Everyday Mathematics®

The University of Chicago School Mathematics Project

Teacher's Reference Manual

Grades 4–6

McGraw Hill Education

Chicago, IL • Columbus, OH • New York, NY

The University of Chicago School Mathematics Project (UCSMP)

Max Bell, Director, UCSMP Elementary Materials Component; Director, *Everyday Mathematics* First Edition
James McBride, Director, *Everyday Mathematics* Second Edition
Andy Isaacs, Director, *Everyday Mathematics* Third Edition
Amy Dillard, Associate Director, *Everyday Mathematics* Third Edition
Rachel Malpass McCall, Associate Director, *Everyday Mathematics* Common Core State Standards Edition

Authors

Max Bell
Jean Bell
John Bretzlauf
Amy Dillard

James Flanders
Robert Hartfield
Andy Isaacs
James McBride

Kathleen Pitvorec
Peter Saecker

Technical Art

Diana Barrie

UCSMP Editorial

Kathryn M. Rich

Photo Credits

Cover (l)John W Banagan/Iconica/Getty Images, (c)Jupiterimages/Getty Images, (tr)Digital Vision/Getty Images, (br)Pier/Stone/Getty Images; **Back Cover** Gregory Adams/Getty Images; iii iv The McGraw-Hill Companies; **v** (tl)Photodisc/Getty Images, (bl br)The McGraw-Hill Companies; **vi** (l)Image Source/Alamy, (r)The McGraw-Hill Companies; **vii** The McGraw-Hill Companies; 1 Image Source/Getty Images; 7 Ryan McVay/Photodisc/Getty Images; **30 45 46** The McGraw-Hill Companies; **71** DILBERT: Scott Adams/Dist. By United Feature Syndicate, Inc.; **72-187** The McGraw-Hill Companies; **205** Adam Woolfitt/CORBIS; **211 228** The McGraw-Hill Companies; **232** Gregory Sams/Photo Researchers, Inc; **233** Dr. Fred Espenak/SPL/Photo Researchers, Inc.; **236 237** The McGraw-Hill Companies; **239** 1989 by NEA, Inc./Tom Thaves; **240 241** The McGraw-Hill Companies; **242** (t)Image Source/Alamy (b)The McGraw-Hill Companies; **250-264** (b)The McGraw-Hill Companies; **311** Image Source/Alamy; **315-356** The McGraw-Hill Companies.

This material is based upon the work supported by the National Science Foundation under Grant No. ESI-9252984. Any opinions, findings, and conclusions or recommendations expressed in this material are those of the authors and do not necessarily reflect the views of the National Science Foundation.

everyday**math**.com

 **Education**

Printed in the United States of America.

Send all inquiries to:
McGraw-Hill Education
STEM Learning Solutions Center
P.O. Box 812960
Chicago, IL 60681

ISBN 978-0-07-657721-7
MHID 0-07-657721-X

5 6 7 8 9 RMN 17 16 15 14 13 12

McGraw-Hill is committed to providing instructional materials in Science, Technology, Engineering, and Mathematics (STEM) that give all students a solid foundation, one that prepares them for college and careers in the 21st century.

The *McGraw-Hill* Companies

Table of Contents

Mathematical Strands and Threads

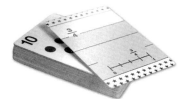

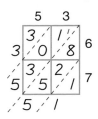

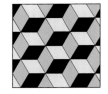

Introduction

i How to Use this Book

This *Everyday Mathematics Teacher's Reference Manual*™ has three main parts: an eight-chapter Management Guide, ten chapters discussing Mathematical Strands and Threads, and a Glossary. The Management Guide includes suggestions on implementing the *Everyday Mathematics*® program; ideas for organizing the curriculum, the students, and the program materials; and descriptions of important program features. The Mathematical Strands and Threads chapters contain reliable information on the mathematics in the curriculum. *Strands* are the familiar topics of mathematics such as numeration and geometry; *threads* are ways of thinking about mathematics that cross the strands, such as problem solving and estimation. These chapters are followed by a detailed Glossary of mathematical and special terms used in *Everyday Mathematics*.

In order to familiarize yourself with the program's features and routines, you may find it helpful to read all eight chapters of the Management Guide before you begin teaching with *Everyday Mathematics*. This reading will also help you decide on organizational strategies for your classroom. Then, as the school year progresses, you may want to refer to some sections again in order to gain further insights.

The ten Mathematical Strands and Threads chapters do not have to be read in their entirety or in any particular order. The topics presented in each chapter are summarized in a table of contents at the beginning of the chapter. You can skim the chapter, consult its table of contents for a specific topic, or read it straight through.

Selected terms in the Glossary refer to sections in the 18 chapters of the manual. For example, the Glossary defines *fact power* as "the ability to automatically recall basic arithmetic facts." The definition is linked to Section 16.3.2: Basic Facts and Fact Power, which details how *Everyday Mathematics* approaches the basic facts, why basic facts are so important, and how the program works to ensure that all students achieve fact power.

Every effort has been made to make this manual easy to use. The authors hope you find it worthwhile and invite your suggestions on how it could be improved.

ii The *Everyday Mathematics* Program

Everyday Mathematics is a comprehensive Pre-Kindergarten through sixth-grade mathematics curriculum embracing many of the traditional goals of school mathematics as well as two ambitious goals for the 21st century:

- To substantially raise expectations regarding the amount and range of mathematics that students can learn;
- To support teachers and students with the materials necessary to enable the students to meet these higher expectations.

Philosophy

Students need a mathematics curriculum that is rigorous and balanced and that:

- Emphasizes conceptual understanding while building a mastery of basic skills;
- Explores a broad mathematics spectrum, not just basic arithmetic;
- Is based on how students learn and what they're interested in while preparing them for their future mathematical needs.

An ever-increasing demand for mathematics competence and problem-solving agility both in and out of school requires us to continue to change both the mathematics we teach and how we teach it. Beginning in Kindergarten, *Everyday Mathematics* makes these changes by introducing students to these six major mathematical content domains: number sense, algebra, measurement, geometry, data analysis, and probability. The program helps students build and maintain basic skills, including automatic fact recall, while helping you use everyday, real-world problems and situations to nurture their higher-order and critical-thinking skills.

Everyday Mathematics differs from traditional, textbook-centered instruction in a number of ways:

- It is consistent with how students actually learn mathematics as it builds understanding over a period of time, first through informal exposure and then through more formal and directed instruction. Because learning proceeds from the known to the unknown, new learning needs to be connected to, and built upon, an existing knowledge base.
- Mathematical content is taught in a repeated fashion, beginning with concrete experiences. Students using *Everyday Mathematics* are expected to master a variety of mathematical skills and concepts, but not the first time they are encountered. It is a mistake to proceed too quickly from the concrete to the abstract or to isolate

concepts and skills from one another or from problem contexts. Students also need to "double back" by revisiting topics, concepts, and skills and then relating them to each other in new and different ways.

- Pacing is important. Students learn best when new topics are presented briskly and in an interesting way. Most students will not master a new topic the first time it is presented, so *Everyday Mathematics* allows students to revisit content in varied contexts, integrating new learning with previous knowledge and experiences. When newly learned concepts and skills are periodically reviewed, practiced, and applied in a wide variety of contexts, they are better retained.

It is important to note how the differences between *Everyday Mathematics* and other programs may affect your day-to-day planning and teaching. Daily routines and games are a necessary part of the program, not optional extensions. Routines and games are designed to build conceptual understanding and ensure mastery of basic skills in authentic and interesting contexts. *Everyday Mathematics* also differs from other programs in that it is designed for the teacher. Rather than being centered on a student textbook, it offers materials that provide students with a rich variety of experiences across mathematical content strands and threads.

Because language, communication, social interaction, tools, and manipulatives all play important roles in helping students acquire skills, *Everyday Mathematics* employs cooperative-learning activities, Explorations, and Projects. The program gives guidance on how to set up your classroom to accommodate group work and on how to help students work together without direct supervision.

For more information, see Chapter 4: Organizing Students.

Through a comprehensive approach to differentiating instruction, *Everyday Mathematics* provides a variety of ways to help students and teachers manage different learning backgrounds, styles, and pacing needs. Mental Math and Reflexes exercises, games, and Math Boxes are just three features included to help students practice skills to keep them sharp throughout the year and into future years. Advice on how to adjust activities for students with different needs is integrated throughout the *Teacher's Lesson Guide*™.

For more information, see Chapter 6: Differentiating Instruction and the *Differentiation Handbook*.

In *Everyday Mathematics,* assessment is closely linked with instruction. While some formal assessment is necessary, a balanced approach including less formal, ongoing methods provides a more complete picture of each student's progress. A number of assessment tools are built into the *Everyday Mathematics* program to help you get feedback about your students' instructional needs and information you can use to assign grades.

For more information, see Chapter 7: Managing Assessment and the *Assessment Handbook*.

In summary, *Everyday Mathematics* is committed to establishing world-class mathematics standards for our nation's schools. The program assumes that virtually all students are capable of a much greater understanding of and proficiency in mathematics than has been traditionally expected, so it provides the features and materials you need to help them meet those higher expectations.

A Note about *Everyday Mathematics* and the NCTM Curriculum Focal Points

The 2006 *Curriculum Focal Points for Prekindergarten through Grade 8 Mathematics: A Quest for Coherence* (*Focal Points* for short) state that, "A curriculum is more than a collection of activities: it must be coherent, focused on important mathematics, and well articulated across the grades" (p. 3[1]). They continue:

> "Curriculum focal points are important mathematical topics for each grade level, pre-K–8. These areas of instructional emphasis can serve as organizing structures for curriculum design and instruction at and across grade levels. . . . [T]o organize instruction around focal points assumes that the learning of mathematics is cumulative, with work in the later grades building on and deepening what students have learned in the earlier grades, without repetitious or inefficient reteaching" (p. 5).

The *Focal Points* propose a broad grade-by-grade outline of important mathematical concepts and skills but do not aim to answer all questions about curriculum. They leave many issues to be resolved by curriculum developers, including instructional approaches, sequencing of topics within grades, teaching tools, and professional development.

The *Everyday Mathematics* authors agree that coherence in curriculum design is critical and have worked hard to ensure that the program is well articulated and coherent. The program's Grade-Level Goals clearly define its focal points, which consistently agree with the topics suggested in the *Focal Points*. Furthermore, the Grade-Level Goals articulate when closure is expected on each skill and concept. *Everyday Mathematics* explicitly maps out how mathematical content builds coherently both within and across the elementary school grades.

As you use this *Teacher's Reference Manual,* you will see how *Everyday Mathematics* specifically addresses the challenges outlined in the *Focal Points.* You will also learn more about how the *Everyday Mathematics* authors have addressed other important topics in elementary school mathematics that go beyond the content strands, such as a flexible use of calculators, estimation and mental arithmetic, and mathematical modeling to aid problem solving.

NOTE: Grade-Level Goals are summarized after the glossary in each *Teacher's Lesson Guide* for Grades 1–6, at the back of the *Teacher's Guide to Activities* for Grades Pre-K and K, and in the *Assessment Handbook* for each grade.

For more information and details about how *Everyday Mathematics* goals correlate with specific *Focal Points* suggestions, see *Everyday Mathematics and the NCTM Curriculum Focal Points* and the *Teacher's Lesson Guide* for each grade.

---

[1] Passages reprinted with permission from the National Council of Teachers of Mathematics. (2006). *Curriculum Focal Points for Prekindergarten through Grade 8 Mathematics: A Quest for Coherence.* Reston, VA: Author.

A Note about *Everyday Mathematics* and the Common Core State Standards[2]

The release of the *Common Core State Standards* (CCSS) continues a national movement aimed at long-term improvement of student performance in mathematics and language arts. Most states have formally adopted the new standards and the U.S. Department of Education has awarded grants to state partnerships that will produce CCSS-aligned standardized tests by 2014–2015.

The *Common Core State Standards for Mathematics* are based on much of the same research and expertise as *Everyday Mathematics*. For example, the CCSS look to internationally high-achieving nations to benchmark the new standards, something that University of Chicago School Mathematics Project authors have been doing for more than 25 years. The CCSS call for challenging, research-based, mathematically accurate curricula that teach students to be powerful mathematical thinkers and problem solvers, which is precisely what *Everyday Mathematics* has always been.

The CCSS for mathematics are *minimum* standards for all students. This CCSS Edition of *Everyday Mathematics* supports students' deep understanding of that minimum set of topics both through direct instruction and by embedding those topics in the context of everyday life. Further, *Everyday Mathematics* takes students beyond a minimum set of standards to a fully integrated mathematics experience from Pre-K through sixth grade.

Many of the *Everyday Mathematics* context-based activities support the *Common Core Standards for Mathematical Practice*. *Everyday Mathematics* students have always approached mathematical content through applications, modeling, and problem solving. The program has also always stressed multiple representations, communication, tools, reasoning, and sense making. So the outcomes that the CCSS standards for mathematical practice call for have always been integral to *Everyday Mathematics*.

Everyday Mathematics is well aligned not only with the CCSS for mathematics, but also with the *Common Core State Standards for English Language Arts & Literacy*. For example, the *Everyday Mathematics Student Reference Books*, which are full of mathematical exposition and worked examples, are exactly the sort of information-rich texts that that CCSS for language arts recommend that students learn to read with growing comprehension. In addition, promoting students' abilities to connect ideas, deal with generalities, and critique their own and others' reasoning has always been a central goal of the *Everyday Mathematics* curriculum.

For more information on the research behind *Everyday Mathematics*, see Introduction Section ii: The *Everyday Mathematics* Program.

---

[2] Common Core State Standards Initiative. (2010). *Common Core State Standards for Mathematics*. Retrieved from http://www.corestandards.org/the-standards

By design, both the CCSS and *Everyday Mathematics* are to be adjusted over time as educators learn more about how students learn mathematics. The *Everyday Mathematics* authors believe the *Common Core State Standards* provide a wonderful opportunity to continue to refine and improve the program, as has been done over many years and three editions. This CCSS Edition of *Everyday Mathematics* takes full advantage of that opportunity.

As you use this *Teacher's Reference Manual*, you will see further details of how *Everyday Mathematics* supports the *Common Core State Standards*.

iii Program Highlights

Highlights of the *Everyday Mathematics* program include:

- *Problem solving in everyday situations* Research and experience show that students who are unable to solve problems presented in purely symbolic form often have little trouble solving them when they are presented in everyday contexts.

- *Developing readiness through hands-on activities* *Everyday Mathematics* offers many suggestions for Explorations and Projects on which students work together. These activities pave the way for the introduction of new mathematical ideas.

- *Establishing links between past experiences and explorations of new concepts* Ideas that have been explored with concrete materials or pictorial representations are revisited through oral descriptions and symbolic representations. Students learn to shift comfortably among various representations and to select models that are most appropriate for given situations.

- *Sharing ideas through discussion* Students gain important insights about mathematics by building on each others' discoveries—one idea leads to another or to refinements of a student's own understanding. Discussion promotes good listening habits and fosters a receptive attitude to the ideas of classmates. Because verbalization often clarifies concepts, talking about mathematics is an important part of thinking about mathematics.

- *Cooperative learning through partner and small-group activities* Students discover that working together is usually more enjoyable and stimulating than working independently. Moreover, as students learn to work as a team, cooperation replaces competition and the less-skilled among them benefit by drawing support from the more-skilled.

- *Practice through games* Students need frequent practice to master a skill. Unfortunately, drills become monotonous and lose effectiveness over time. Games, however, relieve the tedium of rote repetition, reduce the need for worksheets, and offer an almost unlimited source of problem material because, in most cases, numbers are generated randomly.

- *Ongoing review throughout the year* It is rare that students master something the first time they encounter it. For this reason, repeated exposure to key ideas presented in slightly different contexts is built into the *Everyday Mathematics* program. In addition, Math Boxes provide opportunities for cumulative review or assessment.

- *Daily routines* The program suggests routines that students can perform on a regular basis. The Math Message and Mental Math and Reflexes exercises are part of the daily routine. Other regular classroom tasks help students develop a sense of order, initiative, and responsibility while reinforcing numerous mathematical concepts.

- *Informal assessment* In addition to independent review exercises, *Everyday Mathematics* provides many suggestions for small-group activities to help you assess students' progress. Through your interactions with small groups of students, you obtain a clearer understanding of individual strengths and weaknesses.

- *Home-and-school partnership* Optimal learning occurs if it involves the student, the teacher, and people at home. The *Home Connection Handbook*™ offers many suggestions for this. Family Letters help inform parents and guardians about each unit's topics and terms, offering ideas for home-based mathematics activities that supplement classroom work. Also, parents or other caregivers are invited to participate in their child's mathematics experiences through Study Links®.

iv Mathematical Content

Fourth through *Sixth Grade Everyday Mathematics* is organized into the following content strands:

- Numeration and Order
- Arithmetic Operations
- Data and Chance
- Geometry
- Measurement
- Reference Frames
- Patterns, Sequences, Functions, and Algebra

Woven throughout the content strands are three important mathematical threads:

- Algorithms
- Estimation, Mental Arithmetic, and Number Sense
- Problem Solving

Special emphasis is placed on:

- Establishing links between new and past experiences through activities with concrete materials, pictures, oral statements, and symbolic mathematical statements. For example, students might act out a problem or talk about it to get a feel for what is happening. Or they might draw simple pictures or diagrams, or do some mental arithmetic, which eventually leads them to write a number model.

- Discussing and sharing ideas. *Can you tell us how you do that? Why do you think so? Does everyone agree?*

- Using and comparing equivalent expressions. *What other ways can we say or write . . .?*

- Expressing quantities and measurements in context by including labels or units. *Five what?*

- Learning about the reversibility of most things: put in, take out; add, subtract; take apart, put together; go away, come back; expand, shrink; spend money, earn money; positive, negative; and so on.

- Using calculators as tools for counting, displaying numbers, developing concepts and skills, and solving problems—especially real-life problems in which numbers are not always "nice."

By becoming a part of everyday work and play, the lessons, exercises, and concepts in *Everyday Mathematics* gradually shape students' ways of thinking about mathematics and foster the development of their mathematical intuition and understanding.

Management Guide

Contents

NOTE: Teachers report that *Everyday Mathematics* requires at least 60 minutes per day of instructional time. As with any new curriculum, teachers may need a bit more instructional time during the first year.

For specific suggestions on how to set up and maintain daily routines, see Chapter 5: Organizing Daily Routines and Displays.

1 Managing the Curriculum

Perhaps the single greatest difference between *Everyday Mathematics* and other programs is that *Everyday Mathematics* is written for you, the teacher, rather than focused on a student textbook. Student materials are supplements to facilitate your use of the program. This section discusses features of the curriculum and describes materials that support its instruction. Central to the *Everyday Mathematics* approach is the introduction and management of three general types of routines: *Daily, Program,* and *Math-Modeling.*

▶ 1.1 Daily Routines

Students learn a great deal of mathematics through the daily routines they perform both independently and as a class. In Grades 4 through 6, you may wish to extend some of the routines begun in Kindergarten through Grade 3. Two important program routines, Math Messages and Mental Math and Reflexes, are also daily routines.

Most of the daily routines in *Everyday Mathematics* should be introduced in the first unit and then maintained throughout the year. Although these routines require special attention and extra time at the beginning of the year, you will find that investing this time will make teaching easier in the long run. Once routines have been established, they become self-sustaining, as much by the students' energy as by your efforts. Learning becomes much more efficient and effective.

▶ 1.2 Program Routines

Program routines are mathematical activities built into lessons in the *Teacher's Lesson Guide* and maintained across units and grade levels. They are described here in alphabetical order.

1.2.1 *5-Minute Math*

5-Minute Math is a collection of short mathematics activities that require little or no preparation, can be done anywhere, and are brief enough to do in 5 to 10 minutes. They can be used with large or small groups of students at any time of the day.

5-Minute Math activities provide students with:

- Reinforcement and continuous review of mathematics content;
- Preparation for a variety of testing situations;
- Practice with mental arithmetic and logical thinking;
- Opportunities to think and talk about mathematics and to try out new ideas;
- Experience with the problem-solving process and sharing strategies with others;
- Increased time learning and reviewing mathematics without increasing lesson time.

5-Minute Math activities give students an opportunity to solve a variety of number, operations, geometry, data, probability, and measurement problems. Each activity begins by introducing a topic and posing a question. This is followed by two or three progressively more challenging questions so that each activity can be tailored to fit different needs and time slots.

1.2.2 Games

Many parents and educators make a sharp distinction between work and play. They tend to "allow" play only during prescribed times. However, students naturally carry their playfulness into all of their activities. This is why *Everyday Mathematics* sees playing games as an enjoyable way to practice number skills, especially those that help students develop *fact power*.

For more information, see Section 16.3.2: Basic Facts and Fact Power.

Games are an integral part of *Everyday Mathematics* rather than the optional extra activities that supplement traditional programs. Make sure that all students have time to play games, especially those who work at a slower pace or encounter more difficulty than do their classmates. If students play games only after finishing other work, those who could benefit the most will have fewer opportunities.

Because the numbers in exercises are generated randomly, games make fact practice more fun than arithmetic worksheets. Also, the game format eliminates the tedium typical of most drills. Here are some suggestions for integrating games into your classroom:

- Include games as part of your daily routine.
- Devote the first or last 10 minutes of each math class to playing the games specified in the unit.
- Set up a "Games Corner" of favorite games. Students can get additional skills practice while playing games of their own choosing during free time. Rotate games often to keep the Games Corner fresh and interesting.

For more information, see Section 16.3.4: Games for Fact Practice.

Game masters are in the *Math Masters*™ book. Rules for many popular games are included in the Grades 3 through 6 *Student Reference Books*™. Game masters can be copied for use in a Games Corner and for students to take home.

Competition

Some people are concerned that including games in the curriculum promotes competition between students. As one teacher writes, "I prefer to have students work in cooperative groupings, staying away from win-or-lose games. I can't think of a quicker way to turn a child off to the concept one is trying to teach than to inject the emotional disaster of 'I've lost!' into the experience."

It is true that many of the games in *Everyday Mathematics* are competitive. Fair and friendly competition can generate many good things, such as excitement, determination, independence, and challenge. However, game rules may also be changed to fit player and teacher needs for fairness, harmony, and equality. It is possible to modify most of the games so that students practice the same number skills while working cooperatively. The challenge and excitement can come from working together, making joint decisions, and doing one's best while having fun.

To demonstrate how a competitive game can be modified to make it noncompetitive, consider *Multiplication Top-It*. In this game, students use a 40-card deck of 1 through 10 number cards with four cards of each number. Each child turns over two cards and calls out the product of the numbers on them. The player with the highest product takes all the cards played in that turn. The player with the most cards at the end of the game wins.

Suppose, however, that two or three students are asked to play the same game but are given this group objective: *Play until all 40 cards are used, putting all the used cards into a single discard pile. Time the game. Play again until all 40 cards are used. Try to beat your best time to play the whole deck.*

This modified game allows practice of the same multiplication skills but does not declare winners and losers. Instead, the focus is on the group objective of achieving a faster time.

As written, many of the *Everyday Mathematics* games identify the winner as the player with the highest total after a certain number of turns. Here are some strategies for converting these games to relatively noncompetitive games:

- Have the students take turns as usual, but ask them to record their results for each round on the same sheet of paper. A game total will then represent the combined efforts of all group members.
- Redefine the game objective. For example, ask groups to play a sequence of games and report the highest and lowest single game totals. This modification may inspire some measure of healthy competition among groups, but the one-on-one competitive nature of the standard game will be reduced.

These are only examples. The best ideas for modifying games are likely to come from your own classroom experiences. Involve your students in the revisions. If they realize that their input improves the games, they are likely to become more eager players and learners.

The Everything Math Deck

The Everything Math Deck is a deck of 54 number cards used for a variety of *Everyday Mathematics* games and activities. The deck can be purchased through the publisher. It has four of each card for the numbers 0 through 10 and one of each card for the numbers 11 through 20. On the reverse of the 0-through-10 cards are fractions represented in a variety of ways.

To transform an ordinary deck of 54 playing cards to function like the whole-number side of an Everything Math Deck:

- Change the four queens to 0s.
- Remove the four jacks, four kings, and two jokers. Label each of these ten cards with one of the numbers from 11 to 20.
- Change the four aces to 1s.
- Let all number cards represent their face value.

For more information, see Section 16.3.4: Games for Fact Practice.

1.2.3 Math Boxes

Math Boxes are a main part of review and skills maintenance in *Everyday Mathematics*. Originally developed by *Everyday Mathematics* teacher Mary Ellen Dairyko, Math Boxes are an excellent way to help students review material on a regular basis. Once this routine has been introduced in each grade level, every lesson includes a Math Boxes page in the *Math Journal*™.

Math Boxes problems are not intended to reinforce the content of the lesson in which they appear. Rather, they provide continuous distributed practice of skills and concepts that students have seen up to that point in the program. The Math Boxes page does not need to be completed on the same day as the lesson, but it should not be skipped.

The first four or five problems on a Math Boxes page are about mathematics in the current and previous units, including those from previous grades, and the final problem or two preview the math found in the next unit. Paired or tripled problems are included to give repeated practice on selected mathematics concepts and skills.

Math Boxes in the Progress Check lesson summarize all the preview problems in the unit. Student performance on these problems informs you of their preparedness for the mathematics in the next unit.

Math Boxes are designed as independent activities, but expect that your guidance will be needed, especially at the beginning of the school year when some problems review skills from prior years. If students struggle with a problem set, it is not necessary to create a lesson to develop these skills. You can modify or skip problems that you know are not review for the students, knowing that the necessary skills will be revisited in subsequent lessons. Math Boxes also provide ongoing assessment information on skills.

NOTE: Although Math Boxes are designed primarily as an independent activity, at times it may be useful to have students work through some problems with partners or as a class.

1.2.4 Math Messages

Beginning early in first grade, a *Math Message* is provided at the beginning of each lesson. The Math Message leads into the lesson for the day. Students should complete the Math Message before the start of each lesson.

You can display Math Messages in several ways:

- Write them on the board, the Class Data Pad, or overhead transparencies.
- Post them on the bulletin board.
- Duplicate them on quarter-sheets of paper to hand out.

You may find it useful to have students record their answers to the Math Message. In some classrooms, students keep a daily math journal in which they enter Math Message questions and answers. In other classrooms, students record their answers on quarter- or half-sheets of paper, which teachers collect from time to time.

Although the *Teacher's Lesson Guide* contains many suggestions for Math Messages, you are encouraged to create your own, designed around the needs of your students and the activities that take place in your classroom. You may also want to provide a Suggestion Box into which students can put their own Math Message, number story, or other math ideas.

1.2.5 Mental Math and Reflexes

Mental Math and Reflexes exercises help students:

- Get ready to think about math;
- Warm up the skills they need for the lesson;
- Continually build mental-math and reflex skills;
- Inform you of their skill and concept development.

As shown in the example below, each exercise is given at three levels of difficulty to help meet students' individual needs.

Mental Math and Reflexes

Pose addition facts and extended facts.

○○○	$6 + 1 = 7$	○○○	$6 + 7 = 13$	○○○	$50 + 50 = 100$
	$8 + 0 = 8$		$8 + 4 = 12$		$20 + 30 = 50$
	$4 + 4 = 8$		$7 + 9 = 16$		$60 + 80 = 140$
	$9 + 2 = 11$		$5 + 8 = 13$		$90 + 90 = 180$

For more information, see Section 1.2.8: Slates.

Mental Math and Reflexes problems are typically answered orally, with body language, or on slates. A session should be brief, lasting no more than five minutes. Numerous short interactions are far more effective than fewer prolonged sessions.

The *Teacher's Lesson Guide* suggests several kinds of Mental Math and Reflexes problems for Grades 4 through 6, including:

- *Choral counting routines* such as counting on or back, skip counting with calculators, stop-and-start counting, or problems on a number grid;

- *Place-value problems* such as writing the largest number from a set of dictated digits, identifying a particular place value in a dictated number, or recording dictated numbers and comparing them using > and < symbols;

- *Mental computation problems* with some or all of the four basic arithmetic operations both in and out of the contexts of number stories;

- *Mental estimation and approximation problems* such as finding measures, making ballpark estimates for sums and products in number stories, or rounding whole numbers and decimals to dictated place values.

For more information, see Section 16.3: Mental Arithmetic.

The *Teacher's Lesson Guide* suggests Mental Math and Reflexes exercises for every lesson except the Progress Checks. You are encouraged to use these exercises based on your students' needs and your classroom activities. If the suggested exercises do not meet the needs of your class, feel free to substitute.

1.2.6 Museums

Everyday Mathematics encourages the development of classroom museums using a bulletin board or table where related items can be collected, categorized, and labeled. Museums could include:

- *Fractions, Decimals, and Percents Museum* Students collect examples of advertisements and articles that contain fractions, decimals, and percents.
- *Grams and Ounces Museum* Students collect objects of different weights measured in grams and in ounces.
- *Graphs Museum* Students collect data representations from newspapers and magazines.
- *Rates and Ratios Museum* Students collect examples of rates, such as speeds and prices per pound, and ratios, such as students to teacher and wins to losses.
- *Tessellations Museum* Students collect pictures of tessellations, such as floor and ceiling tiles, brickwork, and wallpaper patterns.

Everyday Mathematics museums are often supplemented with posters of 2-dimensional representations of items. The posters help students to categorize the solid objects they manipulate and to connect concepts across dimensions.

If you take your class to a museum in your community, encourage the students to look for the uses of mathematics that abound there. Examples include statistics about objects in exhibits and ways of categorizing those objects that often have some underlying frame of reference, such as size or time.

1.2.7 Projects

The Projects suggested in *Everyday Mathematics* cover a wide array of mathematics activities and concepts created around themes that interest students. Project ideas are found in the Projects Appendix of the *Teacher's Lesson Guide* for each grade. Project Masters are in the *Math Masters* book.

The Projects are cross-curricular, drawing on and developing skills and concepts in reading and language arts, social studies, art, and especially science. They often include the following science processes:

- Observing
- Communicating
- Reading for mathematical content
- Identifying
- Collecting, organizing, and graphing data
- Using numbers
- Measuring
- Determining patterns and relationships

Some Unit Organizers in the *Teacher's Lesson Guide* suggest Projects that are appropriate at particular points during the school year. You are given enough ideas in Projects for you to choose those that

NOTE: You can consider many Projects and other activities suggested in the *Everyday Mathematics* program to be a part of other areas in your curriculum including reading, language arts, social studies, art, and science.

interest the students, and you are encouraged to add your own as well. Projects may take a day or more to complete. Please take the time to do these important parts of the curriculum that are memorable to students.

In addition to the projects described in the Projects Appendix of the *Teacher's Lesson Guide,* there are also projects that appear in the *Student Reference Book* for each grade. In Grades 4 and 5, these are special yearlong projects that focus on a particular topic.

- Fourth-grade students take a World Tour, which is easily linked to geography and other social studies and language arts topics.
- Fifth-grade students take an American Tour, a series of activities that examine the history, demographics, politics, and environment of the United States.
- *Sixth Grade Everyday Mathematics* includes a set of projects that explore uses of mathematics in art, design, and astronomy.

Materials for each of these special projects are found in a separate section in the *Student Reference Book* for each grade level. Lessons tied to the projects appear throughout the *Teacher's Lesson Guide.*

1.2.8 Slates

Most students and teachers genuinely enjoy using slates. They afford an excellent opportunity for everyone to answer a question quietly and simultaneously, and they help you to see at a glance which students may need extra help. They also save paper. Two kinds of slates are particularly easy to use:

- *Plastic Write-On/Wipe-Off Slates* Students write on these small, white slates with dry-erase markers. They can store both the markers and the slates in their tool kits or stack them on a counter or shelf for easy distribution when needed.
- *Chalkboard Slates* Chalk may be kept in old socks that can also double as erasers. Small rug scraps or pieces of cloth also make good erasers; one teacher recommends small, cotton-quilt cosmetic pads.

Establish a routine for using slates. To help prevent confusion, you might want to use a procedure with 1-word cues, such as *Listen, Think, Write, Show,* and *Erase:*

- Tell students to *Listen.* Explain each exercise aloud. If students find the problems too challenging, you may want to write them on the board or an overhead transparency.
- Be sure to give students time to *Think.* Have them work problems mentally.
- Instruct students to *Write* their answers on their slates and keep them covered.
- When most students have written their answers, tell them to *Show* their slates at the same time by holding them up facing you. When appropriate, take a few minutes to have the students share their problem-solving strategies.
- Have students *Erase* their slates.

You can use laminated tagboard and dry-erase markers as an alternative to slates, or simply have students fold a piece of paper into fourths, giving them eight cells in which to write answers.

Instead of doing oral and slate assessments with the whole class, you might work with one small group of students per day over several days. While you do this, the rest of the class can work on Assessment Masters. When students use slates, it is not necessary to record each student's performance on every problem. You primarily need to keep a record of students who are struggling. At a later time, you can record positive comments for students you know were doing well.

1.2.9 Student Reference Book

My Reference Book™ is an *Everyday Mathematics* resource for children in the second half of first grade and all through second grade. Beginning in Grade 3, students receive a *Student Reference Book* to look up and review information on the major mathematical topics introduced in their grade, including many worked examples. In Grades 4 through 6, the book also has sections on:

- How to use scientific and fraction calculators;
- Rules of many popular games;
- A glossary of mathematical terms;
- Descriptions of projects;
- Tables of measures;
- Fraction-decimal-percent conversion tables;
- Place-value charts.

Math Boxes and Study Links® are cross-referenced to the *Student Reference Book* so that both teachers and parents may appreciate this resource.

NOTE: In fourth and fifth grade, the *Student Reference Book* also has sections on the World and American Tours, respectively.

NOTE: Unlike journals, the *Student Reference Book* is a nonconsumable resource.

1.2.10 Study Links

Study Links are the *Everyday Mathematics* version of homework assignments. Each lesson has a Study Link which can be found in the *Math Masters* book. Study Links problems review the content of the lesson, and most contain ongoing computational practice exercises. The next lesson has a follow-up to the previous Study Link. The Study Link for the last lesson in each unit is a Family Letter outlining the next unit. You are also encouraged to make custom Study Links to fit your individual needs.

▶ 1.3 Math-Modeling Routines

This section briefly summarizes the major *Everyday Mathematics* routines for students to practice mathematical modeling. Detailed descriptions of the routines and how they are used throughout *Everyday Mathematics* are included in the 10 Mathematical Strands and Threads chapters later in this manual.

1.3.1 Fact Families/Fact Triangles

A *fact family* is a collection of four related facts linking inverse operations. For example, the four equations in the left diagram below symbolize the fact family relating 8, 9, and 17 by addition and subtraction.

Fact Triangles are the *Everyday Mathematics* version of flash cards to help students develop their mental arithmetic reflexes. Fact Triangles are more effective than traditional flash cards because they emphasize fact families. An addition/subtraction Fact Triangle has two addends and a sum; a multiplication/division Fact Triangle has two factors and a product.

For more information, see Section 16.3.3: Fact Practice.

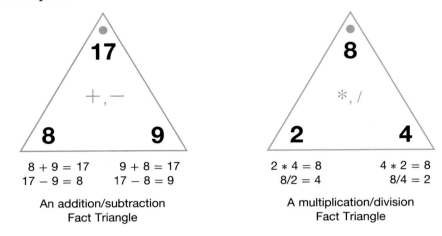

$8 + 9 = 17$ $\quad$ $9 + 8 = 17$	$2 * 4 = 8$ $\quad$ $4 * 2 = 8$
$17 - 9 = 8$ $\quad$ $17 - 8 = 9$	$8/2 = 4$ $\quad$ $8/4 = 2$

An addition/subtraction
Fact Triangle

A multiplication/division
Fact Triangle

1.3.2 Frames-and-Arrows Diagrams

Frames-and-Arrows diagrams help students organize their work with sequences. Each frame contains a number in the sequence, and each arrow represents a rule that defines the number that goes in the next frame.

For more information on Frames-and-Arrows, see Section 17.1.2: Sequences.

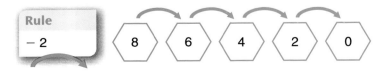

Rule
$- 2$

8   6   4   2   0

1.3.3 Name-Collection Boxes

A *name-collection box* is a diagram that helps students learn equivalent names for numbers. It is a box headed with a label that identifies the number whose names are collected in the box. For example, the box shown below is a 16-box, a name-collection box for the number 16.

For more information, see Section 9.9.3: Name-Collection Boxes.

16
4^2
$\sqrt{256}$
$(4 + 6) * 6 - 4 * 11$
XVI

A 16-box

1.3.4 Number Grids/Number Lines

A *number grid* is a matrix that consists of rows of boxes, ten to each row, containing a set of consecutive integers. Students use number grids to explore number patterns, reinforce place-value concepts, and calculate sums and differences. By attaching grids of larger or smaller numbers to a starting grid, students make *number scrolls*.

−9	−8	−7	−6	−5	−4	−3	−2	−1	0
1	2	3	4	5	6	7	8	9	10
11	12	13	14	15	16	17	18	19	20
21	22	23	24	25	26	27	28	29	30
31	32	33	34	35	36	37	38	39	40
41	42	43	44	45	46	47	48	49	50
51	52	53	54	55	56	57	58	59	60
61	62	63	64	65	66	67	68	69	70
71	72	73	74	75	76	77	78	79	80
81	82	83	84	85	86	87	88	89	90
91	92	93	94	95	96	97	98	99	100
101	102	103	104	105	106	107	108	109	110

A number grid

A *number line* is a line on which points correspond to numbers called *coordinates*. There is one point for every number and one number for every point. Students use number lines when counting and skip counting, performing measuring activities, and adding and subtracting. Number lines are also used as the axes in coordinate graphing systems. The Real Number Line poster used in sixth grade summarizes and orders the kinds of numbers students have used since Kindergarten and gives a preview of other numbers that they will use in later grades. This poster is shown on the next page.

For more information, see Section 9.9.2: Number Grids, Scrolls, and Lines.

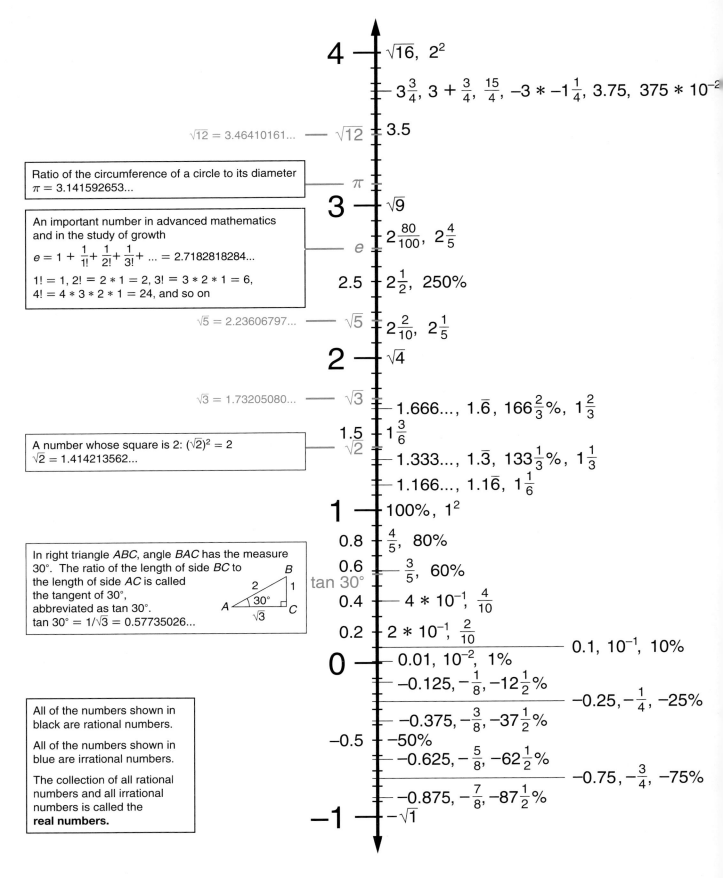

The Real Number Line poster

1.3.5 Situation Diagrams

In *Everyday Mathematics,* students are encouraged to use *situation diagrams* to help sort out various kinds of problem situations. These diagrams organize the information in simple 1-step number stories. Examples include the *parts-and-total, comparison, change,* and *rate* situations that are diagramed below. Diagrams do not have to be fancy, and you can omit or change words, as in the rate diagram.

For more information, see Section 10.3: Use Classes and Situation Diagrams.

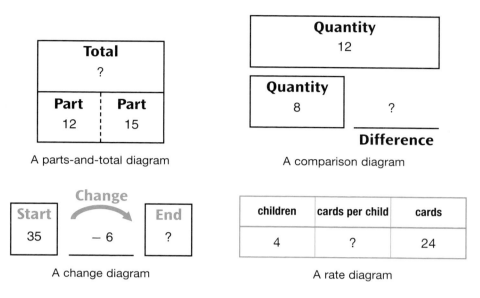

A parts-and-total diagram

A comparison diagram

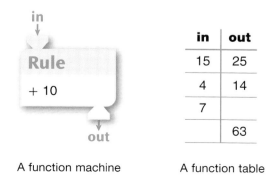

A change diagram

A rate diagram

1.3.6 Unit Boxes

A *unit box,* such as the one in the margin, is a rectangular box that is displayed next to a problem or a set of problems. Unit boxes contain the labels or units of measure used in the corresponding problem(s). Unit boxes help students to think symbolically by encouraging them to see numbers as quantities or measurements of real objects.

A unit box

1.3.7 "What's My Rule?"/Function Machines

"What's My Rule?" is an activity in which students analyze a set of number pairs to determine a rule that relates the numbers in each pair. The data are often represented using a *function machine,* an imaginary device that receives inputs and pairs them with outputs. For example, the function machine below takes an input number and outputs 10 more than the input. The input/output pairs can then be displayed in a function table.

For more information, see Section 17.1.3: Functions.

in	out
15	25
4	14
7	
	63

A function machine

A function table

▶ 1.4 Reading Mathematics

In *Kindergarten* through *Sixth Grade Everyday Mathematics,* students encounter a balance of problem representations based on the model shown below.

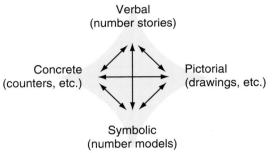

Four problem-solving representations

In early grades, much more attention is given to verbal and concrete representations than in traditional mathematics curricula, and less attention to symbolic ones. Students in Grades 4 through 6 are expected to spend more time reading and writing mathematics for several reasons:

- The symbolic language of algebra was invented so that people could communicate efficiently. It is also a core part of all computer languages.
- Being able to read mathematics and about mathematics allows students more independence. In particular, it allows them to develop an opinion other than yours.
- Secondary school mathematics requires students to be able to read mathematical text and symbols. *Everyday Mathematics* has a responsibility to help prepare students for such experiences.

Throughout the program, you are given hints on how to help students read and write numbers, number models, and sentences containing variables. This section is intended to give you additional suggestions on how to help your students read mathematics text.

There are three main levels of comprehension of mathematical text: *literal, inferential,* and *analytic.* Each has its own challenges for readers and for teachers.

Literal Comprehension

The first task in achieving a literal comprehension of text is *decoding,* or the simple recognition of words and symbols. Unless symbols are recognized and defined, a reader has no hope of understanding a passage. For example, the square-root symbol is introduced to students of *Fourth Grade Everyday Mathematics.* While the symbol itself is not too difficult to learn, its unfamiliarity and peculiar look may mean that students need time to use it comfortably.

The fact that English text is always read from left to right and down a page is a potential obstacle to literal comprehension of mathematics. For example, correctly reading a sum of two fractions means reading down first, then across, and then down again as illustrated at right.

$$\frac{1}{2} + \frac{1}{3} =$$

It is understandable that good English readers might incorrectly add the numerators and then add the denominators. Decoding the mathematics expression means modifying old habits, which takes time. Reading a coordinate graph can have even more unpredictable consequences.

How can you help students at this literal decoding level? A key word is patience—although such tasks may seem trivial to experienced readers, it is probably due to extensive practice rather than some innate understanding. A little time spent having students read equations aloud, describe graphs, or name symbols can lead to greater success with more difficult comprehension tasks later on.

In some ways, symbols, or even the arrangement of a fraction, can be easier to comprehend than words that have a mathematical meaning along with one or more other meanings in everyday language. For example, words like *function, difference,* or *solution* have distinctly different meanings in a mathematical context than in other contexts.

How do you help students assign appropriate meanings to mathematical symbols and words? Mostly, make yourself aware of as many possible misinterpretations or different interpretations as you can. It is surprising how many of us assume that a meaning we have for a word is "the" meaning, when actually we haven't thought about alternatives at all. Some general categories of questions that can be used to encourage accurate literal comprehension of mathematics are listed below. These may be presented verbally, as homework, or in quizzes.

Ask students to:

- Identify whether a given symbol is the same as or different from one in the text;
- Rewrite or redraw a given symbol on their slates;
- Pronounce a given symbol;
- Decide whether alternative forms of a given symbol are acceptable replacements;
- Define a given symbol;
- Interpret between variations of symbol meaning;
- Describe characteristics of a symbol;
- Identify examples or instances of use of a symbol;
- Make representations of a symbol.

As basic as many of these activities may seem, they are well worth the time it takes to do them, especially when symbols and words are first introduced. Keep in mind that a student having any trouble understanding words or symbols at this level of comprehension is unlikely to be successful understanding or solving problems that use them.

Inferential Comprehension

A reader has *inferential comprehension* of text if he or she understands the "signals" in the text. Signals include:

- Cues to relational structures, such as *first . . ., second . . ., third, . . .;*
- Premature abstractions of a concept, such as *The main ideas of this lesson are . . .;*
- Summary statements such as *In short, . . .;*
- "Pointer" words or phrases such as *more importantly* and *unfortunately.*

Inferential comprehension is finding meaning in the way that literal symbols and words are connected. In the sentence *My dog has fleas,* a reader may know the meaning of dog and fleas, but not understand the ownership of the dog; the fact that the fleas are here now, not in the past; and that the fleas are somehow in contact with the dog. The latter conclusions are meanings that are inferred from the sentence.

Questions for inferential comprehension should focus on relationships. Some general categories of questions that can be used to improve inferential comprehension of mathematics are listed below.

Ask students to:

- Complete a sentence;
- Verify relationships of symbols in a sentence;
- Give their opinion about the meaning of relationships of symbols;
- Determine the cause and/or effect of relationships in and between sentences;
- Use an algorithm;
- Sort mixed-up steps of algorithms;
- Fill in missing steps in an algorithm.

Analytic Comprehension

If readers of text can creatively *apply* what they have read to new situations, or responsibly *critique* the text, then they have *analytic comprehension.*

Applying the Reading

Solving written mathematical problems requires the literal and inferential comprehension described in the previous sections and then the realization that certain mathematical skills and models will help. The difficulty that most people have in decoding and interpreting mathematical text and symbols is a major reason *Everyday Mathematics* is based on a concrete, informal experience with mathematical ideas well before the ideas are expressed formally and symbolically.

How can you help students achieve greater analytic comprehension in reading mathematical applications such as number stories? Once again, the answer is to be patient. Give them time and opportunity to read many new stories that require previous mathematical knowledge and time to read progressively more challenging text. During and outside of mathematics class time, have all students read material that is rich in ideas; full of connections—containing words such as *then, but,* and *unless;* and relatively dense, that is, with much information packed into few words or symbols.

Patience is needed especially for older students who may be transferring into your class. Ask about their background in talking about mathematics before assuming they have the same expertise as students already familiar with *Everyday Mathematics* expectations.

Critical Reading

Understanding text well enough to judge its value is arguably the highest level of comprehension, provided the criticism is backed with reasonable evidence.

Critical readers ask themselves good questions. The challenge for you is to help students ask good questions. If the quality of the questions asked is weak, then much of the benefit of motivating students to learn mathematics through applications is lost. However, if questions require careful, critical thinking, then both you and the reader are likely to be much more engaged. Often, the necessary first step of understanding an interesting problem makes doing subsequent mathematics steps trivial.

How can you help students become more critical readers? Ask the following types of questions.

Ask students to:

- Make generalizations from specific instances;
- Find exceptions to a rule;
- Complete and make analogies;
- Identify missing information in text;
- Identify irrelevant information in text;
- Tell whether an algorithm is appropriate in a given problem situation;
- Generate logical consequences from stated facts;
- Simplify details to describe global meanings;
- Guess and check;
- Make mathematical models.

For more information, see Section 18.3: Mathematical Modeling.

1.4.1 Reading Strategies

Beginning in *Fourth Grade Everyday Mathematics,* students are asked to do more reading than in previous grades. In particular, they are expected to read chapters in their journals and in the *Student Reference Book.*

Group Reading Strategies

Strategies to help a class read a chapter together include:

- *Round Robin* Choose a student to read a portion of the text aloud while the rest of the class listens. At a convenient stopping point, the teacher or the reader chooses another student to read aloud.

- *Choral Reading* One student begins reading aloud. At some point another student "jumps in" and "picks up" the reading. Continue in this way until the chapter is complete.
- *Independent Read* Students first read a paragraph to themselves. The paragraph is then read aloud to the class by the teacher or another student. Continue in this way until the chapter is complete.
- *Partner Read* Students read a passage in partnerships or small groups. When all students have completed the reading, the class discusses the passage as a whole group. You might have the small groups or partnerships write one question and one comment about the passage before the class meets. In this way, each small group is responsible for interacting with the text.

Independent Reading Strategies

Strategies to help students become independent readers include:

The Three-Minute Pause When reading text aloud during class or when students are reading silently to themselves, stop several times for about three minutes each time and have students turn to partners and summarize what they have read or heard so far, ask questions about something that is still confusing, or relate what they have read to something in their own lives.

The K-W-L Strategy Before reading text, ask students to write anything that they think they *know* about the topic being presented *(K)*. Also have them write anything they *would like to know* about the topic *(W)*. After reading the text, students identify what they have *learned (L)*.

Advance Organizer Questions Prior to having students read the text, provide students with questions about the key points of the text. In this way, their reading can focus on what you consider most important. Also, identify key vocabulary in the reading and discuss it beforehand. Create a "word wall" of key vocabulary.

Graphic Organizers To help students sort information:

- Provide time for students to make an outline or flowchart of a procedure or other information in the text.
- Provide Venn diagrams or other visual devices for sorting information.

Note-Taking Strategies Suggest the following ideas for note taking:

- Draw pictures in the margin of the page to illustrate the text.
- Highlight key information or the answers to advance organizer questions.
- Put a check mark in the margin next to paragraphs which make sense and a question mark next to paragraphs in which the information is unclear.

Interact with the Text Better readers do things to relate information to their lives and to clarify questions they may have about the material. For example, they:

- Write questions in the margin as they read;

- Picture in their mind what is being described in the text;
- Think about how the information relates to something they already know;
- Summarize the main points of the text;
- Write three questions that are answered by the text.

Resources for Reading Mathematics

Barton, M. L., and Heidema, C. (2002). *Teaching Reading in Mathematics, Second Edition: Supplement to Teaching Reading in the Content Areas: If Not Me, Then Who?* Alexandria, VA: Association for Supervision and Curriculum Development.

Billmeyer, R., and Barton, M. L. (1998). *Teaching Reading in the Content Areas: If Not Me, Then Who?* Alexandria, VA: Association for Supervision and Curriculum Development.

Earle, R. (1983). *Teaching Reading and Mathematics.* Newark, DE: International Reading Association.

1.5 Support for Substitute Teachers

Substitute teachers can handle many *Everyday Mathematics* lessons, especially if they let the students think things through for themselves. However, the program's approach may be unfamiliar to some of the substitutes, so it is wise to prepare additional materials for when you are absent. Here are some suggestions:

- Reserve the Math Boxes from several lessons or create extra Math Boxes of your own. Name-collection boxes and "What's My Rule?" routines can also be included. Use the blank masters in the *Math Masters* book.
- Plan two or three Games Days which substitutes can easily manage.
- Prepare suggestions for practice with Fact Triangles. Students can sort the facts by the different strategies they use to verify them or into facts that they know and those they still need to practice. Partners can take turns quizzing each other. Known facts can be recorded in the Math Journal.
- Make an "emergency box" with activities to be done on days when your absence is unexpected. As you teach, identify activities from *Everyday Mathematics* that could be included.

2 The Importance of Problem Solving

In *Everyday Mathematics,* problem solving is much more than solving word problems. Problem solving is a process of building a *mathematical model* of a situation and then reasoning with the model to draw conclusions about the situation. The process typically involves some or all of the following stages, not necessarily in the order presented:

- Identify precisely what the problem is.
- Analyze what is known and seek out further data as necessary.
- Play with the data to try to discover patterns and meaning.

- Identify mathematical techniques that can help a solution.
- Look back and ask *Does the solution make sense?*

This figure shows how these stages interact in the modeling process.

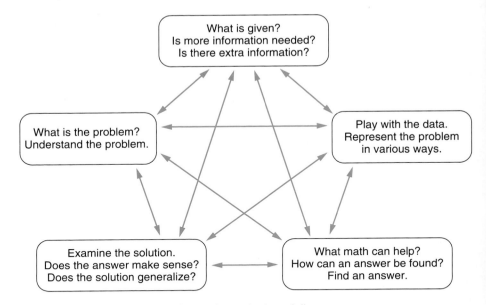

What is given?
Is more information needed?
Is there extra information?

Play with the data.
Represent the problem
in various ways.

What is the problem?
Understand the problem.

What math can help?
How can an answer be found?
Find an answer.

Examine the solution.
Does the answer make sense?
Does the solution generalize?

Stages in the mathematical-modeling process

The *Everyday Mathematics* approach to problem solving and mathematical modeling is described in detail in Chapter 18. The remainder of this chapter defines what the authors of *Everyday Mathematics* call *mathematical sense* and suggests ways to manage students' problem solving in your classroom.

▶ 2.1 Mathematical Sense

The range of experiences provided by *Everyday Mathematics* is designed to help students develop *mathematical sense,* which includes both an understanding of the body of mathematical knowledge and students' abilities to do mathematics to solve problems. Mathematical sense has the following principal components:

- *Number sense* is a feeling for where numbers come from and what they mean. Students need a great deal of experience using numbers of various kinds and sizes in order to understand which numbers make sense in a given situation. Number sense leads them to continually ask *What is a reasonable answer?* It helps students check the accuracy of answers whether they were obtained mentally, with pencil and paper, with a calculator, or by other means.
- *Operations sense* is a feeling for what addition, subtraction, multiplication, and division mean. For example, *Why is it that products of whole numbers greater than zero are greater than one or both factors, but products of fractions or decimals can be less than the factors?*
- *Measure sense* is a feeling for what measurement means, what kinds of measures and units are appropriate in different situations, and what range of results are reasonable to accept. *Is 20 square*

feet a sensible measure of the area of the backyard? Might my dog really weigh 800 kilograms?

- *Data sense* is an appreciation of a collection of numbers as a whole. *How reliable are the numbers? How might they be used? What are the "spread" and "landmarks" of a collection, such as the range and middle value?*

- *Spatial sense* comes from extensive experience with 2-dimensional and 3-dimensional geometric objects and from hands-on constructions that apply geometric principles. *How many grocery bags will fit in the trunk of my car? Can I cover all the walls in my bedroom with a quart of paint?*

- *Function sense,* or *pattern sense,* comes from looking for visual and number patterns and predicting outcomes from applying a rule. It helps students develop multiple perspectives by relating pictorial, symbolic, verbal, and concrete representations of a pattern. *Which is better, doubling $2 every year or adding $50 every year?*

In addition to mathematical sense, *Everyday Mathematics* is committed to helping students recognize and develop their own common sense. By *common sense,* the authors mean an understanding of one's own basic ideas and how they are useful for judging among reasonable alternatives in everyday situations.

2.2 Sharing Students' Strategies and Solutions

Research indicates that students develop a variety of problem-solving strategies if they are given the opportunity to share their ideas with their peers. If this sharing takes place in an open, receptive environment, students will learn that inventing creative, innovative ways of solving problems is acceptable in mathematics. The practice of gathering together to share solutions after individual or group problem solving continues throughout *Everyday Mathematics.*

For more information, see "Exploring Mathematics through Talking and Writing" by Whitin and Whitin (2000). A full reference is on page 309.

Number stories are an excellent context for developing habits of sharing. Students can share their strategies, both correct and incorrect. They can record their solutions on the board, illustrating with pictures and number models. Students develop a better understanding of various mathematical processes when asked to think and strategize rather than when they are merely asked to repeat the steps of a standard written algorithm.

Discussing students' solutions can be extremely valuable, but care should be taken to ensure that students are not embarrassed if their efforts fall short. Students with correct answers are usually happy to share their models and strategies with the class, but discussing incorrect answers can also be very instructive. Here are several suggestions for dealing with wrong answers:

- Emphasize that it is OK to make mistakes. In fact, errors are inevitable. What is *not* OK is failing to learn from one's mistakes.

- Frame discussions of incorrect solutions by saying *Some students in last year's class did _____ .* [Describe the incorrect approach.] *Why do you think they did that? How would you help them see their mistake?*

- Emphasize that answers obtained using different methods should agree, so if there is not agreement, something must be wrong. Encourage students to resolve the dilemma.
- Compare and contrast different strategies and help students see advantages and disadvantages of each. An incorrect method may have some good ideas that can be used to improve another method.

At the beginning of each school year, *Everyday Mathematics* includes specific occasions for students to share strategies and solutions. Many other opportunities occur over the course of the year. With practice, students eventually become comfortable sharing their strategies and are able to talk about them freely and fluently, listen to one another attentively, and revise their own strategies and adopt new ones based on the discussions.

▶ 2.3 Problem-Solving Strategies for Beginners

The diagram of the mathematical-modeling process shown on page 26 generally fits what experts do when they solve problems but is too complicated to be of much help for beginners. On the other hand, many elementary school mathematics textbooks include long lists of strategies and tips; but these lists are often little help even with simple real-life problems, and are essentially useless for dealing with complicated problems such as those found in the workplace.

Students need a guide that is more useful than a list of tips but simpler than a diagram of expert behavior. To this end, *Third* through *Sixth Grade Everyday Mathematics* outlines general guidelines for managing problem solving, such as those in the margin, which are taken from the Grade 4 *Student Reference Book.*

Because problems from everyday life are usually complicated, the first need is often to simplify the situation and figure out exactly what is known and what is to be found out. For example, problem situations in daily life often contain many irrelevant numbers. Sometimes relevant numbers are missing and must be inferred or derived from what is known. Often, the problem solver must deal not only with just a few counts or measures but also with large sets of data. Considerable effort may be required to make the data consistent in format and to devise a display that suggests useful patterns or interesting questions. The process seldom follows one predictable step after another.

A Guide to Number Stories

1. Understand the problem.
2. Plan what to do.
3. Carry out the plan.
4. Look back.

3 Managing Tools

Tools are extremely important in the *Everyday Mathematics* program. The authors define tools broadly to include anything that can be used to facilitate mathematical thinking and problem solving. Calculators, rulers, manipulatives such as pattern blocks and geoboards, paper and pencil, slates, reference books, and the Internet are all mathematical tools. *Everyday Mathematics* helps students learn the skills they need to use these and other tools and to choose the proper tools to help solve a given problem.

By emphasizing the power of tools and helping students learn how to employ them intelligently, *Everyday Mathematics* is working to make doing mathematics in school resemble how mathematics is done in everyday life. Without this type of approach, school mathematics risks becoming abstract and disconnected from everyday life, a complaint that many adults make about their own mathematics education.

The following sections focus on tools that are often used in *Everyday Mathematics*. More information about these and other tools can be found in some of the Mathematical Strands and Threads chapters, which link specific tools to the teaching, learning, and application of particular mathematical topics.

▶ 3.1 Electronic Tools

Electronic tools for mathematics education include calculators, computers, and computer peripherals such as probes, videodiscs, and CDs. Access to electronic tools is varied, and *Everyday Mathematics* is very conservative in its assumptions about which tools are available to every student. In fact, 4-function calculators are sufficient in Kindergarten through Grade 3, and scientific calculators are sufficient in Grades 4 through 6. Some links to Web sites are included in the materials, but none are required. Spreadsheets are optional in some sixth-grade activities.

3.1.1 Calculators

In the more than a quarter-century since electronic calculators have become widely available, many researchers have studied their effects on how students learn. The preponderance of evidence from these studies suggests that the proper use of calculators can enhance students' understanding and mastery of arithmetic, promote good number sense, and improve problem-solving skills and attitudes toward mathematics.

Three summaries of this research are:

- "Research on Calculators in Mathematics Education" by Ray Hembree and Donald J. Dessart;
- "A Meta-Analysis of Outcomes from the Use of Calculators in Mathematics Education" by Brian A. Smith;
- "A Meta-Analysis of the Effects of Calculators on Students' Achievement and Attitude Levels in Precollege Mathematics Classes" by Aimee J. Ellington.

The Smith and Ellington studies also conclude that calculator usage does not hinder the development of paper-and-pencil skills. Ellington recommends that calculators be used by children in Kindergarten through Grade 2 for experimenting with arithmetic concepts in problem-solving contexts.

Both teacher experience and educational research show that most students develop good judgment about when to use and when not to use calculators. *Everyday Mathematics* supports students' need to

NOTE: Encourage students to respect and care for the tools in their tool kits just as doctors, carpenters, and others respect and take care of the tools they use.

NOTE: For complete references to these studies, and information on other calculator research, see "Resources on Calculators" on pages 34 and 35.

Calculator A: the TI-15

Calculator B: the Casio *fx-55*

learn how to decide when it is appropriate to solve an arithmetic problem by estimating or calculating mentally, by using paper and pencil, or by using a calculator. The evidence indicates that students who use calculators are able to choose appropriately.

Everyday Mathematics encourages students to think about developing algorithms as they solve problems. To foster this habit of mind, students need to study particular paper-and-pencil algorithms, but once the algorithms are understood, repeated use becomes tedious. One reason that calculators are so helpful in the mathematics curriculum is that they free both students and teachers from having to spend so much time on dull, repetitive, and unproductive tasks. Calculators also allow students to solve interesting, everyday problems requiring computations that might otherwise be too difficult for them to perform, including problems that arise outside of mathematics class. There is no evidence to suggest that this will cause students to become dependent on calculators or make them unable to solve problems mentally or with paper and pencil.

Before the availability of inexpensive calculators, the elementary school mathematics curriculum was designed primarily so that students would become skilled at carrying out paper-and-pencil algorithms. Thus, there was little time left for students to learn to think mathematically and solve problems. Calculators enable students to think about the problems themselves rather than focus on carrying out algorithms without mistakes.

How the Authors Used Calculators when Writing *Everyday Mathematics*

In the second edition of *Everyday Mathematics,* one calculator was chosen as representative of all calculators for Kindergarten through Grade 3 materials and another for Grades 4 through 6. This choice allowed the authors to give examples of specific key sequences for a variety of calculations. However, having just one representative calculator led authors to explain features that were available only on the chosen machine and not on most other available calculators. To present a more balanced view, the third edition features key sequences for *two* widely available calculators.

By choosing two calculators, the authors have been able to define a "generic" calculator to support *Everyday Mathematics.* Only those functions that are on *both* calculators, and so likely to be on any other comparable calculator, are considered to be generic tools for problem solving.

For Grades 4 through 6, the authors used TI-15 and Casio *fx-55* fraction calculators. Both calculators offer many of the same functions. The Casio has a random-number generator that the TI does not, so this feature is not generic. The TI offers a number of functions such as an "arithmetic training" mode that neither the Casio nor any other calculators on the market have at the time of this writing. None of these features are considered generic.

Not all keys for common functions are the same on both machines, so *Everyday Mathematics* presents key sequences for both. Because of this, you should be able to find the help you need to use any fraction or scientific calculator.

For political and other reasons, some schools cannot use student materials that mention specific brand names of products. Therefore, in the *Student Reference Book,* the TI-15 is called "Calculator A" and the Casio *fx*-55 is called "Calculator B." Reminders of this convention are also given at appropriate places in the *Teacher's Lesson Guide.*

Types of Calculators

As with all electronic technology, the types of calculators and features they contain are always changing. There are calculators that print on paper; send data via infrared beam to computers or other calculators; and draw pictures, graphs, and geometric constructions. Who knows what they'll do tomorrow? At this writing, there are five general types of calculators: 4-function, scientific, fraction, and graphics calculators; and calculators bundled with computer, personal digital assistant (PDA), and cell-phone operating systems.

Four-Function Calculators These calculators originally got their name because all they did was add, subtract, multiply, and divide. Today, however, it is difficult to find a recently manufactured 4-function calculator that does only the four basic arithmetic operations. Most have at least a percent key and often a square-root key. Even most of the "credit card" calculators that are given as promotional items have a percent key. So today, 4-function calculators usually do more than four functions, but they are still referred to by that name.

The authors encourage you to be less concerned with the number of available functions than with how a 4-function calculator works. Some 4-function calculators are programmed to follow the *algebraic order of operations,* while others are not. To find out whether or not a calculator is an algebraic calculator, try the following test:

- Enter 10 ⊟ 2 ⊠ 4 ⊟ into your calculator.
- If the result is 32, it is *not* an algebraic calculator.
- If the result is 2, it *is* an algebraic calculator.

A nonalgebraic calculator does the operations in the order they were entered: $10 - 2 = 8$ and $8 * 4 = 32$. An algebraic calculator multiplies the 2 and 4 first and subtracts the result, 8, from 10. Both the TI-15 and Casio *fx*-55 are algebraic calculators.

Scientific Calculators So-called scientific calculators have more functions and are more complicated than 4-function calculators. These calculators use scientific notation to display numbers that have more digits than will fit on the display. Such calculators have keys for entering numbers in scientific notation, commonly ⟨E⟩ or ⟨EE⟩ for "exponent" or "enter exponent." For example, to enter $2.345 * 10^8$, press 2.345 ⟨EE⟩ 8.

NOTE: As recently as the mid-1960s, a 4-function calculator cost hundreds of dollars.

NOTE: Although most calculators have a percent key, the key does not necessarily work the same way on all of them. Students in Grades 4 through 6 learn about ways that different calculators find percents.

For more information, see Section 10.2.3: The Order of Operations.

Other keys commonly found on scientific calculators are for:

- Exponentiation with bases other than 10 (for example, [EXP], [x^y], or [∧]);
- Logarithms (for example, [LOG] or [ln x]);
- Trigonometric functions (for example, [COS], [SIN], and [TAN]);
- Statistics functions, including regression and correlation.

Scientific calculators also conform to the conventional order of operations, rather than simply carrying out operations in the order in which they are entered. This is a major reason why *Everyday Mathematics* students in Grades 4 through 6 are expected to have at least scientific calculators.

Fraction Calculators A fraction calculator allows a user to enter and manipulate fractions in fractional form. Such calculators generally allow the user to compute with fractions, simplify fractions, and convert between fractions and decimals. Fraction calculators differ in their procedures for handling fractions, so you may need to check your owner's manual for some details. Fraction calculators often have a key to display division with remainder.

The calculators the authors used in writing *Fourth* through *Sixth Grade Everyday Mathematics* are fraction calculators that do not have the advanced mathematics functions such as trigonometry functions. This choice was made primarily to keep the number of keys on the representative calculators to a minimum.

Graphing Calculators Graphing calculators let a user enter equations and then graph them on a coordinate plane. As with the other types of calculators, new graphing calculators enter the market with even more bells and whistles than the previous versions; nowadays, many are programmable, do statistics, and make tables of values. One such calculator even contains dynamic geometry software. Students do not need a graphing calculator for *Everyday Mathematics*.

Computer, PDA, and Cell-Phone Calculators There are several calculator applications or programs that run on computers. When you run the application, it looks like a calculator on the screen. MacOS X, Windows 7, Palm OS, and some cell-phone operating systems each come with a built-in calculator. Four-function-type calculator programs have been standard features of most computer operating systems since personal computers were invented. If you use computers with students, you might want to check if a 4-function calculator program is available and use the preceding comments to help determine how it works.

Calculator Basics and Key Sequences

Children begin using calculators in *Kindergarten Everyday Mathematics* both to display numbers and to count. If your class has had no previous experience with calculators, you may want to begin with a period of free exploration and then use some of the exercises in the *Student Reference Book* as a warm-up.

NOTE: Of the functions in this list, students in *Everyday Mathematics* use only the exponentiation, or powering, key.

For more information on fraction calculators, see Section 11.4: Algorithms on Calculators.

NOTE: Graphing calculators are often called *graphics* calculators to indicate more than just coordinate graphing capabilities.

As with any tool, proper and effective use of a calculator requires instruction. Research has shown that without instruction, students using calculators do not calculate any better than students not using them. Whenever an operation that can be performed on a calculator is introduced, *Everyday Mathematics* includes an activity that introduces the new calculator key(s). It is recommended that you draw the new key(s) on the board or on an overhead transparency.

The order in which keys are pressed to perform a calculation is called a *key sequence.* In *Everyday Mathematics* key sequences, function keys such as [+] and [−] are written with square brackets or shown as pictures of actual keys. Numbers, including decimals, are not. For example, a key sequence to calculate $12 − 3 + 5$ is 12 [−] 3 [+] 5 [=]. The authors recommend that you also use the square-bracket notation and encourage students to follow it when they are asked to write key sequences. Encouraging students to "discover" an appropriate key sequence is a suitable activity at any grade level and fits well into the *Everyday Mathematics* philosophy.

The four basic arithmetic keys [+], [−], [×], and [÷], along with the number keys, decimal-point key, clear key, and long-term memory keys (with an M on them) are introduced by *Third Grade Everyday Mathematics.* Children also "program" their calculators to skip count using constant operation functions. In Grades 4 through 6, students learn to use a variety of other keys, including those for manipulating fractions, taking square roots, and exponentiation. The best *Everyday Mathematics* resource for using the TI and Casio calculators is the *Student Reference Book* for the grade you teach. The most complete resource is your owner's manual.

Perhaps the most important suggestion about using calculators as a classroom teaching tool is that everyone in the room use the same machine. Because there are variations in calculator symbols and key sequences required to perform various tasks, it can be confusing if several different calculators are being used at the same time.

Interpreting the Display

Calculators compute with programmed algorithms; they do not solve problems. The user must know which keys to press and how to interpret the results. As with any technology, calculators have their own unique challenges when it comes to displaying results.

Calculators often display more digits than are warranted in the context of a problem. In *Fourth* through *Sixth Grade Everyday Mathematics,* students study significant digits formally, but the basic idea is straightforward: The result of a calculation can be no more exact than the numbers used in the calculation. For example, if the ages of a group of children are 9, 12, 7, 13, 8, 6, and 10 years, then reporting the average age as 9.7142857 years is silly; reporting the average as "about 10" would be more reasonable. For the primary grades, it's enough for children to be aware that not all the digits that a calculator displays are meaningful. A rule of thumb is that answers

NOTE: Using calculators may require learning alternative symbols for operations. Refer to your owner's manual to become familiar with the symbols for operations on your calculator.

NOTE: More advanced calculators have a *fix* function to fix the number of decimal places displayed. So fixing the display to two digits means that all decimals will be displayed as dollars and cents without the dollar sign. Both the TI-15 and Casio *fx*-55 have fix keys, but operate differently. Each is described in the *Student Reference Books*.

can have as many meaningful digits as the original numbers. So if the numbers you calculate with have two digits each, then probably only the left most two digits in the calculator display are significant.

Another challenge is that calculators sometimes display fewer digits than are expected. For example, suppose a calculator is used to find the value of 36 nickels. The key sequence 36 [×] .05 [=] leads to a display of 1.8, not $1.80 or even 1.80. This cutting off, or *truncating,* of trailing zeros to the right of the decimal point can be confusing to beginning calculator users.

Perhaps the greatest challenge to interpreting calculator results is common to all forms of calculation, including paper-and-pencil algorithms. That is, sometimes the result is nonsense in the context of the problem being solved. Reasons for a nonsensical calculator result might include:

- The calculator wasn't properly cleared.
- A number or operation was entered incorrectly.
- The analysis of the problem was faulty and incorrect calculations were made.

Whatever the reason, sometimes a calculator's answer just doesn't make sense. When this happens, a user must determine whether an answer is reasonable by asking whether it makes sense in terms of the original problem situation, just as he or she must after using paper and pencil or mental arithmetic.

Resources on Calculators

Campbell, P. F., and Stewart, E. L. (1993). "Calculators and Computers." In Jensen, R. (Ed.) *Research Ideas for the Classroom: Early Childhood Mathematics.* New York: Macmillan.

Demana, F., and Leitzel, J. (1988). "Establishing Fundamental Concepts Through Numerical Problem Solving." In Coxford, A. F., and Shulte, A. P. (Eds.) *The Ideas of Algebra, K–12: 1988 Yearbook.* Reston, VA: National Council of Teachers of Mathematics.

Groves, S., and Stacey, K. (1998). "Calculators in Primary Mathematics: Exploring Numbers before Teaching Algorithms." In Morrow, L. J., and Kenney, M. J. (Eds.) *The Teaching and Learning of Algorithms in School Mathematics.* Reston, VA: National Council of Teachers of Mathematics.

Ellington, A. J. (2003). "A Meta-Analysis of the Effects of Calculators on Students' Achievement and Attitude Levels in Precollege Mathematics Classes." *Journal for Research in Mathematics Education 34(5):* pp. 433–463.

Hembree, R., and Dessart, D. J. (1992). "Research on Calculators in Mathematics Education." In Fey, J. T., and Hirsch, C. R. (Eds.) *Calculators in Mathematics Education: 1992 Yearbook.* Reston, VA: National Council of Teachers of Mathematics.

National Council of Teachers of Mathematics. (2005). *Position Statement: Computation, Calculators, and Common Sense.* Reston, VA: Author. Retrieved from www.nctm.org/about/content.aspx?id=6358

National Council of Teachers of Mathematics. (2008). *Position Statement: The Role of Technology in the Teaching and Learning of Mathematics.* Reston, VA: Author. Retrieved from www.nctm.org/about/content.aspx?id=14233

Smith, B. A. (1997). "A Meta-Analysis of Outcomes from the Use of Calculators in Mathematics Education." *Dissertation Abstracts International 58:787A.*

Waits, B. K., and Demana, F. (2000). "Calculators in Mathematics Teaching and Learning: Past, Present, and Future." In Burke, M. J., and Curcio, F. R. (Eds.) *Learning Mathematics for a New Century: 2000 Yearbook.* Reston, VA: National Council of Teachers of Mathematics.

3.1.2 Computers

Because computer access and availability vary widely across the United States, computer-based activities are currently not integrated into the core curriculum but are occasionally included as optional investigations. For example, *Sixth Grade Everyday Mathematics* provides optional activities in which students use spreadsheets.

Many existing software programs can be used with *Everyday Mathematics.* Some of these software programs are designed as instructional tools that can be used by teachers to model, demonstrate, or explain mathematical concepts. Students can use other software for concept development, practice, enrichment, motivation, or exploration.

3.1.3 Spreadsheets

A *spreadsheet* has been a business tool for a long time. It gets its name from a ledger sheet for financial records, similar to the one shown in the margin. Such sheets were often large pages, folded or taped, that were spread out for examination.

When one or more numbers in a spreadsheet are changed, related numbers on the sheet may need to be recalculated and changed. This is called *updating,* or revising, a spreadsheet. For example, if Amala got another hit, then cell B3 in the spreadsheet at right would be updated to a 6. The total in cell B12 would also need to be changed to 54.

When done by hand on ledger paper, spreadsheets are a practical way of organizing data, but their usefulness is limited. What if you forget to update the total? When computerized spreadsheets became available, their usefulness exploded, primarily because values in cells in the sheet could be *dynamically linked* to other values by formulas. This means that changing one value, such as Amala's hits in B3, automatically changes the values of any linked cells, in this case the total number of hits for the team in B12.

	A	B	C
1	**Player**	**Hits**	**Runs**
2	Carl	9	4
3	Amala	5	2
4	Noreen	1	0
5	Doug	11	5
6	David	3	3
7	Annina	2	1
8	Ted	7	3
9	Raoul	12	7
10	Cheryl	3	0
11			
12	**Total**	**53**	**25**

As one of the first practical applications of microcomputers in business, spreadsheet programs were instantly successful. They put the microcomputer revolution into high gear and revolutionized business practice at the same time. Over the years, spreadsheet programs from Lotus 1-2-3 to Microsoft Excel have become increasingly sophisticated. They can solve complicated financial problems, do a variety of statistical analyses, and create wonderfully informative graphs and charts. Most of your students will probably use some form of computer spreadsheet in their lives.

As optional activities, sixth graders use spreadsheets to:

- Calculate and compare mean and median values of data sets;
- Practice using formulas for calculating sums and products dynamically;
- Examine graphs based on the data and formulas they have entered.

3.1.4 The Internet

As the Internet has become more widely available to the public and to schools, *Everyday Mathematics* has incorporated it into the program in a modest way. This section lists Web sites that seem destined to survive over the years and that supplement activities in a substantive way. At this writing these include the Web sites listed in the following tables:

Mathematics Web Sites: Cross-Grade Resources	
Organization	**Web Site**
UCSMP *Everyday Mathematics* Center	everydaymath.uchicago.edu
National Council of Teachers of Mathematics (NCTM)	www.nctm.org
The Math Forum	mathforum.org
Shell Centre	www.mathshell.com

Mathematics Web Sites: Fourth-Grade Resources	
Organization	**Web Site**
OANDA Currency Converter	www.oanda.com/currency/converter
Indo.com Internet Travel and Technology	www.indo.com/cgi-bin/dist
International Orienteering Federation	www.orienteering.org
Infoplease: Latitude and Longitude of World Cities	www.infoplease.com/ipa/A0001769.html
National Library of Virtual Manipulatives for Interactive Mathematics	nlvm.usu.edu/nav/vlibrary.html
NCTM Illuminations Activities	illuminations.nctm.org/ActivitySearch.aspx
Tropical Rainfall Measuring Mission	kids.earth.nasa.gov/trmm/locator.html
U.S. Census Bureau U.S. Gazetteer	www.census.gov/geo/www/gazetteer/gazette.html

Mathematics Web Sites: Fifth-Grade Resources	
Organization	**Web Site**
Annenberg/CPB Taxicab Treasure Hunt	www.learner.org/teacherslab/math/geometry/shape/taxicab
Google Maps	maps.google.com
National Weather Service	www.nws.noaa.gov
Pi Through the Ages	www-groups.dcs.st-and.ac.uk/~history/HistTopics/Pi_through_the_ages.html
University of Michigan Weather	cirrus.sprl.umich.edu/wxnet

Mathematics Web Sites: Sixth-Grade Resources	
Organization	**Web Site**
NASA for grades 5-8	www.nasa.gov/audience/forstudents/5-8/index.html

3.2 Topical Tools

There is a variety of conceptual devices, manipulatives, and other tools that students use to help them understand *Everyday Mathematics* topics. This section summarizes them and discusses some management strategies. More information on each tool is then found in the last section of appropriate Mathematical Strands and Threads chapters.

3.2.1 Numeration and Order Tools

Tools to explore numeration and order are among those commonly called manipulatives. Highlighted here are a commonly used manipulative, base-10 blocks, and three made specifically for *Everyday Mathematics:* Fact Triangles, Fraction Sticks, and Fraction-Stick Charts.

For more information, see Section 9.9: Numeration and Order Tools and Techniques.

Base-10 Blocks

In *Everyday Mathematics,* students use base-10 blocks starting in first grade. Although these blocks have a variety of names, it helps to have a common vocabulary for discussions and written work with the blocks. In *Everyday Mathematics,* the following names are used: *cube* for the smaller 1-cm cube, *long* for the block consisting of ten 1-cm cubes (1×10), *flat* for the block consisting of one hundred 1-cm cubes (10×10), and *big cube* for the larger cube consisting of one thousand 1-cm cubes ($10 \times 10 \times 10$).

Sometimes you may want to make a written record of work with base-10 blocks. The shorthand shown on page 38 is handy for drawing quick pictures of base-10 blocks. Such pictures are often more convenient to use than are the actual blocks, especially the larger blocks, and can be useful for explaining and recording solutions.

For more information, see Section 9.9.1: Base-10 Blocks.

2,045 in "base-10 shorthand"

Base-10-Block Shorthand		
Name	**Block**	**Shorthand**
cube		
long		
flat		
big cube		

Fraction-Stick Charts and Fraction Sticks

Students in *Fifth Grade Everyday Mathematics* use a *Fraction-Stick Chart* to find equivalent fractions and to compare fractions. Each row in the chart is a *fraction stick* divided into unit fractions, or pieces, for a particular denominator. Fraction sticks are pictorial representations of fractions, with each stick representing a whole, or ONE. The chart and an example of how to use it are in Section 9.9.4.

Fraction sticks can help students visualize the addition of fractions with certain denominators, as the following example illustrates:

$$\frac{3}{16} + \frac{9}{16} = \text{ } = \frac{12}{16}, \text{ or } \frac{3}{4}$$

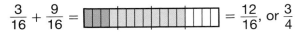

Number Grids, Scrolls, and Lines

A *number grid* consists of rows of boxes, usually ten in each row, containing consecutive integers (positive and negative whole numbers).

Number grids have many wonderful features that can help students with pattern recognition and place value. However, their original use in *Everyday Mathematics* was simply to solve the problem of number lines being unmanageably long. Number lines can be

−9	−8	−7	−6	−5	−4	−3	−2	−1	0
1	2	3	4	5	6	7	8	9	10
11	12	13	14	15	16	17	18	19	20
21	22	23	24	25	26	27	28	29	30
31	32	33	34	35	36	37	38	39	40
41	42	43	44	45	46	47	48	49	50
51	52	53	54	55	56	57	58	59	60
61	62	63	64	65	66	67	68	69	70
71	72	73	74	75	76	77	78	79	80
81	82	83	84	85	86	87	88	89	90
91	92	93	94	95	96	97	98	99	100
101	102	103	104	105	106	107	108	109	110

cumbersome even when stretched along a classroom wall, and it is nearly impossible to print them in students' books without breaking them into chunks. Number grids may be considered number lines that fit nicely on a page or a classroom poster.

Number scrolls are extended number grids. You can make them by adding single sheets of 100 numbers to existing sheets, either forward (positively) or backward (negatively).

A *number line* is a line on which points are indicated by *tick marks* that are usually at regularly spaced intervals from a starting point called the *origin,* the *zero point,* or simply 0. Numbers are associated with the tick marks, and the interval from 0 to 1 on the line is called the *unit interval.*

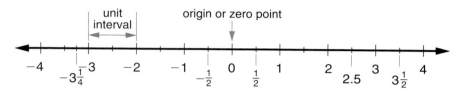

Students use number lines when counting and skip counting, performing measuring activities, and adding and subtracting. Number lines are also used as the axes in coordinate graphing systems.

For more details, see Section 9.9.2: Number Grids, Scrolls, and Lines.

3.2.2 Arithmetic Operations Tools

There are three main tools that students use to develop their skills for problem solving with arithmetic operations: paper-and-pencil algorithms, situation diagrams and calculators. The summaries here are to put each tool in context. In-depth discussions of them are found in other parts of this manual as indicated by margin references.

Paper-and-Pencil Algorithms

An *algorithm* is a well-defined, step-by-step procedure guaranteed to achieve a certain objective, often with several steps that "loop" as many times as necessary. For example, an algorithm for multiplication will produce the correct product no matter what the factors are.

During the early phases of learning an operation, *Everyday Mathematics* encourages students to invent their own algorithms. Students are asked to solve arithmetic problems from first principles about situations in which operations are used, before they develop or learn systematic procedures for solving such problems. This helps them understand the operations better and also gives them valuable experience solving nonroutine problems.

Later, when students thoroughly understand the concept of the operation, several alternative algorithms are introduced. Some of these algorithms are based on approaches that many students devise on their own. Others are less likely to be discovered by students but have a variety of desirable characteristics. Students are urged to experiment with various algorithms in order to become proficient at using at least one alternative.

For more information, see
Chapter 11: Algorithms.

Everyday Mathematics also designates one of the alternative algorithms for each operation as a *focus algorithm*. Focus algorithms are powerful, relatively efficient, and easy to understand and learn. All students are expected to learn the focus algorithm for each operation. In solving problems, however, students may use either the focus algorithm or any other methods they choose. The aim of this approach is to promote flexibility while ensuring that all students know at least one reliable method for each operation.

Situation Diagrams

In *Everyday Mathematics,* students are encouraged to use *situation diagrams* to help them sort the information in simple 1-step number stories. Examples include the *parts-and-total, comparison, change,* and *rate* situations diagramed below. Diagrams do not have to be fancy, and you can omit or change words, as in the rate diagram.

For more information, see
Section 10.3: Use Classes
and Situation Diagrams.

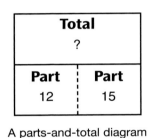

A parts-and-total diagram

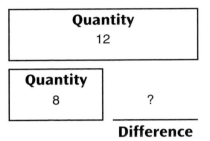

A comparison diagram

A change diagram

A rate diagram

Calculator Operations

For more information, see
Section 3.1.1: Calculators
and Section 11.4: Algorithms
on Calculators.

Scientific calculators get their name from a shared ability to use scientific notation. Beginning in Grade 4, *Everyday Mathematics* expects students to learn to operate scientific calculators, to check results for correctness, and to think about whether using a calculator is appropriate or not. They also learn to use fraction calculators if available.

3.2.3 Data and Chance Tools

For more information, see
Section 12.4: Data and
Chance Tools and Techniques.

Everyday Mathematics highlights two types of tools for exploring data and chance, the *Probability Meter* and a variety of random-number generators.

The Probability Meter

Students encounter informal games and activities dealing with probability beginning in first grade. Starting in fourth grade, probability ideas are extended and made more formal. In fifth grade, the concept of probability is extended by means of a Probability Meter. The *Probability Meter* visually represents the likelihood of the occurrence of a given event. Throughout the year, the probabilities of events occurring are recorded on stick-on notes and placed on the meter.

Numerical representations of chance events are presented as fractions, decimals, and/or percents to familiarize students with the different ways probability is expressed. The Probability Meter also serves as an expanded number line for rational numbers between 0 and 1. Equivalent names are shown for some numbers, such as the repeating decimal $0.3\overline{3}$ and $\frac{1}{3}$.

Random-Number Generators

Many games generate numbers randomly to inject both an element of chance and a sense of fairness. Several tools for helping students generate random numbers are listed below. Often these devices do not generate perfectly random outcomes, but they are good enough for most purposes.

Calculator Random-Number Keys Some scientific calculators have one or more keys for generating random numbers. See your owner's manual if have one you'd like to use. The Casio *fx-55* has a random-number key $\boxed{\text{RAN\#}}$. This key and most like it generate a decimal greater than or equal to 0 and less than 1. You can then multiply the number by an appropriate factor and truncate (ignore) the decimal part. For example, to generate numbers from 0 through 9, multiply by 10 and truncate. If a calculator generates 0.659, you would get $10 * 0.659 = 6.59$, which rounds down to 6.

Dice Use a regular die to generate the numbers 1 through 6. Use a polyhedral die (with 12 or 20 sides) to extend the range of numbers to be generated. Note that rolling more than one die and adding the resulting number of dots produces a *nonuniform distribution* of possible outcomes. For example, if you roll two standard dice, there are 36 possible ways for them to land.

Egg Cartons Label each egg-carton cup with a number. For example, you might label the cups 0 through 11. Place one or more pennies, beans, or centimeter cubes inside the carton, close the lid, shake the carton, and then open it to see in which cups the objects have landed. Randomness depends on how thoroughly the carton is shaken. This is probably the least random method of this list.

The Everything Math Deck This deck of cards consists of four sets of number cards 0 through 10 and one set of number cards 11 through 20. Fractions are on the reverse side of the 0 through 10 cards. You can limit the range of numbers to be generated simply by removing some of the cards from the deck. For a uniform distribution of the

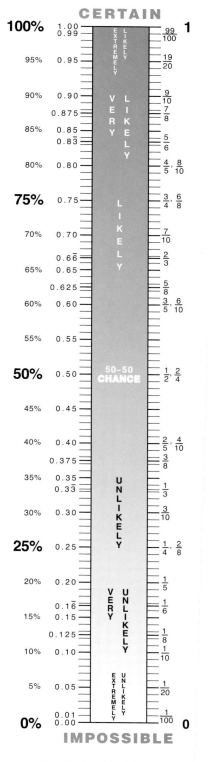

The Probability Meter

numbers 0 through 20, for example, use only one set of 0 through 10 cards and the set of 11 through 20 cards. To use the cards, simply shuffle and draw. The better the shuffle, the more unpredictable the draw will be.

You can transform an ordinary deck of 54 playing cards to function like the whole-number side of an Everything Math Deck as follows:

- Change the four queens to 0s.
- Remove the four jacks, four kings, and two jokers. Label each of these ten cards with one of the numbers from 11 through 20.
- Change the four aces to 1s.
- Let all number cards represent their face value.

Spinners Spinners are used throughout *Everyday Mathematics,* usually in games. They are extremely useful for helping students visualize the idea of chance. There are many commercially available spinners, though it is not necessary to purchase them. Students can use a pencil and paper clip with a spinner mat as shown in the margin. Use either a large (about 2-inch) or standard (about 1-inch) paper clip for the part that spins. The larger size is preferred because it spins more easily. Make a mark as a pointer at one end of the paper clip using a permanent felt-tip marker.

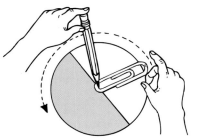

The spinning mat may be drawn on cardstock or paper. Sometimes a mat is supplied as a master or journal page. If you make your own mat, start with a circle or square large enough to accommodate the paper clip. Mark the center of the circle, choose the number and sizes of the regions, and then measure and draw the appropriate angles. For example, the central angles of six equal-sized regions would each measure $360°/6 = 60°$. You can use shapes other than circles for a spinner, and the regions do not have to be the same size, as in the square mat in the margin.

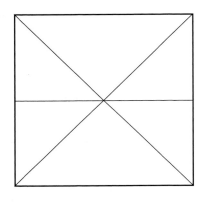

Before spinning, tape the mat to a level surface. You need only two small pieces of tape, one at the top and one at the bottom. To spin, place the tip of a pen or pencil on the center of the circle and within the paper clip as shown in the diagram. Flick the paper clip about halfway between the center of the circle and the tip of the paper clip, as flicking the paper clip near the pointer end will generate less of a spin.

Standard Playing Cards Use the 2 through 9 cards, the aces for 1s, and the queens for 0s. Draw one card to get a 1-in-10 chance for each one of the digits 0 through 9. Draw two cards to make 2-digit numbers, three cards for 3-digit numbers, and so on. If more than one card is drawn, you will need to decide whether to replace it before another card is drawn. If the first card is replaced in the deck and the deck is reshuffled, the probability will remain the same for each draw. If the card is not replaced, the chance of drawing that digit decreases.

3.2.4 Geometry Tools

The study of geometry in *Everyday Mathematics* involves many hands-on experiences, such as manipulating pattern blocks and attribute blocks, tracing shapes from templates, working with geoboards, cutting out shapes, folding shapes, drawing shapes with a compass and straightedge, constructing shapes out of straws, and constructing 3-dimensional figures from 2-dimensional nets (flat figures that can be folded to form closed, 3-dimensional models).

Compass and Straightedge

Students use a compass and straightedge for geometry constructions beginning in *Fourth Grade Everyday Mathematics.* Students need plenty of practice in simply drawing a circle with a compass. There are two main methods: fix the paper and rotate the compass or hold the compass still and rotate the paper. Students experiment and select the method they find easier.

Use a board compass and straightedge to demonstrate constructions at the chalkboard, or an overhead projector and a compass with a felt-tip marker. Remind students that a straightedge is for drawing straight lines in constructions, not for measuring. The primary difference between a compass-and-straightedge construction and a drawing or sketch of a geometric figure is that measuring is not allowed in constructions.

Pattern-Block and Geometry Templates

In *Kindergarten* through *Third Grade Everyday Mathematics,* children use a Pattern-Block Template for explorations of plane figures. Beginning in fourth grade, students use a Geometry Template with more shapes and measurement scales to help them in more detailed explorations of categories of triangles and quadrangles. The measuring devices include inch and centimeter scales, a Percent Circle useful for making circle graphs, and both full-circle and half-circle protractors.

Pattern Blocks and Geometric Solids

In *Kindergarten* through *Third Grade Everyday Mathematics,* children use building blocks and pattern blocks to motivate the study of 1- and 2-dimensional geometry. These activities serve as background for a methodical approach, beginning in fourth grade, to making 2-dimensional maps of structures and 3-dimensional models of prisms and pyramids from 2-dimensional patterns. Pattern blocks are also used to explore fractions in Grades 2 through 5.

Straws and Twist-Ties

Constructing 2- and 3-dimensional objects with straws and twist-ties is a popular activity, beginning in *First Grade Everyday Mathematics.*

Teachers find that most students have little trouble constructing polygons with straws and connectors. The ends of the ties may need to be pinched a little to slide into the straws. If you have to use large-diameter straws, fold back an inch or so of the end of the connector for a tighter joint. To keep the size of polygons with more than five sides to sensible limits, use shorter straws. Except for triangles, polygons are easily twisted so that they don't lie "flat."

For more information, see Section 13.13: Geometry Tools and Techniques.

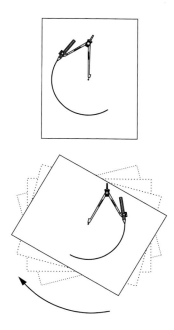

For more information, see Section 13.13.1: Compass-and-Straightedge Constructions.

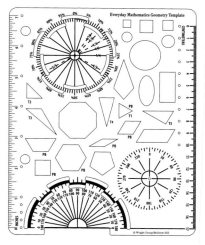

The Geometry Template

For more information, see Section 13.4: Planes and Plane Figures and Section 13.5: Space and 3-D Figures.

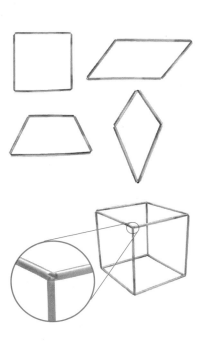

For more information, see Section 13.13.4: Straws and Twist-Ties.

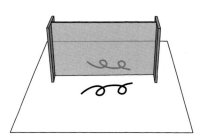

A transparent mirror

For details on body-part measures, see Section 14.1: Personal Measures.

When they are not lying flat, the figures are no longer in a plane and are no longer 2-dimensional figures. Have students make polygons on flat surfaces and encourage them to try to keep the polygons flat when picking them up.

For 3-dimensional figures, students can begin by putting two connectors, or one folded connector, into one end of a straw, so that it can be connected to two other straws. When more than three straws need to meet at a vertex, additional connectors may be inserted as needed, or students can first connect several pairs of straws and then make a bundle of one straw from each pair held together with an additional connector.

Transparent Mirrors

Students in *Fourth Grade Everyday Mathematics* experiment with reflections using transparent mirrors to move and draw reflection images. You are familiar with a regular mirror and the symmetric image you see in it. A transparent mirror also reflects an image, but it has the advantage that you can see through it and trace the mirror image. The drawing in the margin illustrates the reflection of a squiggle as you might see it in a transparent mirror.

As with any new tool, students need time, practice, and patience to develop skills using a transparent mirror. For accurate placement of images, students should:

- Lean down and look directly through the transparent mirror.
- Use the ends of the mirror to keep it perpendicular to the paper, that is, not hold the mirror off the desk or table.
- Use the inner part of the recessed edge along the bottom of the mirror to place the mirror on points or lines, or to draw mirror lines.
- Hold the transparent mirror firmly in position with one hand while doing any tracing behind it or while drawing lines along its recessed edge.

Students use transparent mirrors to study lines of symmetry in figures and to draw reflection images of their own artistic designs. The mirrors are especially useful for drawing reflections in tessellations.

3.2.5 Measuring Tools

Children in *Kindergarten* through *Third Grade Everyday Mathematics* use a wide variety of informal and formal tools for measuring. The informal ones, including body parts such as hands and feet or the edges of their journals, are relatively easy to manage. This section discusses some of the more formal, or *standardized*, measuring tools.

Protractors and the Percent Circle

In *Third Grade Everyday Mathematics,* children explore rotations and angles using straws and measure angles informally, identifying, for example, a right angle as a quarter-turn. Fourth graders review angles with straws and then use both kinds of protractors to find more precise measures of angles. First, they make 360° angle measurers from journal drawings and straws. Next they use full-circle protractors on transparencies made from a Math Master. To use a full-circle protractor, students must measure angles in a clockwise direction.

Later, students graduate to half-circle protractors, which are slightly more complicated to use because, unlike full-circle protractors that measure angles in a clockwise direction, half-circle protractors have scales for measuring in either a clockwise or counterclockwise direction.

The authors of *Everyday Mathematics* developed the Percent Circle to make measuring and constructing circle graphs easier. The *Percent Circle* is a full-circle protractor on the Geometry Template with the circumference marked in percents rather than degrees. This allows fifth graders to interpret and construct circle graphs before they tackle the complicated calculations needed to construct circle graphs with a protractor, which they learn in sixth grade.

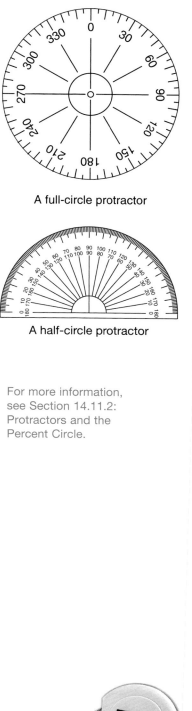

A full-circle protractor

A half-circle protractor

For more information, see Section 14.11.2: Protractors and the Percent Circle.

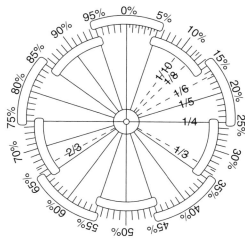

The Percent Circle

Rulers and Tape Measures

Along with weighing scales and balances, rulers and tape measures are among the first tools used for practical everyday measurements, both in human history and in the lives of students. In the early grades, students learn to give ballpark estimates of heights and lengths; then, over the years, they get progressively more sophisticated in their use of measuring instruments to find approximate lengths. In later grades, *carpenters' rules* are important tools for applying the "half" fractions—$\frac{1}{2}$, $\frac{1}{4}$, $\frac{1}{8}$, and so on, each fraction being half the previous one. Metersticks and centimeter rulers are instructive when teaching about decimals.

If your students use retractable tape measures, teach and enforce the "2-inch, 5-centimeter no-zap rule": Do not "zap" the tape measure until no more than 2 inches or 5 centimeters show. This will extend the life of these tools, as well as make your own life quieter and easier.

For more information, see Section 14.11.4: Scales and Balances.

For more information, see Section 17.2.4: Solving Open Sentences.

Scales and Balances

A scale is another historically old measuring tool. *Scales* are used to measure how heavy things are according to a standard weight. Different scales are used for different purposes, both in everyday life and in *Everyday Mathematics.*

In first grade, pan balances are used to introduce the symbols for relations such as $<$, $>$, and $=$. Through third grade, children write number models using these symbols. Beginning in fifth grade, pan balances serve as concrete models for open sentences.

4 Organizing Students

The following sections outline ideas for managing your classroom as students do mathematics.

▶ 4.1 Cooperative Groupings

Cooperative learning helps students by:

- Improving attitudes toward learning and academic achievement;
- Improving social skills and time spent on task;
- Helping develop speaking, listening, and writing skills;
- Creating an atmosphere for sharing ideas and problem-solving strategies that they may not have discovered on their own;
- Preparing them for real-life situations in which people often share responsibilities with others and need to cooperate and work together toward common goals.

The next few sections give suggestions for forming and managing partnerships and small groups.

Groups and Partnerships

For simplicity, the word *group* is used to refer to both partners and small groups. Learning becomes a dynamic process during group activities, as interaction among group members encourages an inquisitive spirit and introduces new avenues for exploration while instilling a spirit of teamwork.

Because *Everyday Mathematics* provides many group activities, both teacher-directed and independent, you may want to plan seating arrangements accordingly so that students can make the transition from whole-class work to group work with minimal disruption.

Use careful thought and planning when assigning students to groups. The best lessons can fail if groups are poorly formed. Having students work with their best friends does not always create a constructive learning environment. And if teams are formed at random, for example, students with the lowest skill levels could all end up in one group. Along with your personal knowledge of each student's skill level, the following teacher-tested strategies may be helpful:

- Make groups heterogeneous with regard to skill, gender, and race or ethnicity. The mixed achievement levels within groups allow for peer tutoring. Randomly selected groups or special-interest groups can be formed occasionally to vary the learning experience, but heterogeneous groupings usually work best.

- To arrange the class into groups, list the students from highest to lowest skill or achievement level. Take one student from the beginning of the list, one from the end, and two from the middle to form each group. When it is necessary to break a team into partners, match high with medium or medium with low achievers.

- A good size for small groups is four students, which also allows for pairs working together within the group. If the number of children is not divisible by 4, place one or two remaining students in a group that will best fit their needs. If three students remain, form another group.

- Keep group assignments for about six weeks. If situations impede a group's progress, make changes as necessary.

Team Building and Group Etiquette

For students to work cooperatively in groups, there often needs to be a team-building process to establish the team's identity, spirit, and responsibility to one another. If students don't know one another, "getting to know you" activities can help. For example, have students make lists of likes and dislikes, and then have them look for differences and common interests.

Even though students have worked in groups before, it is important that you take time during the first few weeks of school to review partner and small-group etiquette. The value of group study is diminished if social interaction replaces purposeful learning.

Post the three basic principles of constructive partner and group interaction: *Guide, Check,* and *Praise.* Then, during the first few days of the year, have students share what they think these terms mean. Guide the discussion to cover the following points:

Guide

- Help and demonstrate what to do without telling or doing everything yourself.
- Take turns.
- Choose only one student to get help from the teacher if the group needs it.

Check

- Pay attention and listen to others.
- If someone makes a mistake, respond positively in a helpful way. (Supply a list of helpful phrases such as *Try again, Good try,* and *Close.*)
- Help fellow group members find correct responses.

Praise

- Let others know they are doing a good job.
- Praise others. (Help students compile a list of appropriate praise words and phrases.)

> *Partnership Principles*
> 1. Guide
> 2. Check
> 3. Praise

To establish a positive learning environment, have students brainstorm with you about a good set of general rules of behavior. Post these rules on the bulletin board so that you can refer students to them as needed. Such rules might include the following:

- Be polite to one another.
- Use quiet voices.
- Talk about problems, but don't argue.
- Do not let others do all of the work.
- Share materials.
- Move quietly.

Duties of Group Members

Each group member may be assigned a specific role that changes daily or weekly. Some roles can be eliminated or modified depending on the activity and grade level. This list suggests possible roles and duties:

Recorder Writes group answers and strategies used; can also act as the reporter for the group.

Reader Reads problems, text selections, directions, and so on.

Facilitator Makes sure that everyone is on task and encourages participation from each group member. Uses positive encouragement such as the following:

- *We need to work on problem 3.*
- *Which step is next?*

Gatekeeper Makes sure one person does not monopolize the activity and ensures equal participation. Uses positive questions such as the following:

- *Denise, how would you do this?*
- *Do you agree, Eric?*
- *What do you think, Shawna?*

Materials/Supply Handler Gathers and returns all materials needed for group activities.

Summarizer Sums up group solutions, opinions, or findings.

Duties of the Teacher

You may also want to share with students some specific classroom roles for the teacher such as those in the following list:

- Explains the activity.
- Monitors groups to make sure they are working in the right direction and that behavior is appropriate.
- Answers group questions and assists as necessary.
- Assesses group/individual skills.
- Provides closure for each lesson or activity.

Resources for Cooperative Learning

Artzt, A. F., and Newman, C. M. (1997). *How to Use Cooperative Learning in the Mathematics Class (Second Edition)*. Reston, VA: National Council of Teachers of Mathematics.

Andrini, B., and Kagan, S. (1992). *Cooperative Learning and Mathematics*. San Juan Capistrano, CA: Kagan Cooperative Learning.

Johnson, D. W., and Johnson, R. T. (1991). *Learning Mathematics and Cooperative Learning*. Edina, MN: Interaction Book Company.

Johnson, D. W., Johnson, R. T., and Holubec, E. J. (1994). *The Nuts and Bolts of Cooperative Learning*. Edina, MN: Interaction Book Company.

Kagan, S. (1992). *Cooperative Learning*. San Juan Capistrano, CA: Kagan Cooperative Learning.

Shulman, J. H., Lotan, R. A., and Whitcomb, J. A. (Eds.) (1998). *Groupwork in Diverse Classrooms: A Casebook for Educators*. New York: Teachers College Press.

▶ 4.2 Group Responses

Group-response activities allow all students to participate at their own levels without being put on the spot. More-skilled students have the opportunity to lead, while others hear them and are thereby strengthened in the concepts in which they are weak.

Establish a brisk rhythm, with responses given simultaneously and clearly. Keep group-response activities brief. If you have students work in small groups or sit around tables, you can focus on one group at a time, even if the whole class is responding. This will help you identify students who may need extra help.

▶ 4.3 Ideas for "Built-In" Mathematics

Teachers who piloted the *Everyday Mathematics* program contributed the following suggestions:

- When disputes between two students arise that could be settled in either one's favor, have each student choose a number between 1 and 100. Pick a number yourself and tell it to a third party or write it down secretly. Explain that the one who guesses closest to your number will be the "winner." After settling the issue, ask questions such as *Is this fair? What makes it fair?* You can extend or limit the range of numbers as appropriate for the situation or the grade level.

- Whenever the opportunity to choose an option presents itself, have the students vote. Tell them to vote for what they want but that they can only vote once. Be sure they understand that the option receiving the most votes is the one by which they all must abide. Students can then tally, count, and compare totals. In the case of ties, ask students to suggest a fair way to proceed.

- When you give directions, quantify as often as you can. For example, *Six students may use the Reading Corner, and five may use the Math Center.*

management guide

- Whenever possible, have students line up according to specified categories such as *everyone wearing something red, everyone wearing a belt,* or *everyone wearing brown shoes.* Extend the routine using *or, and, not,* and so on: *everyone wearing a belt or shorts and not wearing brown shoes.*

- Alternatively, have students line up without revealing the category to them. For this version of "What's My Rule?" determine a category and then call out the names of students who fit the category. Then ask the class to explain why you chose those particular students. Don't insist on your rule if students see one that is equally valid. You might say *What I had in mind was . . ., but yours works, too,* or *I didn't think of yours.*

- Dice and spinners are good random-number generators. You can make nonstandard dice by putting self-sticking number labels on standard dice or wooden cubes. Vary the numbers to make new games.

- When minor decisions need to be made or when you can't quite think of a way to perform a particular task, take a few minutes to have students think about the problem. Discuss their ideas, as they are often great. This also gives students a chance to solve real problems.

- If you have a Math Center, don't let it get too cluttered. Introduce new items and remove old ones to maintain students' interest.

- Assign an *identification number* to each student at the beginning of the year, possibly using large numbers such as 10,001 with older students. Then use the numbers to label nonconsumable items such as books, calculators, and rulers that the students borrow during the year. This will help you match a misplaced item with its user. You can also use the numbers in various games and activities such as the following:
  - Tell students *Prime numbers stand up* or *Multiples of 5 line up (*or *count off) in order.*
  - Write the identification numbers on small slips of paper and put them in a container. Draw a number at random when you need to pick someone for an activity or task.

5 Organizing Daily Routines and Displays

Most classes have routines for daily activities such as taking attendance or keeping track of the date. *Everyday Mathematics* strongly suggests that students take an active part in these routines, which provide many examples of mathematics in everyday contexts. The following sections contain general advice and tips from fellow teachers.

Semipermanent Chalk, a Useful Display Tool

There will be times when you will want to write or draw things on the board that cannot be erased with a standard board eraser. For example, you could draw a semipermanent array of dots to represent a geoboard. Figures drawn with regular chalk could be erased, leaving the array behind.

If you can't or don't want to buy semipermanent chalk, here are two ways to make semipermanent chalk drawings:

- Dissolve sugar in some hot water until the water can no longer absorb any additional sugar. Drop a piece of porous (not dustless) chalk into the sugar solution and let it stand overnight. The chalk will soak up the sugar solution and become resistant to erasure. When not in use, keep the chalk in a sealed container so that it stays moist. When you make a mark on the board with this chalk, the mark may not be visible at first. It will become visible when it has dried. Once dried, the marks can be easily erased with a wet cloth or sponge but not with a board eraser.

- Thoroughly wet the area where you want a semipermanent drawing. Draw with regular chalk while the board is wet. Let it dry completely. Now you will be able to write on the base drawing and erase a number of times without losing the base drawing. To remove the base drawing, simply wash it off with water.

5.1 Kindergarten through Grade 3 Daily Routines

In *Kindergarten* through *Third Grade Everyday Mathematics,* children take an active role in the daily routines of taking attendance, keeping track of the date, counting the days in school, observing and recording weather conditions, and managing the daily schedule and classroom job assignments. Through these routines, they encounter mathematics in everyday contexts and develop and practice skills in many mathematical strands. While fourth through sixth graders are less likely to benefit from spending time on these routines, you may want to consider extending one or two of them in your classroom as suggested below.

- Use daily attendance data throughout the school year. For example, students might make graphs to discover trends, such as whether certain weekdays or certain months have substantially more absences than others. Follow up by discussing possible reasons for the trends.

- Use a number line to establish a school year timeline. Rotate students through the job of *class historian,* whose responsibility is to write about a memorable event each school day and attach it to the timeline. The number line can also serve as a frame of reference for counting and numeration activities throughout the year.

- Collect daily temperature data. Use both Fahrenheit and Celsius temperature scales so that students can practice comparing and converting between them. Make graphs or other displays to look for trends in the data. In Kindergarten through Grade 3, children made bar graphs of temperature data by color-coding intervals on a thermometer scale. Your students could make line graphs of temperature data for each day or of average temperatures for each week or month.

- Compare weather maps from a local source and a national daily newspaper or Web site on a monthly basis to observe differences in climate changes in different parts of the country. If possible, keep the maps on the Class Data Pad (see below) so that by the end of the school year, nine months of data can be seen and compared. Weather maps also help students become familiar with the United States map in a meaningful way.

▶ 5.2 Class Data Pad

Throughout the year, you and the students will have opportunities to collect information that can greatly enrich the content of the *Everyday Mathematics* program. Data collected in and out of the classroom can be analyzed and graphed, or used to make up number stories, several times over the course of the year. For example, students might find the middle number for a collection of data, graph the data set at some other time, and compare it with a related set of data at still another time.

To use this data repeatedly, record it on a large pad of newsprint and call it the Class Data Pad. With the Class Data Pad you can save sheets on the pad for later use. If you label large, stick-on notes and position them so that they extend over the edges of pages, you can easily index and retrieve stored data for students to write their own number stories or when you need information for problems.

6 Differentiating Instruction

This edition of *Everyday Mathematics* includes extended support for teachers to recognize and individualize the program for students with different learning needs. Major initiatives include:

- Adding Key Concepts and Skills tied to Year-End Goals to each lesson;
- Relating optional *Readiness* and *Enrichment* activities to the Key Concepts and Skills;
- Suggesting modifications to assessing children's performance on the Progress Check written assessments in the *Assessment Handbook*™;
- Providing more variations to games and routines;
- Highlighting opportunities for students to respond to open-ended questions and problems;
- Providing ideas for adjusting lesson activities;
- Highlighting assessment opportunities in a variety of forms;
- Providing ideas for supporting mathematical language in lessons.

For more information about managing your classroom to meet students' special needs and supporting English language learners, see the *Differentiation Handbook*™.

Resources on Differentiation

Baxter, J., Woodward, J., and Olson, D. (2001). "Effects of Reform-Based Mathematics Instruction on Low Achievers in Five Third-Grade Classrooms." *The Elementary School Journal 101(5):* pp. 529–547.

NOTE: You can save some data from year to year to explore changes over longer periods of time.

NOTE: You could set aside a portion of a bulletin board or chalkboard to record data, but this might be inconvenient because both have limited surface area.

Garnett, K. (1998). "Math Learning Disabilities." Retrieved from www.ldonline.org/article/5896

Gregory, G. (2003). *Differentiated Instructional Strategies in Practice.* Thousand Oaks, CA: Corwin Press.

Johnson, D. (2000). *Teaching Mathematics to Gifted Students in a Mixed-Ability Classroom.* Arlington, VA: ERIC Clearinghouse on Disabilities and Gifted Education.

Lock, R. (1997). "Adapting Mathematics Instruction in the General Education Classroom for Students with Mathematics Disabilities." *Reprint from the LD Forum: Council for Learning Disabilities (Winter 1996).* Retrieved from www.ldonline.org/article/Adapting_Mathematics_ Instruction_in_the_General_Education_Classroom_for_Students_with_ Mathematics_Disabilities

Tomlinson, C. (1999). *The Differentiated Classroom.* Alexandria, VA: Association for Supervision and Curriculum Development.

Usiskin, Z. (1994). "Individual Differences in the Teaching and Learning of Mathematics." *UCSMP Newsletter 14 (Winter 1994).* Chicago, IL: University of Chicago School Mathematics Project.

Villa, R., and Thousand, J. (Eds.) (2005). *Creating an Inclusive School.* Alexandria, VA: Association for Supervision and Curriculum Development.

Woodward, J., and Baxter, J. (1997). "The Effects of Reform-Based Mathematics Instruction on Low Achieving Students in Inclusive Settings." *Exceptional Students 63(3):* pp. 373–388.

7 Managing Assessment

From the beginning, the philosophy of *Everyday Mathematics* regarding assessment has been clear. From the *Assessment Handbook:*

> Too often, school assessment tends to provide only scattered snapshots of student achievement rather than continuous records of growth. In *Everyday Mathematics,* assessment is like a motion picture, revealing the development of each student's mathematical understanding over time while also giving the teacher useful feedback about the instructional needs of both individual students and the class as a whole.

For assessment to be useful to teachers, students, parents, and others, the *Everyday Mathematics* authors believe that . . .

- teachers need to have a variety of assessment tools and techniques from which to choose so that students can demonstrate what they know in a variety of ways and teachers can have reliable information from multiple sources.

- students should be included in the assessment process. Self assessment and reflection are skills that students will develop over time if encouraged.

- assessment and instruction should be closely aligned. Assessment should assist teachers in making instructional decisions concerning both individual students and the whole class.
- assessment should focus on all important outcomes, not simply on outcomes that are easy to measure.
- a good assessment program makes instruction easier.
- the best assessment plans are those developed by teachers working collaboratively within their own schools and districts.

The third edition of *Everyday Mathematics* provides teachers with extensive support in managing these assessment goals, including:

- Clearly articulated *grade-level goals* for the program organized by mathematics strands across all grades. Specific opportunities for assessment are identified throughout the lessons and are linked to grade-level goals.
- *Ongoing assessment notes* to better support your understanding of the role of your grade-level mathematics content in the context of the grade-level goals. Specifically, these notes help you distinguish activities in which you can:
  - *Recognize student achievement* by collecting assessment data to monitor students' progress with respect to grade-level goals. These data come from a variety of sources, such as journal-page problems, Mental Math and Reflexes problems, game record sheets, and Math Boxes.
  - *Inform instruction* through tips that help you anticipate students' mistakes or misconceptions and highlight their successful solution strategies. Suggestions are given on how to evaluate students' performance and how to adapt your instruction to meet individual needs when appropriate.
- Improved support for *ongoing learning and practice* of mathematics skills by students through games, Math Boxes, and Study Links.
- End-of-unit *Progress Checks* are tied to grade-level goals that students studied in that unit and previous units. Progress Checks include student self-assessments, written assessments that distinguish between summative and formative understanding of concepts, oral and slate questions, and an open-response problem.

Resources on Assessment

Black, P., and William, D. (1998). "Assessment and Classroom Learning." *Assessment in Education 5(1):* pp. 7–74.

Black, P., and William, D. (1998). "Inside the Black Box: Raising Standards Through Classroom Assessment." *Phi Delta Kappan 80(2):* pp. 139–149.

Bush, W. S. (Ed.) (2001). *Mathematics Assessment: Cases and Discussion Questions for Grades K–5.* Reston, VA: National Council of Teachers of Mathematics.

For more information, see the *Assessment Handbook.*

Glanfield, F., Stenmark, J. K., and Bush, W. S. (Eds.) (2003). *Mathematics Assessment: A Practical Handbook for Grades K–2.* Reston, VA: National Council of Teachers of Mathematics.

Kloosterman, P., and Lester, F. K., Jr. (Eds.) (2004). *Results and Interpretations of the 1990 through 2000 Mathematics Assessments of the National Assessment of Educational Progress.* Reston, VA: National Council of Teachers of Mathematics.

Kulm, G. (1994). *Mathematics Assessment: What Works in the Classroom.* San Francisco: Jossey-Bass Publishers.

Mathematical Science Education Board/National Research Council. (1993a). *Measuring Up: Prototypes for Mathematics Assessment.* Washington, DC: National Academy Press.

Mathematical Sciences Education Board/National Research Council. (1993b). *Measuring What Counts: A Conceptual Guide for Mathematics Assessment.* Washington, DC: National Academy Press.

National Assessment Governing Board. (2008). *Mathematics Framework for the 2009 National Assessment of Educational Progress.* Washington, DC: U.S. Department of Education. Retrieved from www.nagb.org/publications/frameworks.htm

National Council of Teachers of Mathematics. (2006). *Position Statement: High-Stakes Tests.* Reston, VA: Author. Retrieved from www.nctm.org/about/content.aspx?id=6356

National Council of Teachers of Mathematics. (2000). *Principles and Standards for School Mathematics.* Reston, VA: Author.

National Council of Teachers of Mathematics. (1995). *Assessment Standards for School Mathematics.* Reston, VA: Author.

Shepard, L. A. (1995). "Using Assessment to Improve Learning." *Educational Leadership 52(5):* pp. 38–43.

Stenmark, J. K., Bush, W. S., and Allen, C. (Eds.) (2001). *Mathematics Assessment: A Practical Handbook for Grades 3–5.* Reston, VA: National Council of Teachers of Mathematics.

Stiggens, R. J. (1997). *Student-Centered Classroom Assessment.* Englewood Cliffs, NJ: Prentice-Hall.

Webb, N. L., and Coxford, A. F. (Eds.) (1993). *Assessment in the Mathematics Classroom: 1993 Yearbook.* Reston, VA: National Council of Teachers of Mathematics.

8 Providing for Home-and-School Communication

Dialogue and discussion, as well as experimentation and discovery, are at the heart of *Everyday Mathematics*. Parents accustomed to conventional mathematics programs may think that because students are not bringing home daily arithmetic drill sheets, they are not learning or doing mathematics. The Study Links and Family Letters described on the next page reassure them that this is not the case.

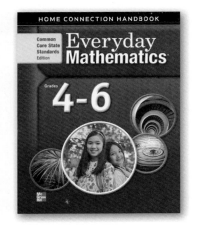

You received a *Home Connection Handbook* in your *Classroom Resource Package* that contains explanatory material about the *Everyday Mathematics* philosophy and program and suggestions for parents regarding how to become involved in their students' mathematics education. Much of the information in the *Home Connection Handbook* can be copied and sent to families to provide information about and promote involvement in the *Everyday Mathematics* curriculum.

▶ 8.1 Study Links and Family Letters

 Study Links activities serve two main purposes: They *promote follow-up* to classroom activities and *involve parents or guardians* in their children's mathematics education.

Study Links activities also:

- Encourage students to take initiative and responsibility;
- Reinforce newly-learned skills and concepts;
- Provide ongoing practice with computation;
- Relate what is learned in school to the students' lives outside of school, tying mathematics to their everyday world;
- Serve as informal assessment tools.

At the beginning of the year, you are encouraged to send home the introductory Family Letter. The last Study Link of each unit is a Family Letter to allow you to continue to involve families throughout the year. Of course, you are encouraged to customize letters to best support your individual needs.

9 Numeration and Order

Contents

The history of mathematics records the invention of increasingly sophisticated systems of numbers in order to solve problems in daily life. The natural numbers 1, 2, 3, . . . enabled people to count and to measure. Later, fractions allowed people to describe parts of objects and to report measurements between whole units. Decimals, which came into use in Europe in the 1500s, greatly simplified computation and provided a unified system of notation. Negative numbers were introduced to represent change relative to a fixed position, as in profit and loss. *Everyday Mathematics* emphasizes the various representations of numbers and the equivalencies among them.

Numbers and counting are integral to most of the topics in this book. This chapter addresses noncomputational aspects of numbers, including number systems and uses of numbers. Numbers are also discussed at length in Chapter 10: Arithmetic Operations; Chapter 16: Estimation, Mental Arithmetic, and Number Sense; and Chapter 17: Patterns, Sequences, Functions, and Algebra.

9.1 Number Uses

If you're looking for one phrase to capture the overall philosophy of *Everyday Mathematics,* it might be "Numbers All Around." In Kindergarten, students explore their surroundings and magazines and other media in search of numbers. In first grade, students create a

"Numbers All Around Museum" and collect numbers about themselves. In second grade, students collect numbers about their worlds and curate another Numbers All Around Museum. Similar lessons using numbers and mathematics from students' everyday experiences continue through *Sixth Grade Everyday Mathematics.*

The numbers that surround us in today's world are not all the same. Some are counts, some are measures, and others are used for identification. The developers of *Everyday Mathematics* have identified five basic categories, or *use classes,* that cover 90% of number uses:

- Counts
- Measures
- Locations
- Ratio comparisons
- Codes

Counts and *measures* are straightforward: 6 eggs, 3 pounds, and so on. *Locations* are a bit trickier: 9:05 A.M. expresses a location in time; 72°C is a location on a temperature scale; pairs of numbers such as 42°N, 87°W mark a location on Earth's surface.

A *ratio comparison* is a number such as *3 times as much* or $\frac{1}{2}$ *as many.* Ratio comparisons are less common in primary grade mathematics than are counts and measures, but they become increasingly important in later grades.

Codes are numbers used as identification tags, which often also include letters. Codes are used for credit cards, Social Security numbers, phone numbers, and so on. Often a code has several parts. For example, in the zip code 60637:

6	refers to Illinois, Missouri, Nebraska, or Kansas.
06	refers to Chicago.
37	refers to the neighborhood in Chicago that includes the University of Chicago.

Students are also interested in the way ancient people used numbers. In *Everyday Mathematics,* they explore the Roman numeral system in which letters used alone and in combination to represent numbers are a sort of code when compared to our decimal system. Roman numerals are still found on clocks, building cornerstones, preliminary pages in books, and copyright dates in some movies.

For more information on numbers as locations, see Chapter 15: Reference Frames.

Roman Numerals

I = 1	XX = 20 (2 tens)	CC = 200
II = 2	XXX = 30 (3 tens)	CCC = 300
III = 3	XL = 40 (50 less 10)	CD = 400
IV = 4	L = 50	D = 500
V = 5	LX = 60 (50 plus 10)	CM = 900
VI = 6	LXX = 70 (50 plus 20)	M = 1,000
VII = 7	LXXX = 80 (50 plus 30)	$\overline{\text{X}}$ = 10,000
VIII = 8	XC = 90 (100 less 10)	$\overline{\text{C}}$ = 100,000
IX = 9	C = 100	∞ = 100,000,000 or infinity
X = 10		

In Grades 4 through 6, students begin to encounter numbers used as constants in formulas, such as the number π in a formula for the circumference of a circle, $C = \pi * d$ or $C = \pi d$. In this formula, π is a ratio comparison. In other formulas, constants may represent counts, measures, or other use classes.

In organizing *Everyday Mathematics,* the authors have been careful to balance the types of numbers that students are exposed to in lessons, journals, and activity sheets. Although use classes are occasionally made explicit, more often than not they are simply implicit in the context of a problem.

For more information see Section 10.3: Use Classes and Situation Diagrams and Section 17.2.1: Uses of Variables.

▶ 9.2 Whole Numbers

Thousands of years ago people managed without numbers or with only the numbers 1, 2, 3, 4, ... Eventually, however, these numbers were found to be inadequate for certain purposes, and other number systems were invented. The inventions of these new number systems were motivated either by the everyday needs of people or mathematical needs, or by both. In this and following sections, we discuss various number systems, including whole numbers, positive and negative rational numbers, and real numbers.

9.2.1 Counting

In the early grades of *Everyday Mathematics*, the most frequent use of the numbers 1, 2, 3, 4, . . . is in counting. The program is committed to having students view numbers in use; and counting involves a counting unit, such as 4 cars, 8 cats, 101 people. The numbers 1, 2, 3, 4, . . . are often referred to as the *counting numbers* or the *natural numbers.*

Sometimes, zero is considered to be a natural number. For example, computer scientists often begin counting with zero. If zero is included with the set of natural numbers, the result is what most elementary school curricula call the *whole numbers.*

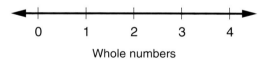

Whole numbers

It is more important for students to understand what zero means than it is for them to know the names for various sets of numbers. Zero does not represent "nothing"; rather, it is the number of cats in the room if there are no cats in the room. It is the starting place for measures and for reference frames such as thermometers. The digit 0 holds places in place-value numeration and permits the use of efficient procedures for adding, subtracting, multiplying, and dividing numbers.

Today, people everywhere write whole numbers in the same way. The system of numeration we all use was invented in India more than a thousand years ago and came to Western Europe via the Middle East and North Africa. This highly efficient system, known as *Hindu-Arabic numeration,* has contributed significantly to the tremendous advances in mathematics and science in the past 500 years.

NOTE: In Arabic, the shapes of the digits differ from those used in most other languages, but the underlying system of numeration is the same.

chapter 9

Hindu-Arabic numeration uses 10 digits to represent whole numbers, called *base-ten numeration*. The digits are placed according to one basic rule: The value of a digit is 10 times the place to its right. Thus the 2 in 72 is worth just 2, but the 2 in 27 is worth 10 times as much, or 20; and the 2 in 275 is worth another 10 times as much, or 200. The system is called a *place-value* system because the value of a digit depends on its place in the number.

By fourth grade, *Everyday Mathematics* students are expected to be familiar with numbers to 1,000,000 and beyond, and to have mastered the following counting skills:

- Counting by 1s up and back, to and from, any number through 10,000 and beyond;
- Counting by 2s, 3s, and 5s to and from any multiples of these numbers in the same range;
- Counting by 10s, 100s, and 1,000s to and from any number in the same range;
- Counting by multiples of 4, 6, 7, 8, and 9, up to 100 and beyond;
- Counting by negative numbers forward and backward from a given number, but especially forward past zero into the positive numbers.

9.2.2 Ordinal Numbers

The counting numbers tell how many; for example, 5 apples, 3 books, or 2 birds. A different kind of number, called an *ordinal number,* tells the order of objects in a sequence, such as first, second, third, and so on.

Ordinal numbers are not as simple as they seem. Suppose, for example, you have an apple, a pear, a peach, a banana, and a plum. Counting these pieces of fruit is easy; there are five 5 of them. But assigning ordinals is not so easy. The apple is listed first, but it could easily be listed third or fifth. Indeed, the apple might be first in alphabetical order and fifth in weight. Also, *5* refers to the entire collection of fruit, but *fifth* refers to only the last piece in a sequential ordering of the five fruits. Fortunately, students can learn to use ordinal numbers without having to bother about these rather abstract issues.

▶ ## 9.3 Fractions, Decimals, Percents, and Rational Numbers

The whole numbers are adequate for counting, but measurement requires numbers between the whole numbers. A pencil, for example, might be more than 5 inches long but less than 6 inches long. The *measure numbers,* or *positive rational numbers,* fill this need. The positive rational numbers include fractions, terminating or repeating decimals, and the numbers {1, 2, 3, . . .}. The efficient and convenient notations we have today for fractions and decimals evolved later, but the numbers themselves were invented thousands of years ago.

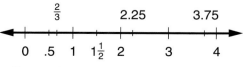

Zero and some positive rational numbers

NOTE: The term *rational number* may be confusing. Rational numbers are no more "reasonable" than other numbers. Rational numbers are called *rational* because they can be written as *ratios* of integers. Every positive rational number can be expressed as a ratio or fraction in which the numerator is a whole number and the denominator is a nonzero whole number. For example, the rational number 7.5 can be expressed as the ratio $\frac{75}{10}$.

The whole numbers are adequate for addition and multiplication of whole numbers in that the sum of any two whole numbers is a whole number and the product of any two whole numbers is a whole number. But not all differences and quotients of whole numbers are whole numbers. For example, $7 \div 2$ and $3 - 5$ do not have whole-number answers. With the positive rational numbers, however, all division problems with whole numbers have answers, except for division by zero.

Fractions are confusing to many people, perhaps because the procedures for adding, subtracting, multiplying, and dividing them seem arbitrary and unpredictable. For example, it is likely that few people really understand the "invert and multiply" rule for division by a fraction. It may be that these mysterious fraction manipulations, often taught without real-life problems or concrete embodiments to give them meaning, are what have convinced so many adults that mathematics is impossible to understand and that getting "correct" results is more a matter of good luck than good comprehension.

One reason many people experience difficulties with fractions may be that many school programs avoid fractions for several years while students work exclusively with whole numbers. When students are finally introduced to fractions, many find them confusing because the results often run counter to what they expect from having dealt only with whole numbers. For example, unlike whole numbers, fractions are generally harder to add than to multiply; a product may be smaller than its factors; a quotient may be larger than the number being divided; and "repeated addition" has little meaning in the multiplication of two fractions.

So, while much of the content of mathematics programs for the primary grades is concerned with whole numbers, including place-value notation, addition, subtraction, and multiplication, *Everyday Mathematics* extends traditional work with these numbers by introducing students to:

- Negative numbers, with temperatures, timelines, and number lines, in Kindergarten;
- Fractions, with measures and "part of" situations, and decimals, mainly with notation, in first grade;
- More fractions such as "1 tenth of . . ." in second grade.

Early attention to fractions, decimals, and percents prepares students for learning about operations with numbers in these notations in Grades 4 through 6.

Students can better understand these new numbers when they are presented as part of everyday experiences. For example, even before the authors began to develop *Everyday Mathematics,* they found, through interviews with 5- and 6-year-olds, that young students respond quickly and accurately when asked for "half of" something, probably as a result of sharing things equally with siblings and friends. Building on these observations, the primary grades program includes negative numbers, fractions, decimals, and percents. These

NOTE: Strictly speaking, only decimals that *terminate* or *repeat,* such as 1.5 and 0.123123 . . . are rational numbers. Decimals that go on forever without repeating, such as 3.14159 . . . and 1.121221222 . . . are not.

NOTE: The numbers used to handle whole-number differences without whole-number answers are the *integers,* which are discussed in Section 9.4: Positive and Negative Numbers.

For more information on division by zero, see Section 11.2.4: Division Algorithms.

NOTE: Fractions may also be difficult for students simply because their symbols are more complicated than those of whole numbers.

are used mainly to convey information, without becoming involved in arithmetic operations. The authors found, in contrast to addition, subtraction, and division of fractions, that multiplication involving *half of . . .* or *1 tenth of . . .* is readily accepted by students, especially in contexts that pair *two of . . .* with *half of . . .* or *ten of . . .* with *1 tenth of . . .*.

9.3.1 Fraction and Decimal Notation

The importance of alternate notations for numbers is emphasized throughout *Everyday Mathematics.* All three notations for rational numbers—fractions, decimals, and percents—can help students see connections between rational numbers and whole numbers. Fractions build on ideas of equal sharing and whole-number operations, decimals extend the whole-number place-value system, and percents connect to the important ideas of ratio and proportion.

For more on repeating decimals, see Section 9.3.4: Rational Numbers and Decimals.

Fractions and decimals are technically interchangeable, but many common situations use one or the other as *standard* notation. For example, although fractions were once standard in stock-market reports, today decimals are used in most financial applications. Measures are commonly expressed as fractions in carpentry and other building trades, but decimals are used for virtually all measures in science and industry.

Representing repeating decimals requires a standardized notation, for example, $\frac{2}{3} = 0.\overline{6}$. The bar is used to indicate a digit or string of digits that repeat in the decimal form of a number.

The history of the development of fractions is fascinating. Fractions were first used in ancient times, probably in response to the need for more precise measures in situations in which whole-number units were insufficient. The ancient Egyptians used *unit fractions*—fractions with a numerator of 1, such as $\frac{1}{2}, \frac{1}{3}$, and $\frac{1}{8}$ —almost exclusively. More complicated fractions were then expressed as the sums of unit fractions, for example, $\frac{1}{2} + \frac{1}{4}$ for $\frac{3}{4}$. Even in modern times, unit fractions are sufficient for the everyday needs of many people.

Equivalent Names for Fractions

Like all numbers, fractions have many equivalent names. In fact, every fraction is just one of an infinite set of equivalent fractions. The fraction $\frac{2}{3}$, for example, is a member of the set $\{\frac{2}{3}, \frac{4}{6}, \frac{6}{9}, \frac{8}{12}, \frac{10}{15}, \cdots\}$. The fraction from such a set that has no common factors in the numerator and denominator is said to be in *simplest* or *standard* form, and this fraction is a convenient label for the entire set. But this simplest-form fraction is not always preferable to all other equivalent names. In fact, flexibility in arithmetic is gained by freely using whichever form is most convenient or appropriate for the purpose at hand. Truly numerate people artfully use one form for a number rather than another to express what they want or need to say. Also, "reducing" fractions to simplest form may result in the loss of important information. For example, saying that the fraction of people voting for a candidate was $\frac{7,500}{10,000}$ conveys more information than either $\frac{3}{4}$ or 75%.

NOTE: You may sometimes encounter the terms *common fraction* and *decimal fraction.* While these terms emphasize that these are two different notations for the same numbers, *Everyday Mathematics* uses the simpler terms *fraction* and *decimal.*

NOTE: The development of decimal notation for rational numbers, which occurred many centuries after fraction notation was first used, has a similarly rich history. For more information, see *The Norton History of the Mathematical Sciences* by Grattan-Guinness (1997) and *Number Words and Number Symbols: A Cultural History of Numbers* by Menninger (1992). Complete references can be found on page 77.

Everyday Mathematics promotes flexibility in using numbers, including fractions. Standard or simplest forms have their place, but to demand their use as the only acceptable form is counterproductive to learning.

9.3.2 Uses of Fractions

One reason fractions may be confusing is that they have many different meanings. The fraction $\frac{1}{4}$, for example, can have any of the following meanings:

- A part of a whole: $\frac{1}{4}$ of a pizza;
- A part of a collection: $\frac{1}{4}$ of a group of students;
- A measurement: $\frac{1}{4}$ mile;
- A division: $1 \div 4$;
- A rate or ratio: 1 part vinegar to 4 parts oil;
- A probability: 1 chance in 4;
- A pure number: the number halfway between 0 and $\frac{1}{2}$.

The idea of a *unit whole* is essential in the first two of these meanings. How big $\frac{1}{4}$ of a pizza is, for example, depends on how big the *whole* pizza is. To know how many students are in $\frac{1}{4}$ of a group, one needs to know how big the whole group is. In order to understand such *part-whole* fractions, students must appreciate the role of the unit whole. They should also understand that the denominator tells how many parts are in the whole and that the numerator tells how many such parts are included in the fraction. In *Everyday Mathematics,* the unit whole is called the *ONE.* Part-whole fractions are perhaps the easiest to understand, and many primary grade activities in *Everyday Mathematics* involve them.

In fractions and in measures, the unit is also vitally important: $\frac{1}{4}$ mile is quite different from $\frac{1}{4}$ inch. Using fractions makes it possible to measure with more precision. With a ruler marked only in whole inches, for example, it is possible to measure precisely to only the nearest inch. But if the spaces between the whole-number marks are subdivided into equal intervals, then more precise measurements become possible. Other measuring tools such as graduated cylinders, measuring cups, and kitchen scales also subdivide the spaces between whole numbers of units. A significant part of learning to use such tools is learning to interpret the marks on the scales correctly.

In most other uses of fractions, there is no clear unit whole. In a ratio, for example, there is no unit whole. A ratio like $\frac{1}{4}$, which can also be written "1:4" or "1 to 4," might mean "one tablespoon of vinegar to four tablespoons of oil in a salad dressing." There is no unit whole in such fractions, nor is there in fractions that indicate division.

Fractions as equal parts of unit wholes and fractions on measurement scales and number lines get a good deal of attention in Grades 1 through 3. These kinds of fractions, along with fractions for division and fractions for rates and ratios, appear often in Grades 4 through 6 in a variety of applications.

NOTE: The notation $a \div b$ is used primarily in elementary school textbooks and ÷ is a common division key on calculators. $\frac{a}{b}$ and a/b, which have identical meanings to $a \div b$, are used virtually everywhere else. Because of computers, the a/b notation is more important than ever. The link between fractions and division is the key to converting fractions to decimals and percents. Therefore, *Fourth* through *Sixth Grade Everyday Mathematics* uses the symbol / to indicate division.

For more information,
see Section 16.4: Number
Sense and Mathematical
Connections.

9.3.3 Rates, Ratios, and Proportions

In both everyday situations and technical work, perhaps the most common use of fraction notation is to express *rates* and *ratios*. Rates, ratios, and what is sometimes called *proportional thinking* are very common in the everyday world, and people with good *number sense* and *measure sense* can handle such number relationships with ease. Unfortunately, everyday uses of rates seem to be difficult for many people. Much of the poor performance in mathematics reported in the professional literature and the popular press reflects failure with rate or ratio problems on inventory tests, or an inability to do proportional thinking in the workplace.

Rates

Rates are comparisons of pairs of quantities by division. The counts or measures in the numerator and denominator of a rate have *different* units, resulting in a compound unit for the rate.

A key to understanding rates is repeated exposure to the many uses of rates in everyday life. A rate of travel, or speed, can be expressed in miles per hour. For example, if a car travels 150 miles in 3 hours, its average speed is 150 miles/3 hours or 50 miles per hour (or 50 mi/hr, or 50 mph). Automobile fuel economy can be expressed in miles per gallon. For example, if a car travels 250 miles and uses 10 gallons of gasoline, its rate of fuel economy is 250 miles/10 gallons or 25 miles per gallon (or 25 mi/gal, or 25 mpg).

For more information on
rate diagrams, see Section
10.3.2: Multiplication and
Division Use Classes.

Beginning in *Fourth Grade Everyday Mathematics,* students solve problems using rate tables, along with the rate diagrams that they have used in previous years. A *rate table* has two rows or columns, one for each unit of measure in a rate problem, and an associated rate, which is used to fill out the table. Students may be given a rate and a table containing values for one measure as in the following example.

Gasoline mileage: 35 miles per gallon

miles	35							
gallons	1	2	3	4	5	6	7	8

Students may also be given a rate table containing some values for each measure, as in the next example.

There are 8 pints in a gallon.

pints	8	16		40			
gallons	1		3				

For more on "What's
My Rule?", see Section
17.1.3: Functions.

Students may recognize rate tables as a special kind of "What's My Rule?" table and may also notice similarities to the incomplete-number-line problems used throughout *Everyday Mathematics.*

Students in Grades 4 through 6 work with rate situations represented in tables, formulas, and graphs as in the following example. Consider the situation *Frank types an average of 45 words per minute.*

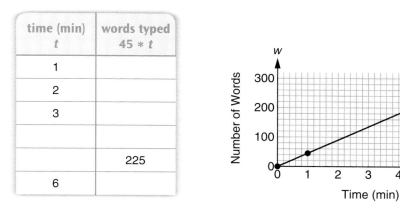

time (min) t	words typed $45 * t$
1	
2	
3	
	225
6	

Rule: Words typed w is 45 times the number of minutes t, or $w = 45 * t$.

A rate formula

A rate table

A rate graph

Each representation has its advantages, and an important goal of the program is to help students shift easily from one to another. Note that rate tables do not have to be oriented horizontally.

Students also learn to find *per-unit* rates. Per-unit rates can be a big help when grocery shopping; for example, *Do I want the 12-ounce can of juice for $1.57 (about 13¢/oz) or the 16-ounce can for $1.95 (about 12¢/oz)?* Per-unit rates are also useful for solving rate problems in other situations, especially before more algebraic methods like cross multiplication are introduced in *Sixth Grade Everyday Mathematics.*

Ratios

Whereas rates compare quantities that have different units, *ratios* compare quantities that have the *same* unit. In effect, the units "cancel" each other, and the resulting number has no unit. For example, the fraction $\frac{2}{20}$ could mean that 2 people out of 20 people in a class got an A on a test or that 2 pears out of 20 pears are ripe. It may even be a simplified fraction that expresses the fact that 20,000 people out of 200,000 people voted for a certain candidate in an election. In part, percents were developed in order to express ratio comparisons in a standardized form that is easy to understand. For example, 10% of the class got an A, 10% of the pears are ripe, and 10% of the people voted for the candidate.

Another frequent use of ratios is to indicate relative size, or *scale*. For example, if a picture of an object is drawn to $\frac{1}{10}$ scale, every length in the picture is $\frac{1}{10}$ the corresponding length in the actual object. In the language of transformations, the picture is a *size-change image* of the object by a factor of $\frac{1}{10}$. Such ratios can be found in dictionaries as well as on maps and scale drawings.

For more information, see Section 13.7.2: Size-Change Transformations.

Children begin making ratio comparisons informally in *Second Grade Everyday Mathematics,* when they look at price data and investigate questions such as *Is the price of a bicycle now more than twice its price in 1897?* By Grade 4, students are applying ratio comparisons to scale drawings. In the Grade 5 American Tour, they make ratio

chapter 9

comparisons of populations and other data using fractions, decimals, and percents. Fifth graders also calculate ratios of circumferences to diameters of circles to explore the value of π. Sixth graders use ratios to explore similar figures and unit ratios to compare ratios with each other. They also investigate an interesting application of scale known as the *Golden Ratio*.

The Golden Ratio

A pleasingly shaped figure called the *Golden Rectangle* appears in ancient Greek art and architecture, as well as in many other works of art throughout history. Students in *Sixth Grade Everyday Mathematics* read about the Golden Rectangle and construct one of their own using the procedure shown below.

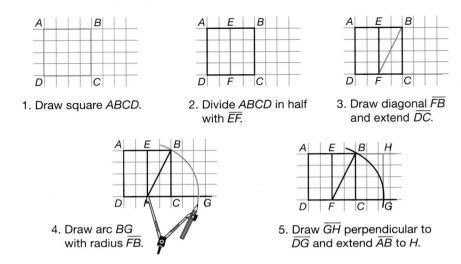

1. Draw square *ABCD*.

2. Divide *ABCD* in half with $\overline{EF}$.

3. Draw diagonal $\overline{FB}$ and extend $\overline{DC}$.

4. Draw arc *BG* with radius $\overline{FB}$.

5. Draw $\overline{GH}$ perpendicular to $\overline{DG}$ and extend $\overline{AB}$ to *H*.

Rectangle *AHGD* is called a *Golden Rectangle* because the ratio of the length of its longer side to the length of its shorter side, $\frac{DG}{AD}$, is the *Golden Ratio*, approximately 1.618 to 1. The Golden Ratio is often denoted by ϕ, the Greek letter *phi*. Students verify the approximation $\phi \approx 1.618$ for several instances, but are not expected to know where it comes from. The following derivation uses a little algebra and the Pythagorean theorem.

To make things simple, suppose that the length of a side of square *ABCD* is 1 inch. So the shorter legs of right triangles *EBF* and *CFB* in the figure in the margin have length $\frac{1}{2}$ inch, and the longer legs have length 1 inch.

By the Pythagorean theorem, the length of hypotenuse $\overline{FB}$, in inches, is

$$\sqrt{1^2 + \left(\tfrac{1}{2}\right)^2} = \sqrt{1 + \tfrac{1}{4}} = \sqrt{\tfrac{5}{4}} = \tfrac{\sqrt{5}}{2}$$

This length is also the length of $\overline{FG}$, because this segment is the rotation image of the hypotenuse $\overline{FB}$.

So the length, in inches, of the longer side $\overline{DG}$ of the Golden Rectangle is

$$\tfrac{1}{2} + \tfrac{\sqrt{5}}{2} = \tfrac{1}{2}(1 + \sqrt{5})$$

For more information on the Pythagorean theorem, see Section 13.4.2: Polygons (*n*-gons).

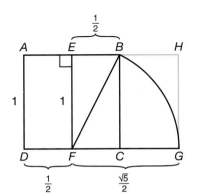

The length of the shorter side $\overline{AD}$ is simply 1 inch. So the Golden Ratio $\frac{\text{length of } \overline{DG}}{\text{length of } \overline{AD}}$ is

$$\phi = \frac{\frac{1}{2}(1 + \sqrt{5}) \text{ in.}}{1 \text{ in.}} = \frac{1}{2} + \frac{\sqrt{5}}{2}$$

As with all ratios, the unit, inches, in the numerator and denominator above "cancels" and the Golden Ratio has no units. To 10 digits, this number is 1.618033989, which rounds to 1.618, the approximate value of the Golden Ratio used in *Sixth Grade Everyday Mathematics*.

The Fibonacci Sequence

The Golden Ratio occurs in a fascinating way in a sequence of numbers called the Fibonacci sequence. The *Fibonacci sequence* starts with two 1s, after which the rule for the sequence is that the next number is the sum of the previous two numbers. The Fibonacci numbers are

$$1, 1, 2, 3, 5, 8, 13, 21, \ldots$$

If you take the ratios of successive terms in the Fibonacci sequence, you get a new sequence

$$\frac{1}{1}, \frac{2}{1}, \frac{3}{2}, \frac{5}{3}, \frac{8}{5}, \frac{13}{8}, \ldots$$

This sequence, expressed in decimal form, is

$$1, 2, 1.5, 1.\overline{6}, 1.6, 1.625, \ldots$$

It has been proven that these ratios of successive terms in the Fibonacci sequence approach the value of the Golden Ratio.

The Golden Ratio has many fascinating properties. For example, if you subtract 1 from the Golden Ratio, you get its reciprocal. That is,

$$\phi * (\phi - 1) = 1$$

Leonardo of Pisa (1170–1250), also known as "Fibonacci," was a great mathematician of medieval Europe who studied the Fibonacci numbers extensively more than 800 years ago. The Fibonacci numbers often appear in models of natural patterns such as the arrangement of leaves on certain plants and the shape of the spirals of the shells of certain shellfish. The Fibonacci sequence, the Golden Ratio, and related topics continue to be investigated today by both pure and applied mathematicians. The *Fibonacci Quarterly* is a journal devoted to the Fibonacci numbers.

A Note on Rate versus Ratio

In many mathematics books and in many dictionaries, rate and ratio are synonymous. But there is a growing tendency among technicians and scientists to use *rate* when the quantities have different units, resulting in a quantity with a compound unit, and *ratio* when the quantities have the same unit, resulting in a number that has no unit, also called a *scalar*.

The authors of *Everyday Mathematics* think this distinction is useful and have maintained it in the program. However, the use of rate and ratio as synonyms is so entrenched in school mathematics and in daily life that *Everyday Mathematics* materials do not make an issue

NOTE: A bar is used to indicate a digit or group of digits that repeats. For more information, see Section 9.3.4: Rational Numbers and Decimals.

NOTE: For more about Fibonacci, see, for example, the *Leonardo Pisano Fibonacci* Web site by O'Connor and Robertson at the mathematics history site of the School of Mathematics and Statistics at the University of St. Andrews, Scotland. A complete reference can be found on page 77.

NOTE: The *Common Core State Standards for Mathematics* do not formally define either rate or ratio. However, the standards are consistent with a ratio being *any* division comparison and a rate being a division comparison of quantities with different units. That means all rates can also be called ratios, but not vice versa. This looser definition of ratio should not affect students using the more scientifically precise definition in *Everyday Mathematics*.

of it. Rate and ratio issues are entangled with the larger concern of how to handle units and units analysis in calculations with counts and measures. Keeping track of units is easy for sums and differences, as only counts or measures with exactly the same unit can be added or subtracted. Keeping track of units becomes more complicated with products, quotients, squares, cubes, and square roots, all of which are important in *Fourth* through *Sixth Grade Everyday Mathematics*.

Proportions

A *proportion* is a number sentence that equates two fractions.

Examples: $\dfrac{1}{2} = \dfrac{50}{100}$ $\qquad$ $\dfrac{2}{3} = \dfrac{60}{90}$ $\qquad$ $\dfrac{n}{5} = \dfrac{30}{75}$

Proportions can be used to model many rate and ratio situations. For example, the following proportion models the fact that a car traveling at a constant rate of 50 miles per hour can travel 300 miles in 6 hours.

$$\frac{50 \text{ mi}}{1 \text{ hr}} = \frac{300 \text{ mi}}{6 \text{ hr}}$$

Proportions are useful in solving problems involving a rate or ratio. If any three numbers in a proportion are known, then the fourth number can be found.

Example: A gray whale's heart beats 24 times in 3 minutes. At this rate, how many times does it beat in 2 minutes?

A simple rate table can help with writing a correct proportion.

beats	24	x
minutes	3	2

The table above leads to this proportion: $\dfrac{24 \text{ beats}}{3 \text{ minutes}} = \dfrac{x \text{ beats}}{2 \text{ minutes}}$

This proportion can be solved in several ways. One way is to use a *unit rate:* $\dfrac{24 \text{ beats}}{3 \text{ minutes}} = \dfrac{8 \text{ beats}}{1 \text{ minute}}$

So the whale's heart would beat 16 times in 2 minutes.

Another approach is to use cross multiplication:

$$\frac{24}{3} = \frac{x}{2}$$
$$24 * 2 = 3 * x$$
$$48 = 3x$$
$$16 = x$$

Again, the whale's heart would beat 16 times in 2 minutes.

9.3.4 Rational Numbers and Decimals

A *rational number* is any number that can be written as a quotient of the form a/b or $\frac{a}{b}$, where a is an integer and b is a nonzero integer. A *rational number* can be positive, negative, or 0.

For more information on solving proportions, see Section 17.2.4: Solving Open Sentences.

Any rational number can be written as either a terminating decimal or a repeating decimal. That is, the decimal for a rational number may terminate, such as

$$\frac{1}{8} = 0.125$$

or it may repeat the same pattern without terminating, as in these examples:

$$\frac{2}{3} = 0.666\ldots = 0.\overline{6}$$

$$\frac{1}{7} = 0.142857142857\ldots = 0.\overline{142857}$$

To find a fraction for a nonterminating, repeating decimal such as $0.123123\ldots$, multiply by an appropriate power of 10 and subtract the original number.

$$
\begin{aligned}
1{,}000n &= 123.123123\ldots \\
- \qquad 1n &= \quad\; 0.123123\ldots \\
\hline
999n &= 123 \\
n &= \frac{123}{999}
\end{aligned}
$$

Not all decimals are rational numbers. For example, there is a pattern in $0.101001000100001\ldots$, but it is not a repeating pattern. This is an *irrational number*. To write an irrational number as a decimal is actually impossible because an infinitely long decimal is required. Although computer scientists have calculated over 200 billion digits of the irrational number π, for example, there are still infinitely many more digits to be calculated.

9.3.5 Percents

Landowner Jones has $\frac{3}{4}$ of an acre and landowner Smith has $\frac{4}{5}$ of an acre. Who has more land?

Answering the question above may be difficult because the denominators of the fractions are not the same. One represents fourths of an acre, while the other represents fifths of an acre. Several methods could be used to rewrite the data in comparable terms, that is, to *standardize* them. Three approaches to standardizing the landowners problem follow.

- *Draw pictures.*

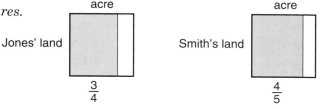

- *Rewrite the fractions with the same denominators.*

$$\frac{3}{4} = \frac{15}{20} \qquad\qquad \frac{4}{5} = \frac{16}{20}$$

- *Rewrite the fractions as decimals or percents.*

$$\frac{3}{4} = \frac{75}{100} = 0.75 = 75\% \qquad\qquad \frac{4}{5} = \frac{80}{100} = 0.80 = 80\%$$

Each approach shows that Smith owns more land than Jones does.

Because it is not always simple to draw a picture or find common denominators, as in the first two methods on page 69, using the percent approach is probably the most convenient and efficient of the three. A *percent* is a ratio comparison based on 100ths. The word "percent" comes from the Latin *per centum*, meaning "for each 100."

The percent symbol % has three equivalent meanings:

Meaning	Example
times 0.01	$5\% = 5 * 0.01 = 0.05$
times $\frac{1}{100}$	$5\% = 5 * \frac{1}{100} = \frac{5}{100}$
divided by 100	$5\% = \frac{5}{100} = 0.05$

Before calculators became a standard tool, the elementary school mathematics curriculum usually treated topics in this order:

- Operations with whole numbers;
- Operations with fractions;
- Operations with decimals;
- Operations with percents.

A key to the old ordering is the long division required to perform the tedious process of rewriting fractions as decimals. These days, even 4-function calculators make the division step of the process much easier and give students access to more interesting applications much earlier in the curriculum. Additionally, fraction calculators give students unprecedented tools for converting between fractions and decimals and vice versa. Thus, students see many kinds of numbers in appropriate contexts in every year of *Everyday Mathematics*. The exception is percent, which is first introduced in third grade.

The payoff for repeated, early, and informal experiences with whole numbers, fractions, and decimals comes later in the program. By seeing relationships among numbers, students use mental computation and estimation with sophistication. For example:

- *How many are 25% of 28 peaches?* Knowing that 25% is equal to $\frac{1}{4}$ makes this easy to do mentally by taking $\frac{1}{4}$ of 28. Taking $\frac{1}{4}$ of 28, or dividing 28 by 4, is much simpler than multiplying 28 by 0.25 to get 7 peaches.

- *Last year 315 seniors out of 435 in the graduating class went on to college. About what percent went to college?* If the numbers in the situation are rounded to 300 out of 400, or $\frac{3}{4}$, it is easy to see that about 75% of seniors went to college. If a more accurate percent is required, then this estimation helps check a calculator or paper-and-pencil result of about 72.4%.

- *Today, 30 fifth graders, or 20% of all the fifth graders in the school, are going to the museum. How many fifth graders are in the school?* Knowing that 20% is $\frac{1}{5}$ of all the fifth graders means there are $5 * 30$, or 150, fifth graders in all.

A goal of *Everyday Mathematics* is for students completing sixth grade to instantly recognize decimal and percent equivalents for many common fractions. These include halves, fourths, eighths, thirds, fifths, and tenths. In fourth grade, students explore strategies for finding equivalencies. In fifth grade, students practice recognizing different forms of numbers by playing a *Frac-Tac-Toe* game. Over the course of Grades 4 through 6, students use real-world contexts to practice operations with rational numbers in these notations.

In the end, *Everyday Mathematics* students should handle everyday percents much more successfully than Dilbert's boss can.

"Easy" Fractions	Decimals	Percents
$\frac{1}{2}$	0.50	50%
$\frac{1}{3}$	$0.\overline{3}$	$33\frac{1}{3}\%$
$\frac{2}{3}$	$0.\overline{6}$	$66\frac{2}{3}\%$
$\frac{1}{4}$	0.25	25%
$\frac{3}{4}$	0.75	75%
$\frac{1}{5}$	0.20	20%
$\frac{2}{5}$	0.40	40%
$\frac{3}{5}$	0.60	60%
$\frac{4}{5}$	0.80	80%
$\frac{1}{8}$	0.125	$12\frac{1}{2}\%$
$\frac{3}{8}$	0.375	$37\frac{1}{2}\%$
$\frac{5}{8}$	0.625	$62\frac{1}{2}\%$
$\frac{7}{8}$	0.875	$87\frac{1}{2}\%$
$\frac{1}{10}$	0.10	10%
$\frac{3}{10}$	0.30	30%
$\frac{7}{10}$	0.70	70%
$\frac{9}{10}$	0.90	90%

DILBERT: @Scott Adams/Dist. by United Feature Syndicate, Inc.

9.4 Positive and Negative Numbers

The invention of negative numbers was prompted by both practical and mathematical considerations. From a mathematical point of view, negative numbers are needed:

- To make subtraction *closed*. When negative numbers are allowed, there is an answer to every subtraction problem, including differences such as $3 - 10$.
- To complete the number line. With negative numbers, the number line can extend below zero.
- To give every number an *additive inverse*. The sum of a number and its additive inverse is zero. The additive inverse of a positive number is negative.

In the everyday world, negative numbers answer the need for specifying locations in reference frames in relation to a *zero point* (starting point) and for naming measures that extend in both directions from the zero point.

Beginning in Kindergarten, students use positive and negative numbers to locate points in reference to a zero point, for example, on a temperature scale, and to represent the result of a change situation, such as using -3 to mean a loss of 3 pounds. Other situations in which positive and negative numbers are used are given in the table below.

Situation	Negative	Zero	Positive
bank account	withdrawal	no change	deposit
time	before	now	after
games	behind	tied	ahead
business	loss	break even	profit
elevation	below sea level	sea level	above sea level

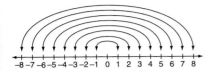

Negative numbers are opposites of positive numbers. Zero is its own opposite.

A Casio *fx*-55

NOTE: A few calculators such as the TI-15 have a ⊝ key for entering the opposite of a number. This key looks like the key for subtraction, but it is not an operation symbol. Trying to use it for subtraction leads to an error message. To enter the opposite on these calculators, press ⊝ before entering the number. For example, to enter −5, press ⊝ 5.

Such situations are useful in helping students understand that negatives are opposites of positives. Positives and negatives come in pairs, and familiarity with negatives can be improved by comparing them with their positive opposites.

One way to represent negative numbers and their relationships to positive numbers is on a number line. The opposite relationship can be illustrated by folding a number line at zero and comparing where points coincide. This demonstration also shows that points on the negative side of zero are reflections of points on the positive side, and vice versa. Encourage students to draw number lines in their journals, on their slates, and on the board, that is, anywhere that may help them visualize the relative locations of positive and negative numbers while they solve problems.

9.4.1 Possibly Confusing Notation with Negative Numbers

Reading and writing expressions with positive and negative numbers has always been a difficult topic for students, and perhaps even for you. Notations with several distinct meanings can be confusing. This is certainly true of the symbol −.

- The symbol − immediately preceding a numeral, as in −3, −0.5, and −37, is read "negative" and is used in naming numbers on the number line (negative 3, negative 5 tenths, negative 37).
- The symbol − preceding parentheses, as in −(+3) and −(−17), is read "opposite of." The opposite of a negative number is a positive number; the opposite of a positive number is a negative number. So the "opposite of positive 3" is negative 3, and the "opposite of negative 17" is positive 17. The number zero is the only number that is its own opposite: −(0) = 0.
- The symbol − in 17 − 3 = 14 is read "minus," "subtract," or "take away" and indicates the operation of subtraction.

The meaning of the symbol − can get tangled in number sentences such as those in the table below.

In symbols	Read it like this
−17 − 3 = −20	"Negative 17 minus 3 is equal to negative 20."
12 − −(−4) = 8	"12 minus the opposite of negative 4 is equal to 8."

Some mathematics programs attempt to reduce confusion by using − only for subtraction. Positive and negative numbers are represented with small raised symbols, for example, ⁻3, ⁻17, and ⁺17; and the opposite may be indicated by "OPP" or "op." But everyday usage and nearly all algebra books continue to use traditional notation, so students eventually have to reconcile the two notations.

The distinction between operation and sign may be clarified using a calculator with an *opposite* or *change-sign* key. It most commonly looks like the +⁄− key on the Casio *fx*-55 calculator shown in the margin that the authors used to write this edition of *Everyday Mathematics*. The change-sign key changes a number to its opposite.

On calculators with a +/- key, enter the number before pressing +/-. For example, to enter −5, press 5 +/-. The negative sign may appear in the margin of the display rather than next to the 5. Other than that, expressions are entered left to right as always.

Third Grade Everyday Mathematics uses the traditional notation for "negative" and "minus" for activities in which students explore opposites of whole numbers. We urge you to help students learn the different meanings of these symbols by reading + as "plus" or "positive" and − as "minus," "negative," or "opposite," as required by the context. Eventually, students in Grades 4 through 6 do likewise when they read mathematical expressions.

9.4.2 Positive and Negative Rational Numbers

In *Everyday Mathematics, negative rational numbers* are presented to students as a natural extension of fractions, or positive rational numbers, in much the same way that negative integers are presented as an extension of whole numbers. Both the idea of negative numbers and the symbols for recording them probably originated in India and were used there in a systematic way by about A.D. 650.

A major use of negative numbers is to express quantities with reference to a zero point. For example, −10° is a temperature of 10 degrees below zero and −2,356 feet is a depth of 2,356 feet below sea level. Positive and negative numbers are also used to express changes in quantities. For example, $+4\frac{1}{2}$ pounds is a weight gain of $4\frac{1}{2}$ pounds and −$1,000 is a decrease of 1,000 dollars.

Students in *Fourth* through *Sixth Grade Everyday Mathematics* learn about the opposites of all rational numbers and decimals. Together with zero, the positive and negative rational numbers form the *rational-number system,* which is sufficient for solving most everyday problems involving counting, measures, locations, and ratio comparisons. All rational numbers can be displayed on a number line such as the following one, but they do not account for every point on the number line. For this, we need both rational and irrational numbers together to form the real-number system described briefly in Section 9.6.

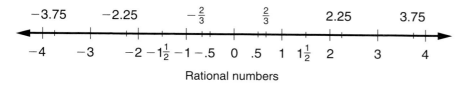

Rational numbers

Integers

An important subset of the rational numbers is the set of *integers,* which include the natural numbers, their opposites, and zero. In practice, *Everyday Mathematics* students investigate negative integers more than negative rational numbers; the latter appear occasionally as answers in fraction subtraction problems in Grade 6.

NOTE: +/- is an example of a *toggle,* a key that switches the display back and forth between two numbers. In this case, it switches back and forth between a number and its opposite each time the key is pressed.

NOTE: Many scientific calculators allow division with remainder, and some call this "integer" division. This is a misnomer, because division with remainder is not defined for negative numbers. For more information, see Section 11.2.4: Division Algorithms.

NOTE: The authors have generally avoided using the term *integer,* choosing instead to call numbers simply positive or negative when a distinction is necessary. The goal is to have students of *Everyday Mathematics* become comfortable with positive and negative numbers in general and not to have undue concern if a problem contains a negative noninteger.

chapter 9

NOTE: By the time students complete *Sixth Grade Everyday Mathematics,* they will have investigated all of the basic properties of the rational-number system, almost all of them in the context of everyday problems. These properties are summarized in the Properties of Rational Numbers tables at the end of this book.

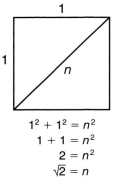

$|-3| = 3$ $|3| = 3$

$$|x| = ABS(x) = \begin{cases} x, & if \quad x \geq 0 \\ OPP(x), & if \quad x < 0 \end{cases}$$

$1^2 + 1^2 = n^2$
$1 + 1 = n^2$
$2 = n^2$
$\sqrt{2} = n$

Length of a unit-square diagonal

There are few everyday uses of negative fractions and decimals, except in finance. Temperatures below zero and elevations below sea level are usually rounded to the nearest integer.

Absolute Value

The absolute value of a number x, written $|x|$ or ABS(x), is the distance of x from 0 on a number line. The absolute value of a positive number is the number itself, and the absolute value of a negative number is the *opposite* of the number. The absolute value of 0 is 0. For example, $|3| = 3$ and $|-3| = 3$ as shown in the margin. An algebraic definition of absolute value of x is also shown in the margin. Students in *Sixth Grade Everyday Mathematics* use absolute value to investigate distances in the coordinate plane and when calculating mean absolute deviations of data sets.

▶ 9.5 Irrational Numbers

If a decimal neither terminates nor has a digit or string of digits that repeats endlessly, then it represents an *irrational number*. An irrational number cannot be rewritten as a fraction, or ratio, $\frac{a}{b}$ where a and b are integers and $b \neq 0$. Examples of irrational numbers include $0.101001000100001\ldots$, $\sqrt{2} = 1.41421356\ldots$, and $\pi = 3.14159265\ldots$. Because a decimal for an irrational number has no repeating pattern, an infinitely long decimal would be required to write it in standard notation. So in practice, special symbols such as $\sqrt{\ }$, π, and $\ldots$ are used to represent irrational numbers.

The ancient Babylonians and Egyptians (c. 3000 B.C.) were able to solve what we now call "algebra" problems, and in so doing they came upon irrational numbers. For example, $\sqrt{2}$ is the answer to *What is the length of the diagonal of a square with sides each 1 unit long?* This problem is solved in the margin using the Pythagorean theorem. A definition of $\sqrt{2}$, in fact, could be *a number that makes the equation* $2 = n^2$ *true.*

The Babylonians and Egyptians did not understand the "irrational" nature of $\sqrt{2}$. They used a fractional approximation of $\sqrt{2}$ as an exact answer. Because most calculations were done in the context of a concrete problem in engineering, architecture, or surveying, a rational approximation was appropriate, as it still is today.

In the fifth or sixth century B.C., Greek mathematicians and philosophers known as the "Pythagoreans" realized that numbers such as $\sqrt{2}$ are not rational, because they do not coincide with points on the rational number line.

The Greeks knew that the whole numbers—negative numbers were unknown at the time—could be represented on a number line by multiples of a unit length. Fractions could be represented by splitting the unit into smaller and smaller pieces such as halves, thirds, fourths, fifths, 99ths, and 120,000ths. By subdividing and adding unit lengths, the Greeks were able, in theory, to generate infinitely many numbers, all those that today we call the positive rational numbers.

In *Great Moments in Mathematics (Before 1650)*, Howard Eves
(pp. 43–44) writes:

> To the early mathematicians it seemed evident, as indeed it
> seems to anyone today who has not been initiated into the deeper
> mysteries of the number line, that all the points on the line are . . .
> used up; ordinary common sense seems to indicate this to us.
>
> It must have been a genuine mental shock for man to learn that
> there are points on the number line not corresponding to any
> rational number. This discovery was certainly one of the greatest
> achievements of the early Greeks, and it seems to have occurred
> some time in the fifth or sixth century B.C. among the ranks of
> the Pythagorean brotherhood. A truly GREAT MOMENT IN
> MATHEMATICS had arisen.

NOTE: A complete reference
to Howard Eves' book can
be found on page 77.

This was a "great moment" because, according to the Pythagorean
philosophy, all of mathematics was based on whole numbers and
their relationships under addition, subtraction, multiplication, and
division, a view not uncommon to many traditional elementary school
mathematics programs. This limited mathematics to rational
numbers, and the discovery of the irrationals was a truly revolutionary
event. According to Eves (p. 53):

> So great was the "logical scandal" that . . . efforts were made for
> a while to keep the matter secret, and one legend has it that the
> Pythagorean Hippasus of Metapontum perished at sea for his
> impiety in disclosing the secret to outsiders, or (according to
> another version) was banished from the Pythagorean community
> and a tomb erected for him as though he were dead.

The crisis was profound. Not only did the rational numbers not
account for all the points on the number line, but there were infinitely
many irrational numbers mixed in with them! Happily, the crisis
was overcome—the irrational numbers were accepted, and *Everyday
Mathematics* students can ponder the results.

It is actually easy to construct on a number line a point with an
irrational coordinate. The number line in the margin shows how to
construct a point at $\sqrt{2}$. First draw a unit square with its base along
the line. Set a compass to the length of the diagonal, and with center
at the zero point, draw an arc so that it intersects the number line
at point P. The length of $\overline{OP}$ is $\sqrt{2}$ units, and it can be proved that
this length cannot be a rational number.

In *Everyday Mathematics,* children begin exploring the irrational
number π in Grade 3 by investigating ratios of circumferences and
diameters in circles. Students work with the square-root operation in
Grade 5 as a process for "unsquaring" numbers. When the square
root of a whole number does not "come out even," then it is irrational.
Sixth graders review square roots when they use a formula for the
area of a circle to find the radius of a circle with known area and also
when they investigate the Pythagorean theorem.

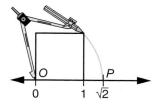

Segment *OP* has length $\sqrt{2}$.

▶ 9.6 Real Numbers

The *real numbers* are simply all the rational and irrational numbers together. The set of real numbers accounts for all the points on the number line. Between any two points on the real number line, there are infinitely many points and a real number corresponding to each point. And, just as important, there are no other kinds of numbers on the number line. Every point on the number line can be matched with a real number, and every real number can be matched with a point on the number line.

Here is part of a real number line from the *Student Reference Book* for *Sixth Grade Everyday Mathematics*.

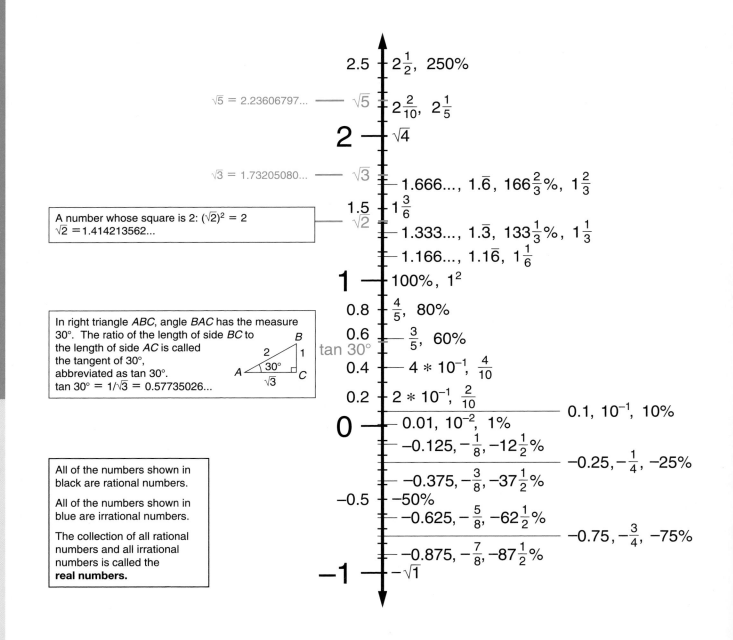

A number whose square is 2: $(\sqrt{2})^2 = 2$
$\sqrt{2} = 1.414213562...$

In right triangle ABC, angle BAC has the measure 30°. The ratio of the length of side BC to the length of side AC is called the tangent of 30°, abbreviated as tan 30°.
tan 30° = $1/\sqrt{3}$ = 0.57735026...

All of the numbers shown in black are rational numbers.

All of the numbers shown in blue are irrational numbers.

The collection of all rational numbers and all irrational numbers is called the **real numbers**.

All the numbers in *Everyday Mathematics* are real numbers, including:

- Counting numbers;
- Positive rational numbers expressed as fractions, decimals, and percents;
- Irrational numbers like $\sqrt{2}$ and π;
- Negative rational numbers.

In the school mathematics curriculum, however, most work with the irrational numbers is reserved for secondary school mathematics, so most of the real numbers that students encounter before high school are rational.

There are infinitely many rational numbers. You could count them, but it would take forever. The number of rational numbers is represented by the symbol $\aleph_0$, which is read "aleph null." There are even more irrational numbers than rational numbers. In the late 19th century, the mathematician Georg Cantor proved that counting the real numbers is impossible, even if you counted forever.

In summary, students in *Everyday Mathematics* explore systems of whole numbers and positive and negative rational numbers. They are introduced to the real-number system in Grade 6. As complete as this may sound, it is just the beginning of the journey. The next new number system they are likely to see includes *imaginary numbers,* which together with the real numbers form the complex-number system. The keystone of the *complex number system* is the number $\sqrt{-1}$, which is defined as the solution to $x^2 = -1$. Students study these numbers in advanced algebra and other pre-calculus courses.

References and Resources for Numeration and Order

Eves, H. (1983). *Great Moments in Mathematics (Before 1650)*. Washington, DC: The Mathematical Association of America.

Grattan-Guinness, I. (1997). *The Norton History of the Mathematical Sciences*. New York: W. W. Norton.

Kline, M. (1972). *Mathematical Thought from Ancient to Modern Times*. New York: Oxford University Press.

Menninger, K. A. (1992). *Number Words and Number Symbols: A Cultural History of Numbers*. New York: Dover.

O'Connor, J. J., and Robertson, E. F. (1998). *Leonardo Pisano Fibonacci*. Retrieved from www-groups.dcs.st-and.ac.uk/~history/Mathematicians/Fibonacci.html

▶ 9.7 Numeric Relations

In mathematics, a *relation* tells how one thing compares to another. This section discusses numeric relations, that is, relations between numbers and expressions. The most common numeric relations are equality ($=$) and inequality ($<$ and $>$), but there are others.

For more information, see Section 13.6: Geometric Relations.

Even preschool students have some idea of "more" and "less." They may be deceived by appearances but, under the right conditions, they can judge bigger/smaller, shorter/taller, heavier/lighter, and so on.

This capacity for judging more/less is the basis for understanding numeric relations.

As students begin to count or measure objects, they learn to write symbols for relationships between the counts or measures of different objects. The table below shows the most common symbols for expressing numeric relations.

Symbols for Numeric Relations		
Symbol	**Read it as**	**Examples**
=	"equals" "is equal to" "is the same as"	$3 = \frac{6}{2}$ 3.0 seconds = 3 seconds $\frac{1}{2} = 50\%$
>	"is greater than"	$12 > 4$ $1.23 > 1.2$ $6{,}000$ ft > 1 mi
<	"is less than"	8 million $<$ 12 million $0.1 < 1.1$ $\frac{5}{2} < 4$
≥	"is greater than or equal to"	attendance ≥ 250 people $2 + 2 \geq 4$ area ≥ 2 acres
≤	"is less than or equal to"	$2 + 2 \leq 4$ fee $\leq \$25$ time ≤ 2 hours
≠	"does not equal" "is not equal to" "is not the same as"	$10 \neq 100$ $\frac{10}{120} \neq \frac{1}{2}$ $85\% \neq 85$

NOTE: *Fifth Grade Everyday Mathematics* introduces the symbol ≈ as shorthand for "is approximately equal to." Although ≈ is not well-enough defined to qualify as a mathematical relation, it is nevertheless useful in situations involving estimation and approximation.

NOTE: Some computer programming languages use "<>" for "not equal."

9.7.1 Equality

Although the concept of equality seems straightforward, students who have been through several years of schooling often have difficulty using the = symbol. Research studies show that many older students reject such number sentences as $5 = 5$ (they say there is no problem), $4 = 2 + 2$ (they say that the answer is on the wrong side), and $4 + 3 = 5 + 2$ (they say there are two problems, but no answers).

The origin of these errors seems clear. Students in school usually see number sentences written only with a problem on the left-hand side of the equal sign and the answer on the right-hand side: $5 + 7 = 12$. So, deliberately write $12 = 5 + 7$ as often as $5 + 7 = 12$, and encourage students to say *means the same as* or *looks different, but is really the same as* when reading the equal symbol.

In large part, arithmetic consists of simply replacing numbers or expressions with equivalent (equal) numbers or expressions. You can replace $7 + 8$ with 15, or substitute 27 for $459 \div 17$. When it suits you, you can use $\frac{1}{2}$ in place of $\frac{1}{3} + \frac{1}{6}$ and vice versa. Number sense and arithmetic skill consist largely of being aware of the many possibilities for equivalent names for numbers and being able to use them flexibly.

chapter 9

For most collections of equivalent names, one name is often recognized as the "simplest" and serves to identify the entire collection. But simplest doesn't necessarily mean best; for example, $\frac{50}{100}$ as in *50 per 100* may convey more information in a given situation than does $\frac{1}{2}$. It also serves as a better bridge to understanding that 50% is equivalent to $\frac{1}{2}$. Unfortunately, much of the traditional mathematics curriculum has made the "simplification" of numbers synonymous with mathematics itself. Students of *Everyday Mathematics* do not have this sterile experience.

▶ 9.8 Number Theory

Beginning in Grade 4, students explore topics in the study of the whole numbers, the branch of mathematics known as *number theory*. Topics such as prime and composite numbers, perfect numbers, and abundant and deficient numbers are described in the following sections.

9.8.1 Prime and Composite Numbers: Divisibility

A fundamental distinction in number theory is the classification of whole numbers greater than 1 as either prime or composite. A *prime number* has exactly two whole-number *divisors* or *factors,* 1 and itself. For example, 2 is prime because it is divisible only by 1 and by 2. Any whole number that has more than two whole-number divisors is a *composite number.* For example, 6 is composite because it is divisible by 2 and 3 as well as 1 and 6. The numbers 0 and 1 are neither prime nor composite.

Beginning in Grade 3, when multiplication becomes a center-stage topic, teachers are advised to find a shorthand notation to record students' solution strategies to problems involving factors. In *Everyday Mathematics,* brackets are used to separate factor pairs. For example, 8 [500s] represents eight 5 hundreds, or 4,000. Students quickly accept whatever notation is adopted as long as it is used consistently.

Prime and composite numbers show interesting features when modeled by rectangular arrays. A prime number can be modeled by only two arrays. For example, arrays for the prime number 5 have either a single column or a single row of five elements. The first array at right models a single column, or 5 * 1, while the second models a single row, or 1 * 5.

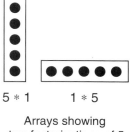

5 * 1   1 * 5

Arrays showing
two factorizations of 5

The number 10 is composite because it can be modeled by four arrays representing 10 * 1, 1 * 10, 5 * 2, and 2 * 5, as shown in the margin.

Students in *Fifth Grade Everyday Mathematics* experiment to find *divisibility rules* to help identify prime numbers. In sixth grade, the rules are used to help simplify fractions. Divisibility rules are extensions of the set of multiplication and division facts. For example:

- All even numbers are divisible by 2. Hence, any number ending in 0, 2, 4, 6, or 8 is divisible by 2.

NOTE: The French mathematician Henri Poincaré (1865–1912) once remarked, "Mathematics is the art of giving the same name to different things." For example, mathematicians give the name "polygon" to many different shapes, including squares, triangles, and pentagons.

NOTE: Finding equivalent names for expressions is an important skill for solving algebraic equations.

NOTE: *Name-collection boxes* are important tools for managing students' work with equivalent names. For more information, see Section 9.9.3.

NOTE: In this section, the terms *divisible, divisibility,* and *divisor* all refer to division of whole numbers by whole numbers.

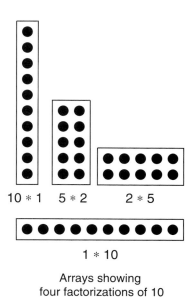

10 * 1   5 * 2   2 * 5

1 * 10

Arrays showing
four factorizations of 10

- A number is divisible by 3 if the sum of its digits is divisible by 3. For example, 57 is divisible by 3 because $5 + 7 = 12$, and 12 is divisible by 3.
- A number is divisible by 4 if the last two digits are divisible by 4. For example, 78,468 is divisible by 4 because 68 is divisible by 4.
- A number ending with 0 or 5 is divisible by 5.
- A number that is divisible by both 2 and 3 is divisible by 6. For example, 12,612 is divisible by 6 because it ends in 2 (and so is divisible by 2) and the sum of its digits is $1 + 2 + 6 + 1 + 2 = 12$ (which is divisible by 3, so 12,612 is also divisible by 3).
- A number is divisible by 8 if the last three digits are divisible by 8. For example, 2,456,864 is divisible by 8 because 864 is divisible by 8.
- A number is divisible by 9 if the sum of its digits is divisible by 9. For example, 567 is divisible by 9 because $5 + 6 + 7 = 18$, and 18 is divisible by 9.

A Note on Divisibility by 9

The divisibility rule for 9 given above is a special case of a general rule about sums of digits and division by 9:

- The remainder of a number divided by 9 is the same as the remainder of the sum of the number's digits divided by 9.

So if the sum of a number's digits is divisible by 9 (the remainder is 0), then the number is also divisible by 9.

Examples: The sum of the digits of 256 is $2 + 5 + 6 = 13$, so 256/9 has the same remainder as 13/9. Because 13/9 has remainder 4, the remainder after 256 is divided by 9 is also 4 *(256/9 → 28 R4)*.

The sum of the digits of 8,793 is $8 + 7 + 9 + 3 = 27$. Because 27 is divisible by 9, so is 8,793 *(8,793/9 = 977)*.

A key to a proof of this rule is that numbers such as 999 and 99 are always divisible by 9. Below is an instance worked out with numbers, followed by a general argument using variables.

$$256/9 = (2 * 100 + 5 * 10 + 6)/9$$
$$= (2 * [99 + 1] + 5 * [9 + 1] + 6)/9$$
$$= (2 * 99 + 2 + 5 * 9 + 5 + 6)/9$$
$$= (2 * 99 + 5 * 9)/9 + (2 + 5 + 6)/9$$

Because 9 divides both 99 and 9 with no remainder, $(2 * 99 + 5 * 9)/9$ has no remainder. So the remainder for 256/9 is the same as the remainder for $2 + 5 + 6$ divided by 9. Because $(2 + 5 + 6)/9$ → 1 R4, the remainder of 256/9 is also 4 *(256/9 → 28 R4)*.

A complete proof of this rule is beyond the scope of this manual, but an argument for 3-digit numbers illustrates the main idea. Represent the digits of a 3-digit number by H (for the hundreds), T (for the tens), and U (for the units or ones digit). Then write the number as $HTU = H * 100 + T * 10 + U$. As in the example above, you can now write:

$$HTU/9 = (H * 100 + T * 10 + U)/9$$
$$= (H * [99 + 1] + T * [9 + 1] + U)/9$$
$$= (H * 99 + H + T * 9 + T + U)/9$$
$$= (H * 99 + T * 9)/9 + (H + T + U)/9$$

Because $H * 99$ and $T * 9$ are both divisible by 9, the remainder for $HTU/9$ comes only from $(H + T + U)/9$. So as the rule states, the remainder of a number divided by 9 is the remainder of the sum of the number's digits divided by 9.

Almost exactly the same argument can be used to show that the remainder of a number divided by 3 is the same as the remainder of the sum of the number's digits divided by 3. Similar arguments can be used to prove the other divisibility rules.

Prime Factors and Factorization

Two important topics in number theory are *prime factors* and *factorization*. For elementary school students, these are useful for arithmetic with fractions. The traditional paper-and-pencil algorithms for finding common denominators, simplifying fractions, and adding and subtracting fractions all require students to factor numbers.

A *factorization* of a number is a product of whole numbers that equals the number. Usually 1s are not included in factorizations, and the order of the factors doesn't matter. For example, 24 has the following distinct factorizations:

$$2 * 12$$
$$3 * 8$$
$$4 * 6$$
$$2 * 2 * 6$$
$$2 * 3 * 4$$
$$2 * 2 * 2 * 3$$

Note that just the last factorization above contains only prime numbers. The *Fundamental Theorem of Arithmetic* states that for each whole number greater than 1, there is only one factorization that consists entirely of prime numbers. The unique factorization of a number into primes is called its *prime factorization.*

In *Everyday Mathematics,* students are encouraged to develop their own approaches to finding prime factorizations. One approach is to use *factor strings.* The first step is to determine whether a number is prime or composite through the use of multiplication and division facts, arrays, and divisibility rules. If a number is composite, then look for *factor pairs,* two factors whose product is that number. For example:

$$24 = 1 * 24 = 2 * 12 = 3 * 8 = 4 * 6$$

Then choose a factor pair and repeat the process. That is, look for factor pairs for each factor in the pair. This creates a factor string. For example:

$$24 = \quad 4 \quad * \quad 6$$
$$= 2 * 2 * 2 * 3$$

Because both 2 and 3 are prime numbers, $2 * 2 * 2 * 3$ is the longest factor string for 24. The factors are all prime, so this is a prime factorization of 24.

A prime factorization can be written using the shorthand notation of exponents. For example:

$$24 = 2 * 2 * 2 * 3 = 2^3 * 3$$

This notation links students to exponential and scientific notations used as shorthand for large numbers, especially in calculators and computers.

To reinforce links between multiplication and division, exploration of factors begins in *Third Grade Everyday Mathematics*. In fifth grade, students are introduced to factor strings and learn to find prime factorizations by making factor trees.

Factor Trees

Making a *factor tree* is an algorithm for finding the prime factorization of a whole number. The algorithm consists of three steps:

1. Write the number to be factored.
2. Underneath the number, write any two factors whose product is the number.
3. Repeat Step 2 for each factor, and each factor's factors, until all the factors are prime numbers.

For example, three factor trees for the number 36 are shown below.

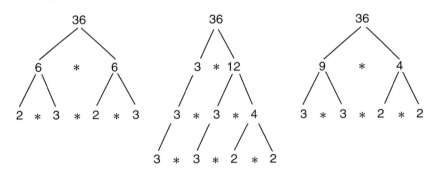

The prime factorization of 36 is $2 * 2 * 3 * 3 = 2^2 * 3^2$. Note that the algorithm gives the same prime factorization regardless of the first pair of factors. Remember that the order of the factors in a factorization doesn't matter.

Students use factor trees to find greatest common factors of two numbers, and, optionally, least common multiples and least common denominators. The latter two activities are optional because the authors of *Everyday Mathematics* believe students have more important, and certainly more interesting, things to do than waste hours writing fractions in an artificially "best" or "simplified" form.

For more information, see Section 10.1.2: Powers and Exponents.

NOTE: Factor trees, like probability tree diagrams, are normally drawn upside down, with their "roots" at the top and their "leaves" at the bottom. This is convenient because you usually don't know in advance how large a factor tree will be; but it can be confusing because the resulting diagrams do not look much like real trees. However, like ordinary trees, mathematical trees do have their "branches" between their roots and their leaves.

9.8.2 Perfect, Deficient, and Abundant Numbers

The Pythagoreans, a group of philosophers and mathematicians in ancient Greece, were interested in the mystical properties of numbers. Among other things, they studied the *proper factors* of a number, that is, all the factors of a number except the number itself. For example, the Pythagoreans found that some numbers are equal to the sum of their proper factors. The least two such perfect numbers are 6 and 28. The proper factors of 6 are 1, 2, and 3, and $1 + 2 + 3 = 6$. The proper factors of 28 are 1, 2, 4, 7, and 14, and $1 + 2 + 4 + 7 + 14 = 28$. The Pythagoreans also found the third and fourth perfect numbers, 496 and 8,128.

St. Augustine (A.D. 354–430) thought perfect numbers had religious significance. He believed that the world could have been created in one day, but God chose to do it in six days because the number 6 was a symbol of perfection. Other scholars linked the perfect number 28 to the number of days it takes the moon to revolve around Earth.

The fifth perfect number is 33,550,336 and the sixth is 8,589,869,056. Recently, computers have been used to find perfect numbers by finding Mersenne prime numbers. In February 2005, researchers found the 42nd Mersenne prime number, which has over 7 million digits, and the associated perfect number has yet to be calculated accurately at this writing. It took 50 days for the computer to calculate the prime number!

All of the perfect numbers found so far are even and all end with either 6 or 8. An odd perfect number has never been found, but it has not been proven that such a number cannot exist. It is also not yet known whether there are infinitely many perfect numbers.

Perfect numbers provide a historical context in which to practice finding factors. Students can also explore two other types of numbers identified by the Pythagoreans, *deficient* and *abundant* numbers.

- The sum of the proper factors of a *deficient number* is less than the number. For example, the proper factors of 10 are 1, 2, and 5. Ten is deficient because the sum of its proper factors is $1 + 2 + 5 = 8$, and 8 is less than 10.

- The sum of the proper factors of an *abundant number* is greater than the number. For example, the proper factors of 12 are 1, 2, 3, 4, and 6. Twelve is abundant because the sum of its proper factors is $1 + 2 + 3 + 4 + 6 = 16$, and 16 is greater than 12.

Students who enjoy playing with these numbers might like to explore *amicable numbers*. Two whole numbers are amicable numbers if each is equal to the sum of the proper factors of the other. For example, the sum of the proper factors of 220 is

$$1 + 2 + 4 + 5 + 10 + 11 + 20 + 22 + 44 + 55 + 110 = 284$$

while the sum of the proper factors of 284 is

$$1 + 2 + 4 + 71 + 142 = 220.$$

So 220 and 284 are amicable, or friendly.

chapter 9

▶ 9.9 Numeration and Order Tools and Techniques

Students in *Fourth* through *Sixth Grade Everyday Mathematics* use a variety of manipulatives including base-10 blocks, counters, coins, straws, number lines, digit cards, name-collection boxes, and dominoes. Some of the more important tools are discussed in the following sections.

9.9.1 Base-10 Blocks

A variety of names are used for base-10 blocks. The following names are used in *Everyday Mathematics: cube* for the smaller 1-cm cube, *long* for the block consisting of ten 1-cm cubes (1 × 10), *flat* for the block consisting of one hundred 1-cm cubes (10 × 10), and *big cube* for the larger cube consisting of one thousand 1-cm cubes (10 × 10 × 10).

In *Third* and *Fourth Grade Everyday Mathematics,* base-10 blocks help students develop decimal exchange concepts. A long may represent the ONE and 1-cm cubes represent tenths. If a flat is assumed to represent the ONE, then 1-cm cubes represent hundredths. Students make this last model pictorial when they color or shade hundredths of a 10-by-10 grid to represent decimals. Students work in the other direction as well, writing decimals for partially shaded grids. In fourth and fifth grades, shaded grids help develop fraction sense and the relationships among fractions, decimals, and percents.

In third grade, children also use base-10 blocks to model the partial-products algorithm for multiplication. First they work out 1-digit by 2-digit problems with arrays of the blocks and, eventually, 2-digit by 2-digit problems.

For more information on the partial-products algorithm, see Section 11.2.3: Multiplication Algorithms.

Sometimes you may want to make a written record of work with base-10 blocks. The shorthand shown below is handy for drawing quick pictures of base-10 blocks. Such pictures are often more convenient to use than are the actual blocks, especially the larger blocks, and can be useful for explaining and recording solutions.

2,045 in base-10-block shorthand

Base-10-Block Shorthand		
Name	**Block**	**Shorthand**
cube		.
long		 |
flat	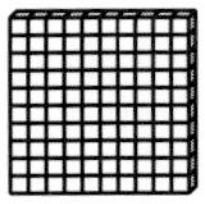	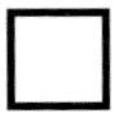 □
big cube	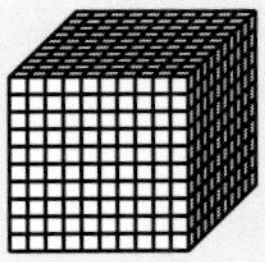	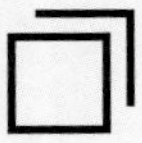

9.9.2 Number Grids, Scrolls, and Lines

Grid is short for *gridiron,* an old English word for a framework of metal bars or wires used to grill meat or fish. Generally, a grid is any set of equally spaced parallel lines, squares, or rectangles used to help establish locations of objects.

In *Everyday Mathematics,* students use many types of grids, including number grids, coordinate grids, grids for estimating area, and grids for interpreting maps. The tick marks on a number line form perhaps the most primitive grid structure. Lattices and arrays are organizations of objects into gridlike formations, a common example of which is a calendar.

Number Grids

A *number grid* consists of rows of boxes, usually ten in each row, containing consecutive integers (positive and negative whole numbers). In *First Grade Everyday Mathematics,* children are introduced to number grids early in the year.

−9	−8	−7	−6	−5	−4	−3	−2	−1	0
1	2	3	4	5	6	7	8	9	10
11	12	13	14	15	16	17	18	19	20
21	22	23	24	25	26	27	28	29	30
31	32	33	34	35	36	37	38	39	40
41	42	43	44	45	46	47	48	49	50
51	52	53	54	55	56	57	58	59	60
61	62	63	64	65	66	67	68	69	70
71	72	73	74	75	76	77	78	79	80
81	82	83	84	85	86	87	88	89	90
91	92	93	94	95	96	97	98	99	100
101	102	103	104	105	106	107	108	109	110

A number grid

Number grids have many wonderful features that can help students with pattern recognition and place value. However, their original use in *Everyday Mathematics* was simply to solve the problem of number lines being unmanageably long. Number lines can be cumbersome even when stretched along a classroom wall, and it is nearly impossible to print them in students' books without breaking them into chunks. Number grids may be considered number lines that fit nicely on a page or a classroom poster.

NOTE: Some readers of past editions of the *Teacher's Reference Manual* feel strongly that this section on number grids, scrolls, and lines belongs in this chapter on numeration and order. Others feel just as strongly that the discussion belongs in Chapter 15: Reference Frames. Believing that teachers should find help wherever they look, it is now included in both chapters.

For more information, see Section 15.3.2: 2- and 3-Dimensional Coordinate Systems.

A number grid lends itself to many activities that reinforce place-value concepts. For example, by exploring the patterns in rows and columns, students discover that any number on the number grid is:

- *1 more* than the number to its left;
- *1 less* than the number to its right;
- *10 more* than the number above it;
- *10 less* than the number below it.

Number grids are useful for addition and subtraction. For example, to find the difference 84 − 37, start at 37, count the tens from 37 to 77 *(4 tens)*, and then count the number of ones from 77 to 84 *(7 ones)*. So 84 − 37 is 4 tens plus 7 ones, or 47. This difference corresponds to the *distance* between the points 37 and 84 on a number line.

From the time they are introduced, students see that number grids can be extended to negative numbers. This is especially useful when ordering negative numbers or finding differences.

−19	−18	−17	−16	−15	−14	−13	−12	−11	−10
−9	−8	−7	−6	−5	−4	−3	−2	−1	0
1	2	3	4	5	6	7	8	9	10
11	12	13	14	15	16	17	18	19	20

A grid extended to −19

Number Scrolls

Number scrolls are extended number grids. You can make them by adding single sheets of 100 numbers to existing sheets, either forward (positively) or backward (negatively). Among other things, scrolls give students the chance to experience the ongoing repetitive patterns of our base-ten number system beyond 100—*101, 102, 103, . . .*—so that they do not continue, as students often do, with *200, 300, 400, . . .*. Teachers have found that many students get excited when they discover these patterns and realize that they are capable of writing bigger and bigger numbers.

Number Lines

A *number line* is a line on which points are indicated by *tick marks* that are usually at regularly spaced intervals from a starting point called the *origin,* the *zero point,* or simply "0." Numbers are associated with the tick marks, and the interval from 0 to 1 on the line is called the *unit interval.*

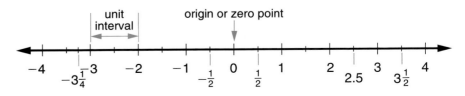

Like any line, a number line extends without end in both directions. Any drawing of a number line is a model of just part of the line. Where you place the zero point is arbitrary, and how you space the numbers depends on the situation you wish to illustrate. You might, for example, mark every other unit-interval point and label by 2s as in Figure 1 below; or you may mark every half-interval point and label by halves as in Figure 2. In *Everyday Mathematics*, students are often asked to solve incomplete-number-line problems that help them understand these concepts.

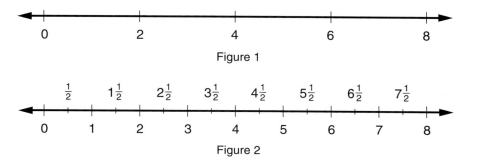

Figure 1

Figure 2

Any scale can be assigned to a number line. For example, a unit interval on a number line could represent one mile on a map. It is also possible to have nonlinear scales on number lines. For example, slide rules and radio dials are based on logarithmic scales, which are beyond the scope of *Everyday Mathematics*.

All number lines have a zero point, although sometimes it is not shown. Or, as in the following line, it is shown along with a break to indicate that a piece of the line has been omitted. This device is often used in technical drawings to focus on important details and still show the reader that part of the object is missing. A variety of broken-line symbols all mean the same thing.

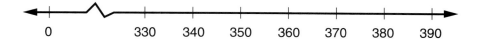

Beginning in Kindergarten, children use number lines in context in counting and measuring activities. Both horizontal and vertical number lines appear. Number lines in coordinate graphing systems are introduced in third grade and are expanded upon and treated more formally in Grades 4 through 6. Number lines also continue to serve as one or more of the axes in data displays such as coordinate graphs, bar graphs, and line plots. In sixth grade, students use a real-number line to order rational and irrational numbers.

9.9.3 Name-Collection Boxes

Beginning in *First Grade Everyday Mathematics*, children use name-collection boxes to help them recognize equivalent names for numbers. These devices give students the opportunity to experience the notion that the same number can be expressed in many different ways. Names can include, for example, sums, differences, products, quotients, the results of combining several operations, words in English or other languages, tally marks, arrays, Roman numerals, and numerals in bases other than ten.

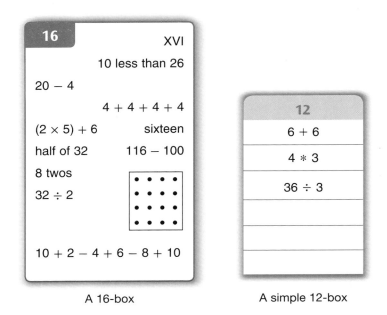

A 16-box   A simple 12-box

In Kindergarten through third grade, a name-collection box diagram is a box with a label attached to it. The name on the label identifies the number whose names are collected in the box. For example, the box shown on the left above is a 16-box, a name-collection box for the number 16. Beginning in fourth grade, students use a more compact name-collection box such as the 12-box shown above.

9.9.4 Fraction-Stick Charts and Fraction Sticks

Students in *Fifth Grade Everyday Mathematics* use a *Fraction-Stick Chart* like the one shown on page 89 to find equivalent fractions and to compare fractions. Each row in the chart is a *fraction stick* divided into unit fractions, or pieces, for a particular denominator. Fraction sticks are pictorial representations of fractions, with each stick representing a whole, or ONE.

To use the Fraction-Stick Chart to find equivalent fractions for $\frac{2}{3}$:

- Use the *thirds* stick to locate the fraction $\frac{2}{3}$. Count the $\frac{1}{3}$ pieces from left to right. The right edge of the second piece is $\frac{2}{3}$.
- Place one edge of a straightedge at $\frac{2}{3}$, that is, along the right edge of the second $\frac{1}{3}$ piece. The straightedge should be parallel to the sides of the Fraction-Stick Chart.
- On the *sixths* stick, the straightedge passes through the end of the fourth piece, which is $\frac{4}{6}$. So $\frac{4}{6} = \frac{2}{3}$.
- On the *ninths* stick, the straightedge passes through the end of the sixth piece, which is $\frac{6}{9}$. So $\frac{6}{9} = \frac{2}{3}$.
- On the *twelfths* stick, the straightedge passes through the end of the eighth piece, which is $\frac{8}{12}$. So $\frac{8}{12} = \frac{2}{3}$.

0    $\frac{1}{4}$ $\frac{2}{4}$ $\frac{3}{4}$ 1

1															
$\frac{1}{2}$								$\frac{1}{2}$							
$\frac{1}{3}$					$\frac{1}{3}$					$\frac{1}{3}$					
$\frac{1}{4}$				$\frac{1}{4}$				$\frac{1}{4}$				$\frac{1}{4}$			
$\frac{1}{5}$			$\frac{1}{5}$			$\frac{1}{5}$			$\frac{1}{5}$			$\frac{1}{5}$			
$\frac{1}{6}$		$\frac{1}{6}$		$\frac{1}{6}$		$\frac{1}{6}$		$\frac{1}{6}$		$\frac{1}{6}$					
$\frac{1}{7}$		$\frac{1}{7}$		$\frac{1}{7}$		$\frac{1}{7}$		$\frac{1}{7}$		$\frac{1}{7}$		$\frac{1}{7}$			
$\frac{1}{8}$	$\frac{1}{8}$		$\frac{1}{8}$		$\frac{1}{8}$		$\frac{1}{8}$		$\frac{1}{8}$		$\frac{1}{8}$		$\frac{1}{8}$		
$\frac{1}{9}$	$\frac{1}{9}$		$\frac{1}{9}$		$\frac{1}{9}$		$\frac{1}{9}$		$\frac{1}{9}$		$\frac{1}{9}$		$\frac{1}{9}$		
$\frac{1}{10}$	$\frac{1}{10}$	$\frac{1}{10}$	$\frac{1}{10}$	$\frac{1}{10}$	$\frac{1}{10}$	$\frac{1}{10}$	$\frac{1}{10}$	$\frac{1}{10}$	$\frac{1}{10}$						
$\frac{1}{12}$	$\frac{1}{12}$	$\frac{1}{12}$	$\frac{1}{12}$	$\frac{1}{12}$	$\frac{1}{12}$	$\frac{1}{12}$	$\frac{1}{12}$	$\frac{1}{12}$	$\frac{1}{12}$	$\frac{1}{12}$	$\frac{1}{12}$				
$\frac{1}{16}$	$\frac{1}{16}$	$\frac{1}{16}$	$\frac{1}{16}$	$\frac{1}{16}$	$\frac{1}{16}$	$\frac{1}{16}$	$\frac{1}{16}$	$\frac{1}{16}$	$\frac{1}{16}$	$\frac{1}{16}$	$\frac{1}{16}$	$\frac{1}{16}$	$\frac{1}{16}$	$\frac{1}{16}$	$\frac{1}{16}$

- On any other stick, the straightedge cuts through one of the pieces, so $\frac{2}{3}$ cannot be written as an equivalent fraction using the pieces on that stick.

To use the chart to find which fraction is greater, $\frac{4}{9}$ or $\frac{3}{8}$:

- Place one edge of a straightedge at $\frac{4}{9}$, the right side of the fourth piece of the *ninths* stick.
- Locate $\frac{3}{8}$ at the right side of the third piece on the *eighths* stick. Because $\frac{4}{9}$ is to the right of $\frac{3}{8}$, $\frac{4}{9}$ is greater than $\frac{3}{8}$. That is, $\frac{4}{9} > \frac{3}{8}$.

Fraction sticks can also help students visualize the addition of fractions with certain denominators, as the following two examples illustrate:

$$\frac{3}{16} + \frac{9}{16} = \boxed{} = \frac{12}{16}, \text{ or } \frac{3}{4}$$

$$\frac{5}{8} + \frac{1}{4} = \boxed{} = \frac{7}{8}$$

NOTE: The Fraction-Stick Chart is available as a master in fifth grade and in the *Student Reference Book* for sixth grade.

chapter 9

10 Arithmetic Operations

Contents

For many adults, elementary school mathematics consisted of little more than learning to add, subtract, multiply, and divide whole numbers, fractions, and decimals. Unfortunately, this is still the experience of many students today. The authors of *Everyday Mathematics* hope that your acquaintance with our texts and your reading of this manual convince you that elementary school mathematics needs to be far more than arithmetic with the four basic operations.

Nevertheless, the importance of arithmetic in mathematics as well as in everyday life cannot be denied. *Everyday Mathematics* combines activities that focus on understanding the basic operations with activities that apply arithmetic in geometry, data exploration, measurement, and other contexts. This ensures that students receive ample practice with arithmetic skills and that they will be better able to use those skills to solve problems. Students in *Everyday Mathematics* see many uses of all the operations from the beginning of the program and build upon these uses year after year. Rather than having multiplication and division delayed until third grade or later, they see these operations as well as addition and subtraction in first and second grades.

Many adults who associate school mathematics with arithmetic also tend to think that an arithmetic operation is what you "do" to get the answer. For example, to these adults division means carrying out the traditional long-division algorithm. In *Everyday Mathematics,* how one "does" an operation is referred to as "applying an algorithm" or "carrying out a computation." Although *Everyday Mathematics* recognizes the importance of knowing algorithms and introduces a variety of algorithms for each operation, it also provides the activities that students need in order to understand the meanings behind each operation. Choosing the proper algorithm and interpreting the result correctly depends on understanding the operation itself. Students need to both understand the meanings of the operations and become proficient at carrying out algorithms to become successful problem solvers.

This chapter begins with discussions about arithmetic symbols, number expressions and sentences, and number models. It then turns to specific approaches to solving number stories using situation diagrams for the four basic arithmetic operations.

▶ 10.1 Arithmetic Symbols

In *Everyday Mathematics,* number models are used to represent situations and to summarize relationships among quantities in problems. Although the first years of the program emphasize concrete, verbal (usually oral), and pictorial models, you are encouraged to write number models on the board or an overhead transparency, and to often include blank response lines for unknown numbers. Symbols for operations such as $+$, $-$, and $\times$ and for relations such as $=$, $>$, and $<$ are introduced informally. In second and third grades, students take on more responsibility for writing the number models.

Writing number models is in some ways similar to writing English sentences. Written English and written mathematics both have rules and conventions about grammar, syntax, punctuation, and usage. These rules clarify thinking and make communication easier. So before looking at a formal definition of number model, the authors discuss the arithmetic symbols themselves and how they are used in number sentences and numerical expressions.

10.1.1 The Four Basic Arithmetic Operations

Many people feel that mathematics has too many symbols. Symbols, however, are vitally important to the subject. They make the language of mathematics more concise and, ultimately, easier to communicate and understand. Symbols can increase mathematical power by relieving the mind of unnecessary work and leaving it free to focus on problem solving.

Writers of school mathematics programs face a dilemma. On one hand, an efficient set of symbols is needed so that activities may progress smoothly in a classroom. But symbols, especially if they are introduced too early, may pose an unnecessary obstacle to the understanding of a concept. With this in mind, the authors of *Everyday Mathematics* have been careful to avoid the premature introduction of symbols and mathematical vocabulary in general. Symbols are introduced only when they help students communicate more efficiently.

For descriptions of various algorithms, see Chapter 11: Algorithms.

For information about managing students' use of number models, see Section 10.2.4: Teaching with Number Sentences and Number Models.

chapter 10

The curriculum must introduce both the symbols needed for classroom activities and the symbols required for real-world general knowledge. Symbols for classroom activities can be introduced on an *ad hoc* basis and could be restricted to a small and efficient set. But the need for students to understand mathematics within a broader social context means that *Everyday Mathematics* must include a more expansive list of symbols. Each group in society, for example, grocers, scientists, engineers, advertisers, and journalists, has a different set of symbols it considers necessary. Even the way we write numbers can spark debate: *Should it be .1 or 0.1? Is 1/2 better than $\frac{1}{2}$, or is $^1/_2$ the best? Should we write -3, −3, or ⁻3?*

Calculators and computers, which might have been expected to help standardize notation, have actually increased the need for understanding that different symbols can mean the same thing. For example, there are several alternative symbols for multiplication, division, powers, and opposites (inverses). *Everyday Mathematics* provides activities to help students become aware of these alternative notations so that they can adapt to different situations as necessary. The program employs several notations for certain operations so students will become familiar with all common symbols.

Addition and Subtraction Symbols

The only symbols for addition and subtraction are + and −. Although the ideas behind the operations are thousands of years old, the symbols first appeared in print in 1498 in a book by the German mathematician Johann Widman. Widman's symbols gradually caught on and are now universally accepted. However, words for these symbols vary: *plus, add*, and *positive* all refer to +; *minus, take away,* and *negative* all refer to −.

Students in *Everyday Mathematics* see these symbols only after they have had informal experiences with the underlying operations. For example, Kindergarten children begin hearing the words *add* and *subtract* in the context of number stories based on their own experiences. Gradually, + and − are introduced in this context to help children link the spoken and symbolic representations. One of the first encounters that Kindergarteners have with the addition symbol occurs when they use the $\boxed{+}$ on their calculators in a counting-on activity. Establishing this informal connection between + and counting supports later use of + in paper-and-pencil representations of addition and the understanding of a rule such as "+ 3" in "What's My Rule?" and Frames-and-Arrows activities. Similar counting-back activities use $\boxed{-}$.

Multiplication and Division Symbols

Multiplication and division are each represented by several symbols in everyday life. All of the symbols are discussed in the *Everyday Mathematics Teacher's Lesson Guide;* but to standardize symbolic representation in the materials, the authors have made some choices that are clarified here.

Mathematics textbooks traditionally use the symbol × (read *times* or *multiplied by*) to indicate multiplication. The Englishman William Oughtred invented this symbol in 1631. The symbol × is used when multiplication models are introduced in *Second* and *Third Grade Everyday Mathematics.* There are at least three disadvantages to using × for multiplication:

- It can be confused with the addition symbol +.
- It does not appear on standard computer or typewriter keyboards, although it is standard on most calculator keypads.
- It can easily be mistaken for the letter *x,* presenting a problem when students use letter variables in Grades 4 through 6.

One solution to these problems is to use a raised dot for multiplication, that is, 5 • 6 rather than 5 × 6. Gottfried Leibniz, one of the inventors of calculus, introduced this dot notation in 1698. But an obvious difficulty with a raised dot is possible confusion with the decimal point. In fact, in some countries a raised dot *is* the decimal point.

After much consideration, the authors of *Everyday Mathematics* decided to use ∗ as the usual symbol for multiplication beginning in fourth grade. It is always the multiplication symbol on computer keyboards, and it is frequently used in print. It is also found on some calculators. The symbol is easy to write or type and is not likely to be confused with other symbols. Using ∗ for multiplication prepares students for the present as well as the future in a world of computers. A disadvantage is that ∗ is less familiar than × to teachers and parents.

Eventually, students learn to indicate multiplication by *juxtaposition,* that is, by writing symbols next to each other. For example, (15)(23) means 15 ∗ 23, $2a$ means $2 ∗ a$, and ab means $a ∗ b$. Juxtaposition to indicate multiplication is common in formulas, which are among the earliest uses of letter variables that *Everyday Mathematics* students encounter. For example, the area A of a rectangle with width w and length l is written as $A = lw$. In fact, almost the only place where this formula is written as $A = l × w$ or $A = l ∗ w$ is in an elementary school mathematics textbook.

Historically, symbols for division have included ÷, ⌐, /, :, and the fraction bar. Their inventors were, respectively, the Swiss Johann Rahn in 1659; the German Michael Stifel in 1544; the Mexican Manuel A. Valdes in 1784; the German Gottfried Leibniz in 1684; and the Arab al-Ḥaṣṣâr in the twelfth century.

In second and third grades, *Everyday Mathematics* uses ÷. Unfortunately, ÷ shares two disadvantages with the multiplication symbol ×: it can easily be misread as +, and it does not appear on standard computer or typewriter keyboards. On the other hand, it is the symbol for division on almost all calculators.

Beginning in fourth grade, *Everyday Mathematics* uses / and the fraction bar, along with ÷, to indicate division. The / has been used for centuries. It appears on some calculators, is easy to write, and is found on computer and typewriter keyboards. The use of / and the

NOTE: A fraction bar is also called a *vinculum.*

fraction bar for indicating division has an additional, very important advantage: the forms a/b and $\frac{a}{b}$ reinforce the relation between division and fractions. The fraction notation also prepares students for the division symbols they are likely to see in middle and high school mathematics and beyond.

Writing division with a remainder can be a bit of a problem. Consider what can happen if equal signs are used:

$$12 \div 5 \ = 2 \text{ R}2$$
$$102 \div 50 = 2 \text{ R}2$$

Because the right-hand sides of the two equations are the same, it appears that the left-hand sides should be equal too. Hence, we should be able to write:

$$12 \div 5 \ = 102 \div 50$$

But, if you do the division, it is apparent that the two sides are *not* equal:

$$12 \div 5 \ = 2.4$$
$$102 \div 50 = 2.04$$

That is, $2.4 \neq 2.04$. The problem is that 2 R2 is not really a number, so using it in equations can lead to trouble. Because $102 \div 50$ is a number, but 2 R2 is not, $102 \div 50$ cannot equal 2 R2. To eliminate this problem, *Everyday Mathematics* uses arrows in number models for divisions with remainders:

$$102 \div 50 \ \rightarrow \ 2 \text{ R}2$$

This notation, although nonstandard, will not mislead students as using $=$ may. Later, when students learn to show remainders as fractions or decimals, the problem disappears altogether:

$$12 \div 5 \ = 2\tfrac{2}{5}$$
$$102 \div 50 = 2.04$$

The symbol $\overline{)}$ is closely linked to the traditional long-division algorithm. Actually, it is really more like a template for carrying out a procedure than a mathematical symbol. Using it, therefore, may suggest the use of the long-division algorithm when another method is warranted. It can be useful, however, for recording answers to division problems with remainders.

10.1.2 Powers and Exponents

Addition, subtraction, multiplication, and division are the four basic arithmetic operations, but there are other operations that are important in school mathematics. One of these is variously called *raising to a power, powering,* or *exponentiation*.

In the early 17th century, René Descartes first used positive whole-number exponents to represent the number of factors in a repeated multiplication. For example, in $2 * 2 * 2 * 2 = 2^4$, the *exponent* 4 is the number of times the *base* 2 is used as a *factor*. 2^4 is read "2 to the fourth power" or simply "2 to the fourth." In most books and with paper and pencil, the exponent is written as a superscript, above and

NOTE: Some scientific and fraction calculators have a key for division with remainder. Some call it "integer division," which is a misnomer, as it implies that the operation is defined for negative numbers, which it is not. In general, how division with a remainder works varies widely across calculators, so please consult an owner's manual on how the function works and how to interpret the display.

slightly to the right of the base. This notation is easy to read and write, but it can be difficult to enter from computer keyboards. Hence, in the computer age, other notations have become common.

In most computer programs, 2^4 is written "2^4," where ^, called a *caret,* means "raise to a power." In some early computer programs, 2^4 was written "2**4," which suggests the connection between multiplication and exponentiation.

Many scientific calculators have a power key that is commonly labeled $\boxed{y^x}$, $\boxed{x^y}$, or occasionally $\boxed{\wedge}$. For example, to calculate 2^4 on the TI-15 and Casio *fx*-55 calculators that the authors used while writing this edition of *Everyday Mathematics,* use these key sequences.

NOTE: On a keyboard, ^ is shift-6.

Powering on a TI-15	
Key Sequence	**Display**
2 $\boxed{\wedge}$ 4 $\boxed{\text{Enter}}$	2^4 = 16

Powering on a Casio *fx*-55	
Key Sequence	**Display**
2 $\boxed{x^y}$ 4 $\boxed{=}$	= 16.

When 2 and 3 are exponents, they are often read "squared" and "cubed," respectively. For example, 4^2 is read "4 to the second power" or "4 squared"; 4^3 is read "4 to the third power" or "4 cubed." These terms reflect the relationship of powering to dimension, in that the area of a 2-dimensional square is the length of a side to the second power and the volume of a 3-dimensional cube is the length of an edge to the third power.

Any nonzero number to the *zero power* is defined to be 1. For example, $4^0 = 1$. This definition may seem peculiar, but it is made to preserve many important properties of exponents. One such property is that every power of a number is the next higher power of the number divided by the number itself. For example:

$$3^2 = \frac{3^3}{3} = \frac{27}{3} = 9$$

Following this pattern for 3^0 yields:

$$3^0 = \frac{3^1}{3} = \frac{3}{3} = 1$$

So $3^0 = 1$, which generalizes for any nonzero number a, $a^0 = 1$.

Any number to the *first power* is equal to itself. For example, $4^1 = 4$.

Although exponents are not used in *Kindergarten* through *Third Grade Everyday Mathematics,* children in Grade 3 are introduced informally to square numbers and square products by observing how such numbers can be displayed in square arrays. Beginning in Grade 4, students use powers of 10, written in exponential notation, to represent large numbers.

Beginning in fifth grade, students learn *scientific notation,* which is shorthand for very large and very small numbers. Students also see

Square numbers

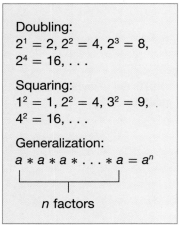

Doubling:
$2^1 = 2$, $2^2 = 4$, $2^3 = 8$,
$2^4 = 16$, . . .

Squaring:
$1^2 = 1$, $2^2 = 4$, $3^2 = 9$,
$4^2 = 16$, . . .

Generalization:
$a * a * a * \ldots * a = a^n$
$\underbrace{\hspace{3cm}}_{n \text{ factors}}$

$10^1 = 10$
$10^2 = 100$
$10^3 = 1,000$
$10^4 = 10,000$
$10^5 = 100,000$
$10^6 = 1,000,000$

how powers of 2 can be used to represent a doubling function, in contrast to using 2 as a power to represent squaring. They generalize the use of exponential notation to represent n factors of a base a as a^n, where a is any number and n is any integer.

Powers of 10 and Negative Exponents

Powers of 10 are used for scientific notation. The nonnegative powers of 10 are easy to remember because the exponent indicates how many zeros appear after the 1 when the number is written in standard decimal notation. For example, $10^6 = 1,000,000$.

Introduced in Grade 5, *negative exponents* are used in Grade 6 to write very small numbers in scientific notation. Powers with negative exponents are read the same way as powers with positive exponents. For example, 10^{-2} is read "10 to the negative second power" or "10 to the negative 2." The -2 exponent signals that 10^2 is a divisor, as shown below.

$$10^{-2} = \frac{1}{10^2} = \frac{1}{100}$$

Negative powers of 10 can be written as fractions or as decimals, as shown in the table at the right.

Power of 10	Fraction		Decimal
10^{-1}	$\frac{1}{10^1}$		0.1
10^{-2}	$\frac{1}{10^2} = \frac{1}{100}$		0.01
10^{-3}	$\frac{1}{10^3} = \frac{1}{1,000}$		0.001
10^{-4}	$\frac{1}{10^4} = \frac{1}{10,000}$		0.0001
10^{-5}	$\frac{1}{10^5} = \frac{1}{100,000}$		0.00001
10^{-6}	$\frac{1}{10^6} = \frac{1}{1,000,000}$		0.000001

The exponent indicates how many zeros follow the 1 in the denominator when a negative power of 10 is written as a fraction. In decimal notation, the exponent indicates how many digits follow the decimal point, that is, a number of zeros and a 1.

Powers of 10 written with negative exponents are a special case of the general rule

$$a^{-b} = \frac{1}{a^b}$$

where a is any nonzero number and b is a positive whole number. For example,

$$2^{-3} = \frac{1}{2^3} = \frac{1}{8}$$

In more advanced mathematics courses, students use fractional exponents. For example,

$$\sqrt{2} = 2^{\frac{1}{2}}$$

Eventually bases and exponents can be any real numbers. For example,

$$\sqrt{2^\pi} = 2^{\frac{\pi}{2}}$$

Such numbers can be approximated using a calculator. For example,

$$2^{\frac{\pi}{2}} \approx 2.9706864$$

A Note on Reciprocals

The product of a number and its *reciprocal,* or *multiplicative inverse,* is 1. For example, 5 and $\frac{1}{5}$ are reciprocals of each other because $5 * \frac{1}{5} = 1$. Every number except zero has a reciprocal. The reciprocal of any nonzero number a is a^{-1}. A bit of algebra verifies this:

$$a * a^{-1} = a * \frac{1}{a} = \frac{a}{a} = 1$$

More generally, for any nonzero a and positive whole number b, a^{-b} is the reciprocal of a^b:

$$a^{-b} = \frac{1}{a^b}$$

Powers of 10 written with negative exponents are a special case of this general rule.

On calculators with an inverse key, the reciprocal is usually labeled $\boxed{1/x}$ or $\boxed{x^{-1}}$. The two symbols are equivalent. On any calculator with an exponentiation key, the reciprocal of a number can be found by raising the number to the -1 power.

Scientific and Other Notations

It is often cumbersome to read and write very large and very small numbers. At times, it may not even be necessary or appropriate to consider all the digits in a large or small number; a rounded number works fine. For this reason, there are shorthand notations for large and small numbers.

For example, in 2003 the *World Fact Book* estimated the area of the Pacific Ocean to be 60,060,900 square miles. This is about 60,000,000 mi², and in *number-and-word* shorthand it is "60 million" mi². Such number-and-word notation is common in newspapers and magazines. *Everyday Mathematics* students begin using it in fourth grade. In Grades 4 and 5, students are introduced to exponential notation for powers of 10 as described above.

In Grades 5 and 6, students use their knowledge of powers of 10 to write large and small numbers in scientific notation. A number written in *scientific notation* is the product of two factors. One factor is a number greater than or equal to 1 and less than 10, and the other factor is a power of 10. Depending on the accuracy that is needed, or justified, the decimal part may be rounded. In scientific notation, estimates of the area of the Pacific Ocean are

$$6.00609 * 10^7 \text{ or } 6.01 * 10^7 \text{ or } 6.0 * 10^7$$

The exponent indicates how many places to the *right* the decimal point needs to be moved in order to write the number in standard decimal form.

The 60,000,000 mi² approximate area of the Pacific Ocean may also be written as $60 * 10^6$ mi². Strictly speaking, this is not scientific notation because 60 is greater than 10. However, it is a convenient and commonly used notation for large numbers.

Very small numbers can be written in scientific notation using powers of 10 with negative exponents. For example,

$$0.0000075 = 7.5 * 10^{-6}$$

The negative exponent indicates the number of places the decimal point in 7.5 is moved to the *left* to write the number in standard decimal notation.

Scientific calculators get their name because they use scientific notation to display large and small numbers. On a scientific calculator, a number that has more digits than will fit in the display is automatically shown in scientific notation. Some calculators use conventional scientific notation, but other calculators do not. The latter types may not even display the 10, but instead use E, EE, or a space to indicate the exponent. Here are some ways $1.3 * 10^9$ may be displayed on such calculators:

For more information on scientific calculators, see Section 3.1.1: Calculators.

$$1.3 \; E9 \qquad 1.3 \; E+9 \qquad 1.3 \; EE9 \qquad 1.3 \; 09$$

▶ 10.2 Reading and Writing Number Sentences

Just as English words become meaningful when they are arranged into sentences, mathematical symbols become meaningful in sentences. And just as proper punctuation and grammar make written English easy to read, rules and conventions for writing number sentences ease mathematical communication.

A *number sentence* is an equation or inequality such as $10 = 7 + 3$, $12/n = 6$, or $14 > 3$. A number sentence has a left-hand side, a relation symbol, and a right-hand side. Symbols for numbers, unknowns, and operations can appear on each side of the relation symbol. Each side of a number sentence is a *numerical expression*. In the sentences above, 10, $7 + 3$, $12/n$, 6, 14, and 3 are expressions. In practice, however, single numbers are usually called just "numbers" or "constants" and expressions usually include one or more operations.

Number sentences can be true, false, or neither true nor false. A number sentence that is neither true nor false is called an *open sentence*. The sentence $5 + 3 = 8$ is true; the sentence $5 + 4 = 8$ is false; the sentence $5 + \_\_ = 8$ is open.

A *number model* is a numerical expression or number sentence that models (represents) some real or hypothetical situation. For example, consider this situation: *Rajiv had 7 pennies and got 3 more. Then he had 10 pennies.* The sentence $7 + 3 = 10$ is a number model of Rajiv's situation. Number models can be based on stories made up by students, on situations invented by you, or on information from everyday life.

An established order of operations eliminates ambiguity about the order in which additions, subtractions, and other operations are to be performed in number sentences. Students begin learning the formal order in *Fifth Grade Everyday Mathematics*. Beginning in Grade 2, children learn to avoid ambiguity by using grouping symbols such as parentheses and brackets.

10.2.1 Grouping Symbols

The four basic operations of arithmetic—addition, subtraction, multiplication, and division—are called *binary operations* because each is carried out on two numbers at a time. Addition and multiplication can certainly involve more than two numbers, but repeatedly adding or multiplying *pairs* of numbers leads to final sums and products. When only two numbers and one operation are involved, there is no need for grouping symbols. Similarly, no grouping symbols are needed in adding several numbers or in multiplying several numbers because these operations may be performed in any order.

However, in situations involving more than two numbers with subtraction, division, or a combination of operations, you may obtain different results depending on the order in which the operations are performed. For example, the value of $4 + 3 * 5$ is 35 if the addition is done first and 19 if the multiplication is done first. To avoid such ambiguity, you can insert parentheses to indicate the order in which operations are to be carried out. If the addition is to be done first in the expression above, write $(4 + 3) * 5$; if the multiplication is to be done first, write $4 + (3 * 5)$.

Parentheses may be *nested,* meaning there are parentheses within parentheses. For example, in $2 * (3 + (2 - 1))$, the $(2 - 1)$ group is nested within the $(3 + (2 - 1))$ group. In nested parentheses, you always begin calculating within the innermost set of parentheses.

Sometimes different symbols are used to help distinguish between sets of grouping symbols. In the previous example, square brackets could be used for either set of parentheses with equivalent results:

$$2 * [3 + (2 - 1)] = 2 * (3 + [2 - 1])$$

Sometimes braces { } are used. Computers and calculators commonly use parentheses, but not brackets or braces, so it is not necessarily helpful in everyday experience to require the use of more than one kind of symbol in nested groups.

A horizontal *fraction bar,* or *vinculum,* is also a grouping symbol. You can imagine a set of parentheses around the entire numerator of a fraction and another set around the entire denominator. For example, an expression such as

$$\frac{22 - (5 + 4)}{1 + (9 - 3) * 2}$$

is equivalent to

$$(22 - (5 + 4))/(1 + (9 - 3) * 2) = (22 - 9)/(1 + 6 * 2)$$
$$= 13/(1 + 12)$$
$$= 13/13$$
$$= 1$$

Brief exercises with parentheses are worth repeating throughout each year of the program. Most students find such exercises to have an appealing, game-like quality. Such exercises also provide students with practice with basic number facts and their extensions, reminders of the effect of multiplying by or adding zero, and practice with expressing solutions in games such as *Name That Number.*

10.2.2 Operations with Positive and Negative Numbers

Children in *Kindergarten* through *Third Grade Everyday Mathematics* learn to represent addition and subtraction by moving counters or other objects from one point to another on a number line. This informal activity helps prepare them for their first formal experience with operations on positive and negative numbers in Grade 4. Using a business situation of credits and debits, students invent and solve number stories, using integers near zero so that problems can be solved mentally. It is important in these situations to name both the operation and the numbers as in the following examples.

Transaction	Read it:	Do *not* read it:
The credit transaction "Add +$3"	"Add positive 3 dollars"	"Add plus 3 dollars."
The debit transaction "Add −$5"	"Add negative 5 dollars"	"Add minus 5 dollars."

In Grades 4 and 5, students use two-color counters to represent debits (negative) and credits (positive) in transactions. In fifth grade, they use a "slide rule" based on integer number lines to help them to visualize addition and subtraction of positive and negative numbers.

Another approach to adding and subtracting positive and negative numbers in Grade 4 is to imagine walking on a number line.

- The first number tells you where to start.
- The operation sign (+ or −) tells you which way to face:
  + means face the positive direction on the number line.
  − means face the negative direction on the number line.
- If the second number is negative (has a − sign), then you walk backward. Otherwise, you walk forward.
- The second number tells you how many steps to walk.
- The number where you end is the answer.

Example: Find $4 - (-3)$.

Start at 4.

Face the negative direction on the number line.

Walk backward 3 steps.

You end at 7. So $4 - (-3) = 7$.

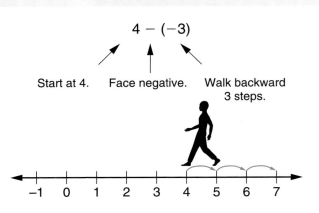

$4 - (-3)$

Start at 4.   Face negative.   Walk backward 3 steps.

Procedures for addition of integers on a number line tend to be reinforced by real-life situations. Many students quickly move beyond using the number line to add integers and develop their own rules for solving such problems. Having students explain their strategies orally or in writing develops and reinforces their understanding of integers.

Building on skills with mental arithmetic and calculators, students in Grades 5 and 6 extend addition and subtraction from integers to all positive and negative numbers, including decimals and rational numbers. Although multiplying and dividing with negative numbers is not as widely applicable in real-life situations as adding and subtracting, students in sixth grade explore these operations as well.

Rules for Subtraction and Multiplication

Because real-life uses of subtraction and multiplication of integers are hard to find, students may need more guidance in developing rules for these operations. This section describes how counters can be used to encourage rule discovery.

Counters that represent positive and negative numbers can help students discover that subtracting a number is equivalent to adding its opposite. You might use two-color counters, with one color representing positive and the other negative, or small slips of paper labeled + or −. For example:

- Model $5 - 3$ with 5 positive counters, from which 3 are removed, leaving 2 positive counters.

$$+ + \boxed{+ + +}$$
$$5 - 3 = 2$$

- Model $5 + (-3)$ with 5 positive and 3 negative counters. Three negative counters are paired with 3 of the 5 positive counters. The sum $3 + (-3)$ equals 0; that is, the 3 positive and 3 negative counters "cancel" each other, leaving 2 positive counters. This shows that $5 + (-3) = 2$.

$$+ + \boxed{\frac{+ + +}{- - -}}$$
$$5 + (-3) = 2$$

- Model $5 - (-3)$ starting with 5 positive counters. There are no negative counters to take away, but 3 positive and 3 negative counters, representing a sum of 0, can be added to the model without changing its value. Then, when 3 negative counters are taken away, 8 positive counters remain. So $5 - (-3) = 8$.

$$+ + + + +$$
$$\downarrow$$
$$+ + + + + \qquad + + +$$
$$\downarrow \qquad \boxed{- - -}$$
$$+ + + + + \qquad + + +$$
$$5 - (-3) = 8$$

Students quickly discover that $5 - (-3)$ has the same answer as $5 + 3$. So they can solve subtraction problems by adding the opposite of the number being subtracted.

Multiplication of a positive integer and a negative number can be related to repeated addition. For example, $3 * (-4)$ is the same as $(-4) + (-4) + (-4) = -12$, and because multiplication is commutative, $-4 * 3$ also equals -12.

It is not as easy to discover a rule for multiplication of two negative numbers. Consider using the following approaches to calculating $-3 * (-4)$, one with patterns and one with properties.

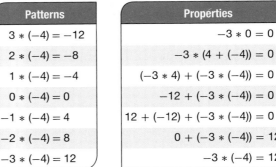

Patterns	Properties
$3 * (-4) = -12$	$-3 * 0 = 0$
$2 * (-4) = -8$	$-3 * (4 + (-4)) = 0$
$1 * (-4) = -4$	$(-3 * 4) + (-3 * (-4)) = 0$
$0 * (-4) = 0$	$-12 + (-3 * (-4)) = 0$
$-1 * (-4) = 4$	$12 + (-12) + (-3 * (-4)) = 0 + 12$
$-2 * (-4) = 8$	$0 + (-3 * (-4)) = 12$
$-3 * (-4) = 12$	$-3 * (-4) = 12$

One benefit of these activities with positive and negative numbers is to show that all four basic operations are possible for all rational numbers with the exception of division by zero.

10.2.3 The Order of Operations

Beginning in Grade 2, children are encouraged to use grouping symbols, particularly parentheses, to make their number sentences clearer. However, once they begin to use variables and scientific calculators in Grade 3, children need to understand the mathematical convention called the *order of operations,* or more formally the *algebraic order of operations,* to distinguish it from other orders that are used in some calculators and computer applications. The order of operations specifies the sequence in which the operations in an expression are to be performed. Grouping symbols are used to specify an order different from the conventional order or simply for greater clarity.

The *algebraic order of operations* is:

1. Do the operations inside *grouping symbols.* Work from the innermost grouping symbols outward. Inside grouping symbols, follow Rules 2 through 4.
2. Calculate all expressions with *exponents.*
3. *Multiply* and *divide* in order, from left to right.
4. *Add* and *subtract* in order, from left to right.

According to this convention, $4 + 3 * 5 = 19$ and

$$8/2^2 - 12/4 + 7 * (9 - 3) = 41.$$

In summary, the algebraic order of operations is used in most of the mathematics that students will encounter in middle school and beyond. The order of operations is formally introduced in *Fifth Grade Everyday Mathematics.* In *Kindergarten* through *Fourth Grade Everyday Mathematics,* grouping symbols such as parentheses and brackets are used primarily to increase clarity.

NOTE: Scientific and other advanced calculators have a formal order of operations built into them. Most 4-function calculators simply calculate with two numbers and an operation in the order that they are entered. If students in your classroom have different types of calculators, take the time to learn how each type handles the order of operations.

NOTE: A mnemonic for the order of operations is *P*lease *E*xcuse *M*y *D*ear *A*unt *S*ally: Do work inside the *P*arentheses first, and then *E*xponentiation, and then *M*ultiplication and *D*ivision, and finally *A*ddition and *S*ubtraction.

NOTE: In each of Rules 3 and 4, neither operation has priority over the other.

10.2.4 Teaching with Number Sentences and Number Models

In *Kindergarten* through *Third Grade Everyday Mathematics*, number models are not used to solve problems. Instead, they are used to represent and clarify the quantitative relationships in a problem. Although writing number models may help some students decide how to solve a problem, more importantly, it helps them learn the mathematical-symbol system. Translating a problem into a number model that is manipulated to find an answer comes later in the curriculum, when students begin to learn formal algebra.

When they are first introduced in *Everyday Mathematics,* number models usually appear after a problem has been solved. A typical instructional sequence might be as follows:

1. You pose a problem.
2. Students solve the problem.
3. Students share their solutions, and you record them on the board. During the discussion of solutions, you write number models and draw situation diagrams on the board. There should be no blanks in the number models or situation diagrams.

For more information, see Section 10.3: Use Classes and Situation Diagrams.

For example, after solving the number story *Marie has 55¢. She wants to buy a notebook that costs 89¢. How much more money does she need?* you or a student might write the number model $55 + n = 89$ on the board. The model shows the relationships between the quantities in the story and may suggest finding the answer by counting up. After solving the story by counting up or some other method, a child might write $55 + 34 = 89$ to summarize the work.

In later grades, an instructional sequence might be as follows:

1. You pose a problem.
2. You and the students discuss the problem and write a number model or draw a situation diagram that corresponds to the problem. The number model or diagram includes a blank or a question mark for the unknown quantity.
3. Students solve the problem. They may use the number model or situation diagram to help them, or they may use another method entirely.
4. Students share their solutions, and you record them on the board. During the discussion of the solutions, you fill in the blanks in the number model or diagram.

In third and fourth grades, more complicated equations are treated informally through puzzles such as *I am the number* x *in* $6 + 5 * x = 16$. *What number am I?* Solving this puzzle requires knowing that the order of operations dictates that x be multiplied by 5 before 6 is added. Students are encouraged to clarify this by rewriting the left-hand side of the number sentence as $6 + (5 * x)$. Students solve such puzzles by trial and error or by working backward.

Students begin solving equations by formal algebraic manipulations in *Fifth Grade Everyday Mathematics* and continue in sixth grade.

NOTE: A use class (read yo͞os class) gets its name by asking *In what situation is this operation* used?

NOTE: The diagrams in *Everyday Mathematics* are adapted from work done by Karen Fuson at Northwestern University.

▶ **10.3 Use Classes and Situation Diagrams**

Everyday Mathematics approaches the four basic operations of arithmetic by examining how they are used. At a certain stage, formal definitions can be valuable, but in the elementary grades it is better to foster understanding of the operations indirectly by looking at how they are used.

Addition, subtraction, multiplication, and division can each be applied in many different situations, but most of those situations can be sorted into just a handful of categories, or *use classes*. In *Everyday Mathematics,* the three basic use classes for addition and subtraction are called *parts and total, change,* and *comparison*. Depending on what is known and what is unknown, each kind of situation can lead to either addition or subtraction problems. Multiplication and division situations are harder to sort out, but several basic use classes can be distinguished: *equal groups, arrays and area, rate and ratio, scaling,* and *Cartesian products*. Each type of situation can lead to either multiplication or division problems, depending on what is unknown.

Everyday Mathematics uses *situation diagrams* to help sort out these various kinds of problem situations. These diagrams help students organize the information in simple 1-step number stories.

10.3.1 Addition and Subtraction Use Classes

Most situations that lead to addition and subtraction problems can be categorized into parts-and-total, change, or comparison use classes.

Although the examples on this and the next page are easy and appropriate for students in second and third grades, the principles they illustrate can be applied to more complicated problems for students in Grades 4 through 6.

Parts-and-Total Diagrams

A *parts-and-total* diagram is used to model situations in which two or more quantities, or parts, are combined to form a total.

In a situation where all the parts are known but the total is unknown, you can solve the problem by adding the parts.

> **Example 1:** Twelve fourth graders, 8 third graders, and 5 first graders are on a bus. How many students in all are on the bus?
>
> The parts are known. You are looking for the total.
>
> Possible number model: 12 + 8 + 5 = __

Total		
?		
Part	**Part**	**Part**
12	8	5

When you and your students draw your own diagrams, quick and easy freehand drawings are best. The words "Part" and "Total" can be omitted or replaced with words that better fit the problem situation.

In situations where the total is known but one of the parts is unknown, you can use subtraction to find the unknown part.

Example 2: Thirty-five students are riding on the bus. Twenty of them are boys. How many girls are riding on the bus?

One part and the total are known. You are looking for the other part.

Possible number models:

$20 +$ __ $= 35$

$35 - 20 =$ __

Total
35

Part	Part
20	?

Change Diagrams

Change diagrams are used to represent problems in which a starting quantity is increased or decreased.

Example 3: Twenty-five students are riding on the bus. At the next stop, 5 more students get on. How many students are on the bus now?

This is a change-to-more situation, or an increase, with the ending quantity unknown.

Possible number model: $25 + 5 =$ __

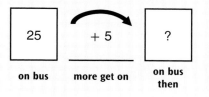

25   + 5   ?

on bus   more get on   on bus
                            then

NOTE: You can simplify change diagrams by omitting words or changing to words that fit the problem as in Example 3.

Example 4: Tom had some money. He bought a magazine for $1.50. Then he had $6.50. How much money did Tom have to start with?

This is a change-to-less situation, or a decrease, with the starting quantity unknown.

Possible number models:

_____ $- \$1.50 = \$6.50$

$\$1.50 + \$6.50 =$ _____

Change

Start	End
?	$6.50

$- \$1.50$

Comparison Diagrams

Comparison situations involve two separate quantities and the difference between them. As with change and parts-and-total situations, comparison situations can lead to addition or subtraction problems depending on what is known and what kind of comparison is being made.

Example 5: There are 12 fourth graders and 8 third graders. How many more fourth graders are there than third graders?

Here both quantities being compared are known and the difference is unknown.

Possible number models:

12 − 8 = __

8 + __ = 12

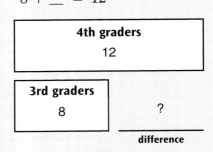

Teaching with Addition/Subtraction Diagrams

It is important to remember that situation diagrams are simply devices to help organize problem solving; they are not ends in themselves. Some students do not need to organize their thinking on paper, and to require them to do so would not be constructive.

For those students who find diagrams useful, *Everyday Mathematics* suggests that they follow these steps, although not necessarily in this order:

- Choose a diagram that fits the problem situation, but keep in mind that more than one diagram may fit. One person might think of a problem as a parts-and-total situation, while another person sees it as a change situation. Don't be too inflexible about which diagram is the most appropriate for a given situation, and remember that many situations are not suitable for any diagram. Multistep problems, for example, do not easily fit into these diagrams.

- Write the known quantities and a question mark for the unknown quantity in the appropriate parts of the diagram.

- Use the diagram to help decide how to solve the problem. Most problems can be solved in more than one way. A change-to-more problem, for example, might be solved by addition, by counting up mentally or on a number grid, by acting out with counters, or by drawing pictures.

- Calculate an answer.

- Write a number model that fits the problem. The number model does not need to reflect how the problem was solved. For example, a child might write "8 + 3 = 11" for a change-to-more problem that she solved using counters. Often, several number models can fit a single situation. Connecting number models to situations can help students understand both the arithmetic operations and the symbols for those operations.

- Write an answer. Be sure to include a measurement unit or other label.

- Check to see if the answer makes sense.

Unit Boxes

The importance of including a unit or other label in an answer cannot be over-emphasized. Numbers and operations make the most sense to students when they are thought of in real-world contexts.

Because labeling each number in a situation diagram can be tedious, *Everyday Mathematics* suggests that you and the students use *unit boxes* for addition and subtraction problems. These rectangular boxes can be displayed beside the problem or at the top of a page of problems. Unit boxes contain the labels or units of measure used in the problem(s). Unit boxes help students organize their mathematics while keeping a particular context in mind.

Some teachers post a unit box for the day on the board so that students will have a context in which to think about all the abstract numbers used in the day's activities, such as facts practice. Or students can supply the context themselves; they can choose topics of current interest or, if they prefer, fanciful or silly labels.

Unit
cents ¢

A unit box

For more information, see Section 16.3.3: Fact Practice.

10.3.2 Multiplication and Division Use Classes

Multiplication and division arise in many different situations, but most of these situations can be sorted into just a few use classes: *equal groups, arrays and area, rate and ratio, scaling,* and *Cartesian products*.

Everyday Mathematics uses diagrams to organize the information in many of these situations. The diagrams have two rows of rectangles. The top row is for the units; the bottom row is for the numbers. As with the diagrams for addition and subtraction situations, these diagrams are meant as problem-solving tools, not as ends in themselves. If using a diagram is not helpful, try some other approach, such as making a table or acting the problem out with objects.

For more information on alternative approaches, see Chapter 18: Problem Solving.

Equal Groups

In an *equal-groups* situation, there are several groups of objects with the same number of objects in each group. Depending on what is unknown, equal-groups situations can lead to either multiplication or division problems.

In an equal-groups situation where the total is unknown but the number of groups and the number of objects in each group are known, you can solve the problem by multiplication.

Example 1: A vase holds 5 flowers with 6 petals on each flower. How many petals are there in all?

Possible number model: $5 * 6 = \_\_$

flowers	petals per flower	total number of petals
5	6	?

In situations where the number of groups and the total number of objects are known, the problem is to find the number in each group. In *Everyday Mathematics*, these are called *equal-sharing* problems. Equal sharing is also known a *partitive division*.

Many students solve equal-sharing problems by "dealing out" the objects to be shared.

Example 2: Twenty-eight baseball cards are to be shared equally by 4 students. How many cards does each child get?

Possible number models:

$$4 * \_\_ = 28$$
$$28/4 = \_\_$$

students	baseball cards per student	total number of cards
4	?	28

In situations where the number in each group and the total number of objects are known, the problem is to find the number of groups. In *Everyday Mathematics*, these are called *equal-grouping* problems.

Many students solve equal-grouping problems by making as many groups of the correct size as possible and then counting the number of groups.

Example 3: Twenty-four Girl Scouts are going on a canoe trip. Each canoe can hold 3 scouts. How many canoes are needed?

Possible number models:

$$3 * \_\_ = 24$$
$$24/3 = \_\_$$

canoes	scouts per canoe	total number of scouts
?	3	24

Equal-grouping problems are also called *measurement division* or *quotitive division*. The term measurement division comes from thinking about using the divisor to "measure" the dividend. For example, consider 26/6. Think *How many 6s would it take to make 26?* Then imagine measuring off 6-unit lengths on a number line:

The figure above shows that there are four 6-unit lengths in 26, with 2 units left over. Thus 26/6 is 4 with remainder 2.

Arrays and Area

Arrays are closely related to equal-groups situations. If the equal groups are arranged in rows and columns, then a rectangular *array* is formed. As with equal-groups situations, arrays can lead to either multiplication or division problems.

Example 4: There are 6 rows with 15 chairs in each row. How many chairs are there in all?

Possible number model: $6 * 15 = \underline{}$

rows	chairs per row	total chairs
6	15	?

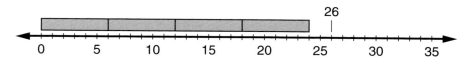

An array of chairs

For more information, see Section 14.4.1: Discrete and Continuous Models of Area.

Arrays are closely related to *area*. An array of square-centimeter tiles with no gaps between the tiles will have an area in square centimeters equal to the number of tiles. Unlike any of the previous multiplication models, an area model generalizes to multiplication with fractions, decimals, and mixed numbers.

Example 5: The area of a rectangle is 48 cm². The rectangle's length is 8 cm. What is its width?

Possible number models:

$8 * \underline{} = 48$

$48/8 = \underline{}$

length (cm)	width (cm)	area (cm²)
8	?	48

Note that because of the Commutative Property of Multiplication, the factors in array and area situations can be interchanged without affecting the value of the product. The total number of chairs in Example 4 would not change if there were 15 rows with 6 chairs in each row. And if the rectangle in Example 5 had a width of 8 cm, its length would be 6 cm to give an area of 48 cm².

However, the difference between a 6-by-15 array and a 15-by-6 array is important not only in the context of some problems, for example, the direction the chairs have to face determines which number represents a row, but in mathematics that students may study later in school. A *matrix* is a mathematical name for an array, and to perform arithmetic with matrices requires keeping track of rows and columns. For these reasons, it is a good idea to always talk about the dimensions of an array as meaning "rows" by "columns," in that order.

This does not mean that students should be penalized for getting rows and columns switched, especially when they correctly answer problems in array situations. If a child has them backward, simply point out *Oh, your array is turned*.

Rates and Ratios

Rate and *ratio* situations are common in higher mathematics and in real-life applications. A *rate* compares two quantities with *different* units. A common situation involving a rate is *speed*, which is the rate of distance per time, but many other situations can also be thought of as rates as well. When you buy apples, for example, the total cost depends on the amount you purchase and the price per pound, a rate.

For more information, see Section 9.3.3: Rates, Ratios, and Proportions.

> **Example 6:** The 8 people on the pep squad worked a total of 20 hours preparing for the school assembly. What was the average number of hours per person?
>
> Possible number models:
>
> $$20/8 = \underline{\quad}$$
> $$8 * \underline{\quad} = 20$$
>
> | people | hours per person | total person-hours |
> | :---: | :---: | :---: |
> | 8 | ? | 20 |

Ratio situations are modeled just like rate situations, but in a ratio, the quantities have the *same* unit.

Scaling

Scaling is another situation that leads to multiplication or division. A *scale factor* tells how much larger or smaller something becomes. For example, when you double a recipe you are scaling by 2. If the scale factor is less than 1, then scaling makes something smaller, such as halving a recipe by a factor of $\frac{1}{2}$.

> **Example 7:** Hector weighed 6 lb at birth. At 1 year, he weighed 3 times his birth weight. What was his weight at 1 year?
>
> Possible number model: $3 * 6 = \underline{\quad}$
>
> | scale factor | birth weight (lb) | 1-year weight (lb) |
> | :---: | :---: | :---: |
> | 3 | 6 | ? |

Scale factors, also known as *scalars,* can be fractions or percents. Scaling problems can involve either multiplication or division, depending on what is known and what is to be found.

Example 8: A store has a $\frac{1}{2}$ price (or 50%) sale. What was the original price of an item that cost $30 on sale?

Possible number models:

$$\frac{1}{2} * \underline{\quad} = 30$$

$$30 / \frac{1}{2} = \underline{\quad}$$

scale factor	original price	sale price
$\frac{1}{2}$	?	$30

Cartesian Products

The last kind of multiplication and division situation in *Everyday Mathematics* involves Cartesian products. Despite the imposing name, the idea is not difficult. A *Cartesian product* is the number of pairings of each item from one set to each item of another set. For example, suppose someone has 3 skirts (black, white, gray) and 5 blouses (black, white, gray, checked, striped). The Cartesian product 3 * 5 tells how many outfits that person has: black skirt and black blouse, black skirt and white blouse, and so on. If the two sets are not too large, this can be shown in a drawing like the one in the margin.

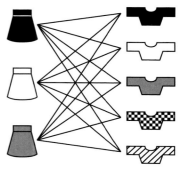

A Cartesian product:
3 * 5 = 15 outfits

Teaching with Multiplication/Division Diagrams

See "Teaching with Addition/Subtraction Diagrams" on page 106 for suggestions on how students might use these diagrams. Keep in mind that the diagrams are devices to help organize problem solving, not ends in themselves. Some students simply do not need to organize their thinking on paper, and to oblige them to do so is not advisable.

10.4 Arithmetic Operations Tools and Techniques

Tools and techniques to help students learn operations and facts include the following:

- Situation diagrams described in Section 10.3: Use Classes and Situation Diagrams;
- Computational algorithms, both traditional and invented, discussed at length in Chapter 11: Algorithms;
- Calculators, discussed in Section 3.1.1: Calculators.

11 Algorithms

Contents

An algorithm is a well-defined procedure or set of rules used to solve a problem. Algorithms are often used in everyday life, and having students become comfortable with algorithmic and procedural thinking is essential to their growth and development as solvers of everyday problems. Skillful use of algorithms can help students to:

- Use a single method to solve an entire class of related problems;
- Improve their use of mental arithmetic skills;
- Develop sound number sense, including a good understanding of place value;
- Strengthen their mathematical power.

This chapter begins with an explanation of how *Everyday Mathematics* approaches computational algorithms, including the role of invented algorithms in developing understanding of operations, place value, and computational procedures.

This discussion is followed by descriptions of the algorithms for the four basic arithmetic operations with whole numbers. For each operation, one algorithm has been designated as a *focus* algorithm. The focus algorithms are not identical to the computational algorithms that are traditionally taught, but they are similar.

In addition to being easier to learn and use than the traditional algorithms, the focus algorithms reveal more about underlying concepts, such as place value, and are less likely to lead to wrong answers.

The chapter ends with a discussion of calculator key sequences as algorithms for manipulating and rewriting fractions.

▶ 11.1 Algorithmic Thinking

People use algorithms every day. A bread recipe is an algorithm giving the ingredients and cooking procedures you need to produce the same type of loaf every time you bake one. The instructions for operating cell phones, home-security systems, or video recorders are all forms of algorithms. As a teacher, you probably establish procedures for students to store their belongings, line up for activities, or use classroom materials. In addition, *Everyday Mathematics* encourages you to establish other, more mathematical routines such as keeping a weather record or class calendar.

Everyday Mathematics includes a variety of both traditional computational algorithms and students' invented procedures. Inventing procedures is valuable because it:

- Promotes conceptual understanding and mental flexibility, both of which are essential for effective problem solving;
- Helps students learn about our base-ten place-value (decimal) system of numeration;
- Involves solving problems that the solver does not already know how to solve. Thus, asking students to devise their own computational methods provides valuable experience in solving nonroutine problems.

Traditional algorithms have advantages, too. They are generally efficient and can help students understand both the decimal number system and the underlying operations. Traditional algorithms also provide a common vocabulary for further development of mathematical ideas.

In addition to studying specific algorithms in *Everyday Mathematics,* students engage in activities to help them understand algorithms in a more general sense. These activities focus on helping students to:

- Understand specific algorithms or procedures provided by other people;
- Apply known algorithms to everyday problems;
- Develop algorithms and procedures when necessary;
- Realize the limitations of algorithms and their procedures so that they are not used inappropriately;
- Adapt known algorithms to fit new situations.

Mathematics advances in part through the development of efficient procedures that reduce difficult tasks to routine exercises. An effective algorithm will solve an entire class of problems, thus

NOTE: The term *algorithm* comes from the name *al-Khwarizmi.* Muhammad ibn Musa al-Khwarizmi (c. 780–850) was one of the greatest mathematicians of the Arab-Islamic world. We also have al-Khwarizmi to thank for the word *algebra,* which comes from *Hisab Aljabr w'al-muqabalah,* the title of one of his books.

NOTE: Algorithmic thinking has its place in geometry, too. The axiomatic method used by Euclid to prove theorems relies on clear definitions and logical deductive steps. Although having students understand geometric proof is not a goal in *Everyday Mathematics,* students in Grades 4 through 6 perform compass-and-straightedge constructions that are step-by-step algorithms proving geometric theorems.

increasing the user's mathematical power. The authors of *Everyday Mathematics* have found that the study of paper-and-pencil computational algorithms can be valuable for developing algorithmic thinking in general.

11.1.1 Computational Algorithms, Algorithm Invention, and Number Sense

Probably the most familiar procedures in the everyday life of elementary school teachers and students are the pencil-and-paper *computational algorithms* for adding, subtracting, multiplying and dividing numbers. There are dozens of computational algorithms that have been used all over the world throughout history in places such as Babylon, sub-Saharan Africa, South America, Europe, ancient Egypt, and the United States. Although algorithms can look very different from one another, they are all well-defined, step-by-step procedures that guarantee correct answers using any numbers.

What makes a *good* algorithm?

A good bread recipe is efficient (has no unnecessary steps or ingredients), unambiguous (has no vague or confusing instructions), and reliable (unless a mistake is made, the loaf comes out as expected). Likewise, a good computational algorithm is efficient, unambiguous, and reliable in applying a basic arithmetic operation to any two numbers.

A computational algorithm is also good if a student "owns" it, meaning that it makes sense, is easy to remember, and inspires the confidence to use it to solve new, unfamiliar problems. *Everyday Mathematics* promotes such ownership by encouraging students to invent their own algorithms.

Algorithm invention encourages students to use skills they already have, exercise their common sense, and gain new skills and knowledge. Students learn to ask questions that are important in problem solving such as, "How long will this take?" or "Is there a better way?" As students create their own procedures, they also develop persistence and the confidence to solve increasingly difficult problems. Students who invent their own algorithms learn that their intuitive methods are valid and that mathematics makes sense. All these benefits qualify students' invented algorithms as good algorithms.

What are the *best* algorithms?

Deciding what is best for an individual student and what is best for a community is always a delicate matter, even when it comes to algorithms.

Your *best algorithms.* For you as an individual, the best bread recipe depends on your situation—on the bread-making "problem" you need to solve. Are you baking the loaf for children or adults; for sandwiches or as soup bowls; in a kitchen or over a campfire? Variations on one recipe, and occasionally a different recipe altogether, can help you meet your different bread needs.

> **NOTE:** A University of Chicago graduate student once counted 17 addition, 18 subtraction, and 32 multiplication algorithms for whole numbers alone!

Similarly, the *best* computational algorithm depends on the problem to be solved and the capabilities of the problem solver. Hopefully, most people use a mental algorithm to calculate 5 – 3, and not a pencil-and-paper one. Calculating 301 – 3 by writing it as shown in the margin and "borrowing" hardly seems to be the best approach. And does it seem best to work from right-to-left to calculate 300 * 20? Unfortunately, students who are taught only one so-called "best" pencil-and-paper algorithm per operation tend to use those algorithms even for these examples. Such students do not use good *number sense*.

People with good number sense:

- Are flexible in their thinking about numbers and arithmetic and look for "shortcuts" to make their efforts more efficient;
- Are continually cultivating good mental-math skills, along with reliable algorithms and procedures for finding results they can't produce mentally;
- Can use their number and arithmetic skills to solve problems in everyday situations;
- Can recognize unreasonable results when they see numbers in print, in other media, or in their own work.

Students with sound number sense do not automatically categorize a given problem, such as 301 – 3, as an addition or subtraction problem. Instead, they think about the problem and use the most efficient and convenient operation and algorithm to solve it. Such students are reflective and creative in their use of the four operations, and they do not blindly use ready-made algorithms as substitutes for thinking and common sense.

To help students develop good number sense, *Everyday Mathematics* shows them a variety of computational algorithms in different problem situations, often challenges them to invent algorithms of their own, and regularly asks them to decide which available algorithm is "best" to perform a given computation.

Our *best algorithms*. Even bread experts can disagree on which recipe is the best. Does the best recipe help bakers learn the principles of making other kinds of breads, or prepare them to make pastries, or help them learn techniques to get into a culinary academy? And even if all the experts agree on one best recipe, can it possibly be best for everyone? For example, to prepare a loaf similar to one prepared by a baker at sea level, a baker at high altitude needs to use less sugar and bake the loaf longer or at a higher temperature—that is, one recipe cannot be best in both circumstances.

Currently in the United States, the traditional algorithms for adding, subtracting, multiplying, and dividing that you probably learned in school are being called "the" *standard algorithms*. These are not scientifically determined standards found by testing all the known algorithms for each operation and measuring the most efficient, unambiguous, and reliable ones. They are not internationally agreed upon standards like standard weights and measures. They are specific

$$
\begin{array}{r}
{}^{2}\ {}^{9}\ {}^{11} \\
\cancel{3}\cancel{0}\cancel{1} \\
-\quad 3 \\
\hline
298
\end{array}
$$

Is all this really necessary?

NOTE: The *Common Core State Standards for Mathematics* also refer to U.S. traditional algorithms as the *standard* algorithms. It is wise for students to learn both terms and to understand why they are called U.S. traditional in *Everyday Mathematics*.

to the United States, so *Everyday Mathematics* calls them U.S. traditional addition, subtraction, multiplication, and division.

After years of research and classroom testing, the authors of *Everyday Mathematics* do not think that the U.S. traditional algorithms are the best for helping students develop *both* computational skill *and* good number sense. To these ends, four *focus algorithms* have been identified that, while being comparably efficient, unambiguous, and reliable to the traditional ones, also offer students richer opportunities to understand the underlying concepts of the operations. Because all students are expected to learn them, the focus algorithms help encourage classroom discussions about algorithmic thinking in general. They also serve as the go-to algorithms for students who may not have mastered any other algorithms. For these reasons, the focus algorithms are the *Everyday Mathematics* community's overall "best" algorithms. (But, of course, even they may not be the best ones to choose for any given problem.)

Yet while *Everyday Mathematics* has its own computational focus algorithms, the authors realize that parents and others often pressure students to master specific algorithms. Many students learn the U.S. traditional algorithms from siblings or adults at home. Projects that you can use to teach these traditional algorithms are included in the *Teacher's Lesson Guides* for Grades 2–6. In any case, *Everyday Mathematics* encourages you to do what is best suited to your situation. The program's aim is to help you teach, not to impose ideas or demands on you.

11.1.2 Alternative and Focus Algorithms

Why not just teach the "best" algorithms?

When baking bread, it is helpful to know more than one recipe. You never know when you might need to bake in a different oven or with substitute ingredients. Your main recipe probably serves you just fine most of the time, but you are a more flexible and creative baker with other recipes in your file. And how do we get new bread recipes? How are old recipes improved? If you know only one recipe, what might prompt you to vary it? Studying a variety of recipes helps beginning bakers to become pastry chefs.

After students have had many opportunities to experiment with computation strategies of their own, *Everyday Mathematics* introduces several alternative algorithms for each operation. Many algorithms are written, but several model the operations with manipulatives or pictures, providing alternative perspectives to meet the diverse learning styles or needs in your classroom.

Students could simply memorize the steps of any algorithm and satisfactorily calculate answers. But having several algorithms to compare gives students a better opportunity to understand the underlying concepts of the operations. Yet, while individual students are encouraged to find their own best procedures, the focus algorithms serve as anchors for everyone in your class to discuss and master one method for each operation.

Some of the alternative algorithms closely resemble methods that students are likely to have devised on their own. Others are traditional algorithms in the United States or in other countries, used either currently or in history. Still others are simplifications of traditional algorithms or wholly new algorithms that have significant advantages in today's technological world. Collecting alternative algorithms could be a class project, or even one that builds from year to year, helping students to be aware that mathematics, even pencil-and-paper computation, is a continually growing subject.

Pencil-and-paper algorithms in a digital world

Who needs a bread recipe? My local bakery is fantastic!

In the modern, high-technology world, most adults reach for calculators when faced with any moderately complicated arithmetic computation. This behavior is sensible and should be an option for students, too. Nevertheless, we hope that this chapter helps you better understand how *Everyday Mathematics* gives students opportunities to benefit in many ways from inventing algorithms and learning traditional and alternative noncalculator procedures. In summary:

- Students are more motivated when they do not have to memorize traditional paper-and-pencil algorithms without understanding why they work. In fact, most people are more interested in things that they can understand, and students generally understand their own methods, as obscure as they may sometimes be to others.

- Students are more able to maneuver among different mathematical models. They readily translate among manipulatives, oral and written words, pictures, and symbols. The ability to represent a problem in more than one way is important in problem solving.

- Students are more able to transform any given problem into an equivalent, easier problem. For example, $301 - 3$ can be transformed to the easier $300 - 2$, because taking 1 from both numbers in a subtraction problem does not change the answer.

- Students gain more experience in nonroutine problem solving by devising creative problem-solving strategies and by refining those strategies for use on a more permanent basis. Students learn to manage their resources efficiently and build on what they already know. They also develop persistence and confidence in dealing with difficult problems.

And last, but not least, students can have fun with algorithms. Just as a baker can enjoy experimenting with different bread recipes, students can enjoy trying out different computational algorithms. As the great German mathematician and calculus inventor Gottfried Wilhelm Leibniz once wrote, "Let us calculate!"

NOTE: In July 2008, a new column-addition algorithm developed by a mathematician and a computer scientist was presented at the International Congress of Mathematics Education in Monterrey, Mexico.

For more on algorithms, you might enjoy reading the following books and articles.

Resources on Algorithms

Albert, L. R. and McAdam, J. F. (2007). "Making Sense of Decimal Fraction Algorithms Using Base-Ten Blocks." In Martin, G. W., Strutchens, M. E., and Elliott, P. C. (Eds.) *The Learning of Mathematics: Sixty-ninth Yearbook.* Reston, VA: National Council of Teachers of Mathematics.

Bass, H. (2003). "Computational Fluency, Algorithms, and Mathematical Proficiency: One Mathematician's Perspective." *Teaching Children Mathematics 9(6):* pp. 322–327.

Morrow, J. J., and Kenney, M. J. (Eds.) (1998). *The Teaching and Learning of Algorithms in School Mathematics: 1998 Yearbook.* Reston, VA: National Council of Teachers of Mathematics.

Prusinkiewicz, P., and Lindenmayer, A. (1990). *The Algorithmic Beauty of Plants.* New York, NY: Springer-Verlag.

Randolph, T. D., and Sherman, H. J. (2001). "Alternative Algorithms: Increasing Options, Reducing Errors." *Teaching Children Mathematics 7(8):* pp. 480–484.

VanLehn, K. (1990). *Mind Bugs: The Origins of Procedural Misconceptions.* Cambridge, MA: MIT Press.

11.2 Algorithms for Whole Numbers and Decimals

Decimal, or base-ten place-value, numeration spread from India to the Middle East and eventually all over the world, in part because it is easier to calculate with it than with other bases. In the thousand years or so that Hindu-Arabic numeration has been in use, many algorithms have been devised for each of the fundamental arithmetic operations. In some sense, all of these algorithms are traditional, or standard, in that at some time and in some place a group of people used each of them. The traditional addition algorithm that many of us learned in school is only one of many alternatives. The same can be said for algorithms for each of the other arithmetic operations.

Over a dozen algorithms for adding, subtracting, multiplying, and dividing whole numbers are presented in the following sections. Some of them are easier to understand than the U.S. traditional algorithms, although they may seem more complicated at first because they are unfamiliar. Several of the algorithms presented are well suited for mental arithmetic or for very large numbers. Some are easier to learn, if perhaps a bit less efficient than others. If efficiency is the goal, however, note that in many situations any paper-and-pencil algorithm will be inferior to mental-arithmetic or technology. Several of these algorithms are based on students' mental-arithmetic efforts and search for procedures. All are procedures that you may suggest to students who need some help getting started.

Many different algorithms for operations with whole numbers and decimals are described in the following sections. For each operation, several alternative algorithms are described, including the *Everyday Mathematics* focus algorithm. Algorithms for fractions are discussed in Section 11.3.

11.2.1 Addition Algorithms

This section discusses several algorithms for whole-number addition: *partial-sums addition, column addition, the opposite-change rule*, and *U. S. traditional addition.*

Focus Algorithm: Partial-Sums Addition

As the name suggests, the *partial-sums-addition algorithm* calculates partial sums, working one place-value column at a time, and then adds all the partial sums to find the total.

		6,802
		+ 453
Add the thousands.	6,000 + 0	6,000
Add the hundreds.	800 + 400	1,200
Add the tens.	0 + 50	50
Add the ones.	2 + 3	+ 5
Add the partial sums.	6,000 + 1,200 + 50 + 5	**7,255**

The partial sums can be found in any order, but working from left to right is the usual procedure. This order seems natural because we read from left to right, and it also focuses on the most important digits in the addends first (thousands before hundreds, hundreds before tens, and so on). A variation on this algorithm can be used to estimate sums quickly: The sum is estimated from only the partial sum(s) for the addends' left-most digits. This is known as *leading-digit estimation.* The partial-sums algorithm can be readily adapted for mental arithmetic.

Partial-sums addition is the algorithm most similar to addition with base-10 blocks. Finding each partial sum corresponds to combining all of one kind of base-10 block. Adding the partial sums corresponds to exchanging blocks as necessary and then combining like blocks.

The partial-sums algorithm, like all the algorithms discussed here, can be easily adapted to work with decimals.

		27.096
		+ 3.507
Add the tens.	20 + 0	20.000
Add the ones.	7 + 3	10.000
Add the tenths.	0.0 + 0.5	0.500
Add the hundredths.	0.09 + 0.00	0.090
Add the thousandths.	0.006 + 0.007	+ 0.013
Add the partial sums.	20 + 10 + 0.5 + 0.09 + 0.013	**30.603**

Column Addition

In the *column-addition algorithm,* vertical lines are drawn to separate ones, tens, hundreds, and so on. Once columns have been created, the usual place-value convention that each place must have only one digit can be broken without confusion. If you wish, you can label the columns "ones," "tens," and so on. The digits in each column are then added, beginning in any column. Finally, any necessary trades are made, again starting in any column. For example, to calculate 967 + 495:

	9	6	7
	+ 4	9	5
Add each column separately, working in any order.	13	15	12
If necessary, adjust, working in any order.	14	5	12
If necessary, adjust, working in any order.	**14**	**6**	**2**

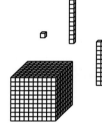

For more information, see Section 9.9.1: Base-10 Blocks.

So $967 + 495 = 1{,}462$. Many students find this algorithm natural and instructive. For some, the process becomes so natural they start at the left and write the answer column by column, adjusting as they go without writing any of the intermediate steps. If asked to explain, they might say something like the following about the sum in the margin:

> *200 plus 400 is 600, but* (looking at the next column) *I need to fix that, so I write 7. Then 60 and 80 is 140, but that needs fixing, so I write 5. The 8 and 3 is 11. With no more to do, I can just write 1.*

$$\begin{array}{r} 268 \\ +\ 483 \\ \hline 751 \end{array}$$

The column-addition algorithm was shown and explained to the *Everyday Mathematics* authors by a first grader. It has become a favorite. The algorithm occurs naturally to many students, and it also has the advantage of quickly producing a rough estimate of the sum. It is also better suited to mental arithmetic than the U.S. traditional algorithm.

The Opposite-Change Rule for Addition

In the *opposite-change rule*, a number is added to one addend and the same number is subtracted from the other addend. So the sum remains the same. For example, consider

$$8 + 7 = 15$$

If 2 is added to the 8 and subtracted from the 7, you have:

$$(8 + 2) + (7 - 2) = 10 + 5 = 15$$

The idea behind this method is to rename the addends so that one ends in one or more zeros. This may take several steps, but eventually the addition becomes trivial.

Example 1: Rename so that the first addend ends in zeros.

$$\begin{array}{rcl} 268 & \xrightarrow{+\,2} & 270 \xrightarrow{+\,30} 300 \\ +\ 483 & \xrightarrow{-\,2} & +\ 481 \xrightarrow{-\,30} +\ 451 \\ & & \text{Add:}\quad 751 \end{array}$$

Example 2: Rename so that the second addend ends in zeros.

$$\begin{array}{rcl} 268 & \xrightarrow{-\,7} & 261 \xrightarrow{-\,10} 251 \\ +\ 483 & \xrightarrow{+\,7} & +\ 490 \xrightarrow{+\,10} +\ 500 \\ & & \text{Add:}\quad 751 \end{array}$$

The opposite-change rule is also well suited to mental arithmetic. With a little practice, students can become quite proficient.

U.S. Traditional Addition

The *U.S. traditional addition algorithm* has many strengths. It is widely known, relatively efficient, and fairly easy to learn. Many students learn how to use this algorithm from their parents or siblings because it is as much a cultural tradition as a mathematical procedure. Therefore, it is likely to be mentioned when you ask students to explain their solutions to multidigit addition problems.

The U.S. traditional addition algorithm is similar to column addition shown on page 120, but it requires the user to proceed column by column from right to left and to observe place values at all times. These requirements make the algorithm more efficient but harder to learn than some of the others.

The user begins with the right-most column, mentally finds the sum of all the digits in that column, writes the ones digit of the sum below the line, and "carries" the tens digit of the sum to the top of the next column to the left. The process is repeated for each column to the left. The "carry" digits can be mysterious to students, so be sure to explain them in terms of place value and renaming when you discuss this algorithm.

$$
\begin{array}{r}
588 \\
+\ 143 \\
\end{array}
$$

Add the ones. *(8 ones + 3 ones = 11 ones)* Regroup.　*(11 ones = 1 ten and 1 one)*	$\begin{array}{r} 1 \\ 588 \\ +\ 143 \\ \hline 1 \end{array}$
Add the tens. *(1 ten + 8 tens + 4 tens = 13 tens)* Regroup.　*(13 tens = 1 hundred and 3 tens)*	$\begin{array}{r} 11 \\ 588 \\ +\ 143 \\ \hline 31 \end{array}$
Add the hundreds. *(1 hundred + 5 hundreds + 1 hundred = 7 hundreds)* **731** is the total.	$\begin{array}{r} 1 \\ 588 \\ +\ 143 \\ \hline 731 \end{array}$

588 + 143 using the U.S. traditional algorithm

In whole-number addition, the starting column is the ones place. In decimal addition, the starting column is the right-most decimal place.

The addition algorithm is probably the best of the U.S. traditional computation algorithms. While *Everyday Mathematics* does not focus on it, it is a viable alternative. If you decide to teach this algorithm, be sure to treat it as one of several possibilities and, as with any algorithm, be sure that students understand how it works.

11.2.2 Subtraction Algorithms

There are even more algorithms for subtraction than for addition, probably because subtraction is more difficult. This section discusses five algorithms for whole-number subtraction: *trade-first, counting-up, European, left-to-right,* and *partial-differences.*

Focus Algorithm: Trade-First Subtraction

The *trade-first subtraction algorithm* resembles the U.S. traditional subtraction algorithm, except that all the trading is done before all the subtraction, allowing the user to concentrate on one thing at a time. The steps involved are listed on the next page.

1. Examine all columns and trade as necessary so that the top number in each place is as large or larger than the bottom number. The trades can be done in any order. Working left to right is perhaps more natural, as with partial-sums addition, but working right to left is a bit more efficient.

2. Check that the top number in each place is at least as large as the bottom number. If necessary, make more trades.

3. Subtract column by column in any order.

Trade-first subtraction is highly efficient, similar to the traditional algorithm, and relatively easy to learn. It is an effective algorithm for paper-and-pencil calculation.

Many teachers find that drawing vertical lines between the places is helpful for students when first learning this algorithm. The vertical lines allow students to focus on one column at a time. They also help students avoid mistakes if unnecessary trades have been made.

$$\begin{array}{r} {}^{8}\;\;{}^{10}\;{}^{5}\;{}^{12} \\ 9{,}0\,6\,2 \\ -\;4{,}7\,3\,8 \\ \hline \end{array}$$

$$\begin{array}{r} {}^{8}\;\;{}^{10}\;{}^{5}\;{}^{12} \\ 9{,}0\,6\,2 \\ -\;4{,}7\,3\,8 \\ \hline 4{,}3\,2\,4 \end{array}$$

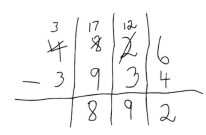

Trade-first subtraction with columns

Trade-first subtraction with an unnecessary trade

Counting-Up Subtraction

The *counting-up subtraction algorithm* is similar to what cashiers do when they give change. In both procedures, the user begins at the lesser number and counts up to the greater number. In giving change, the cashier tenders bills or coins to the purchaser. In counting-up subtraction, the user keeps a running total of the amounts counted up and then totals all of the count-up amounts to find the difference.

The counting-up technique that is the basis for this algorithm is useful in mental computation, although mentally keeping a correct running total requires practice. When the procedure is carried out mentally, it helps to start with the larger places.

Solve 932 − 356 by counting up.

$$\begin{array}{r} 356 \\ +\quad 4 \\ \hline 360 \end{array}$$ Count to the nearest 10.

$$\begin{array}{r} +\quad 40 \\ \hline 400 \end{array}$$ Count to the nearest 100.

$$\begin{array}{r} +\quad 500 \\ \hline 900 \end{array}$$ Count to the largest possible 100.

$$\begin{array}{r} +\quad 32 \\ \hline 932 \end{array}$$ Count to the larger number.

Then add the numbers you circled.

$$\begin{array}{r} 4 \\ 40 \\ 500 \\ +\quad 32 \\ \hline 576 \end{array}$$ So 932 − 356 = 576.

European Subtraction

The U.S. traditional subtraction algorithm involves regrouping, or "borrowing," from the next place to the left. That is, in the problem 623 − 345, one of the 2 tens in 623 is traded for 10 ones. This is written:

$$\begin{array}{r} {\scriptstyle 1\ 13} \\ 6\,2\!\!\!/\,3 \\ -\ 3\,4\,5 \\ \hline \end{array}$$

A variation on this procedure called the *European subtraction algorithm* increases the bottom number in the next column to the left:

$$\begin{array}{r} {\scriptstyle 13} \\ 6\,2\,3 \\ -\ 3_{\!1}4\,5 \\ \hline 8 \end{array}$$

The small mark next to the 4 in 345 is a ten that compensates for adding 10 to the 3 on top. The next step is to subtract 50 instead of 40. Because you can't take 5 tens away from the 2 tens in 623, use the same strategy again, this time increasing the hundreds digit in the bottom number. Then subtract 1 + 4 = 5 tens from 12 tens to get 7 tens.

$$\begin{array}{r} {\scriptstyle 12\ 13} \\ 6\,2\,3 \\ -\ _{\!1}3_{\!1}4\,5 \\ \hline 7\,8 \end{array}$$

The mark next to the 3 on the bottom is a hundred that compensates for adding 10 tens to the top. The final step is to subtract 1 + 3 = 4 hundreds from 6 hundreds to get 2 hundreds.

$$\begin{array}{r} {\scriptstyle 12\ 13} \\ 6\,2\,3 \\ -\ _{\!1}3_{\!1}4\,5 \\ \hline 2\,7\,8 \end{array}$$

You may find the European algorithm confusing, but it is the traditional algorithm used in many countries in the world today. You might want to spend a few minutes thinking about how increasing the number on the bottom has the same effect as decreasing the number on the top. If you want to experience what it might be like for a child to learn the U.S. traditional subtraction algorithm, you might try learning this European subtraction algorithm.

Left-to-Right Subtraction

With the *left-to-right subtraction algorithm,* the user starts at the left and subtracts column by column. For the problem 932 − 356:

	932
Subtract the 100s.	− 300
	632
Subtract the 10s.	− 50
	582
Subtract the 1s.	− 6
	576

Like left-to-right addition, the left-to-right subtraction algorithm can be used to find a rough estimate of a difference.

Partial-Differences Subtraction

The *partial-differences subtraction algorithm* is a fairly unusual method, but one that appeals to some students.

The procedure is fairly simple: Write partial differences for each place, record them, and then add them to find the total difference. A complication is that some of the partial differences may be negative, as in the problem on the next page.

		932
		− 356
Subtract 100s.	*900 − 300*	600
Subtract 10s.	*30 − 50*	−20
Subtract 1s.	*2 − 6*	−4
Add the partial differences.		576

The Same-Change Rule for Subtraction

The *same-change rule for subtraction* states:

- If you add the same number to both numbers in a subtraction problem, the difference remains the same.
- If you subtract the same number from both numbers in a subtraction problem, the difference remains the same.

For example, consider

$$15 − 8 = 7$$

If 2 is added to both the 15 and the 8, you have:

$$(15 + 2) − (8 + 2) = 17 − 10 = 7$$

Or, if 5 is subtracted from both the 15 and the 8, you have:

$$(15 − 5) − (8 − 5) = 10 − 3 = 7$$

The usual strategy for applying this approach to multidigit subtraction is to rename the subtrahend so that it ends in zeros. This may take several steps, but eventually the subtraction becomes trivial.

Example 1: Add the same number.

$$
\begin{array}{r} 932 \\ -\ 356 \end{array}
\overset{+\,4}{\underset{+\,4}{\longrightarrow}}
\begin{array}{r} 936 \\ -\ 360 \end{array}
\overset{+\,40}{\underset{+\,40}{\longrightarrow}}
\begin{array}{r} 976 \\ -\ 400 \end{array}
$$

Subtract: 576

Example 2: Subtract the same number.

$$
\begin{array}{r} 932 \\ -\ 356 \end{array}
\overset{-\,6}{\underset{-\,6}{\longrightarrow}}
\begin{array}{r} 926 \\ -\ 350 \end{array}
\overset{-\,50}{\underset{-\,50}{\longrightarrow}}
\begin{array}{r} 876 \\ -\ 300 \end{array}
$$

Subtract: 576

The same-change rule is also well suited to mental arithmetic.

Adding and Subtracting Decimals

In everyday life, most decimals to be added or subtracted tend to have the same precision, or number of decimal places. A common example is money, where most values are rounded to the nearest cent. In fact, there are very few situations in which you might need to combine or subtract values with different precisions. Even if a data set has such disparate measures, you would probably want to round them all to the same precision to avoid exaggerating the precision of the final answer. So when the numbers all have the same precision it is easy to generalize the addition and subtraction algorithms described above.

For more on precision, see Section 16.2: Approximation and Rounding.

chapter 11

$25 + 1.726 + 0.05 = ?$

$$
\begin{array}{r}
25.000 \\
1.726 \\
+\ 0.050 \\
\end{array}
$$

"Evening out" the decimals

In spite of the everyday reality, on local, state, or national achievement tests students likely will have to add or subtract decimals with different precisions. For this reason, students in *Fifth* and *Sixth Grade Everyday Mathematics* learn to insert zeros as necessary to "even out" the addends to the same number of decimal places. The example in the margin shows how writing the values vertically while aligning the decimal makes this simple to do.

While students can learn to cope with testing demands by inserting zeros, the authors of *Everyday Mathematics* encourage you to help them realize that the process is artificial. In actual work with measures, students should apply the sensible and realistic rule that all data in a problem should be collected or rounded to about the same level of precision. They should also recognize that in complicated computations, calculators help improve accuracy.

11.2.3 Multiplication Algorithms

Adults usually reach for calculators when they have to multiply "difficult" numbers. Similarly, calculators should be available to students when they deal with problems that they understand but that involve calculations beyond their current skills. This allows the curriculum to include more realistic, interesting, and instructive problems. Nevertheless, for the reasons discussed in Section 11.1.1, *Everyday Mathematics* includes a significant amount of work with paper-and-pencil multiplication.

As always, *Everyday Mathematics* suggests that students share their strategies and discuss how they created their computational procedures. Inventing procedures for multiplication and division is more difficult than for addition and subtraction, but students who have experience with the latter two will be well prepared to attempt the former two. When doing mental arithmetic, for example, many students begin to compute partial products: *Ten of these would be . . ., so 30 of them would be . . ., and then we need 5 more, so . . ..* Beginning in *Third Grade Everyday Mathematics,* this approach is formalized as the partial-products algorithm, the focus algorithm for multiplication.

There are many multiplication algorithms besides the partial-products algorithm and traditional right-to-left long multiplication. Former University of Chicago graduate student Raven Deerwater (formerly known as Dan Hirschhorn), after only a few hours' search of old schoolbooks and mathematics education articles, found more than 40 different multiplication algorithms. About 25 of them were special "tricks" for quick mental multiplication of numbers with special characteristics or procedures you may remember from high school algebra. Some were very efficient but difficult to explain. More than 15 of the 40 were general algorithms for multiplying any two whole numbers. Several of these algorithms are discussed on the following pages.

Focus Algorithm: Partial-Products Multiplication

In the *partial-products multiplication algorithm,* each factor is thought of as a sum of ones, tens, hundreds, and so on. For example, in 67 * 53, 67 can be thought of as 60 + 7 and 53 as 50 + 3. Each part of one factor is then multiplied by each part of the other factor. Finally, all of the resulting partial products are added.

$$
\begin{array}{r}
67 \\
* \quad 53 \\
\hline
\end{array}
$$

50	*	60	3000
50	*	7	350
3	*	60	180
3	*	7	+ 21
			3551

You don't have to work from left to right; any order will do as long as all possible partial products are found. Working from left to right, however, does help keep the procedure orderly and also, as with left-to-right procedures for addition and subtraction, produces a quick estimate of the product.

In order to use the partial-products algorithm efficiently, students must be adept at multiplying multiples of 10, 100, and 1,000, such as 60 * 50 in the example above. These skills also help students to make ballpark estimates of products and quotients.

The partial-products algorithm can be demonstrated visually using arrays. The diagram below shows how a 23-by-14 array represents all of the partial products in 23 * 14.

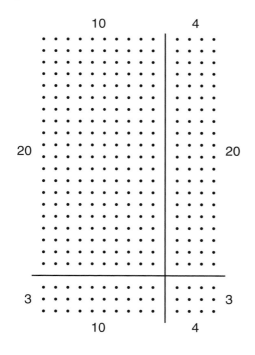

$$
\begin{aligned}
23 * 14 &= (20 + 3) * (10 + 4) \\
&= (20 * 10) + (20 * 4) + (3 * 10) + (3 * 4) \\
&= 200 + 80 + 30 + 12 \\
&= 322
\end{aligned}
$$

> **NOTE:** The partial-products algorithm uses the Distributive Property of Multiplication over Addition repeatedly.
>
> First, $20 * (10 + 4) = (20 * 10) + (20 * 4)$.
> Second, $3 * (10 + 4) = (3 * 10) + (3 * 4)$.

A benefit of the partial-products algorithm is that it previews a procedure for multiplication that is taught in high-school algebra and is related to some algebra in *Sixth Grade Everyday Mathematics*. In multiplying expressions such as $(x + 2)$ and $(x + 3)$, every term in one expression is multiplied by every term in the other expression, and the partial products are added. For example:

$$(x + 2) * (x + 3) = (x * x) + (x * 3) + (2 * x) + (2 * 3)$$
$$= x^2 + 3x + 2x + 6$$
$$= x^2 + 5x + 6$$

Lattice Multiplication

Everyday Mathematics initially included *lattice multiplication* for its recreational value and historical interest and because it provided practice with multiplication facts and adding strings of single-digit numbers. To our surprise, lattice multiplication has become a favorite of many students.

Why the lattice method works is not immediately obvious, but it is very efficient and powerful. The authors have found that with practice, it is more efficient than standard long multiplication for problems involving more than two digits in each factor. And problems that are too large for long multiplication or for most calculators can be solved using lattice multiplication.

To multiply 67 by 53:

1. Draw a 2-by-2 lattice as in the margin.
2. Write one factor along the top of the lattice and the other along the right, one digit for each row or column.
3. Multiply each digit in one factor by each digit in the other factor. Write the products in the cells where the corresponding rows and columns meet. Write the tens digit of these products above the diagonal and the ones digit below the diagonal.
4. Starting at the bottom-right corner, add the numbers inside the lattice along each diagonal. Write these sums along the bottom and left of the lattice. If the sum on a diagonal exceeds 9, carry the tens digit to the next diagonal to the left.

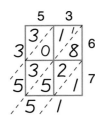

$67 \times 53 = 3{,}551$ by lattice multiplication

Multiplying larger numbers requires a larger lattice.

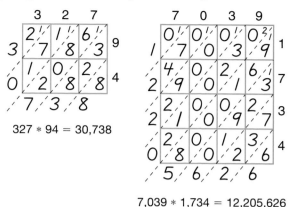

327 * 94 = 30,738

7,039 * 1,734 = 12,205,626

NOTE: In 1478, in Treviso, Italy, lattice multiplication first appeared in what is said to be the first printed arithmetic book. Amazingly, it was in use long before that, with historians tracing it to Hindu origins in India before A.D. 1100.

To understand why lattice multiplication works, note that the diagonals in the lattice correspond to place-value columns. The far right-hand diagonal is the ones place, the next diagonal to the left is the tens place, and so on.

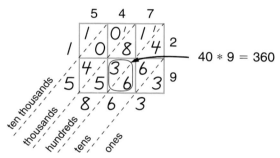

40 * 9 = 360

Modified Repeated Addition

Contrary to what is often taught, multiplication is not merely repeated addition, even for whole numbers and certainly not for decimals and fractions. Moreover, as a computational method for multiplying, repeated addition is inefficient for anything but small numbers. For example, it would be unbearably tedious to add fifty-three 67s in order to compute 67 * 53.

If you think of ten 67s as 670, however, you can first add the 670s (there are five of them) and then add the three 67s, as shown in the margin. This *modified repeated-addition algorithm* is a good "broken calculator" exercise to find a product without using the ⌧ key.

Modified U.S. Traditional Multiplication

Example 1 at right shows the U.S. traditional multiplication algorithm for calculating 67 * 53. Although this algorithm does indeed work and is moderately efficient, many people who use it cannot explain the shifting to the left in successive partial products. Even harder to explain is why the 3 in the 35 from 5 * 7 is written above the 6 in 67. When asked why the 3 is written in the tens place, many adults say that the 3 stands for 3 tens, which is incorrect. The 3 actually stands for 300 because it comes from 50 * 7 = 350.

When many adults say they "understand" this algorithm, what they really mean is simply that they can carry it out correctly. The authors

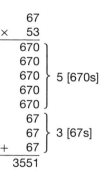

Modified repeated addition

Examples:

1.	2.	3.
$\overset{3}{\underset{2}{}}$ 67	$\overset{3}{\underset{2}{}}$ 67	$\overset{2}{\underset{3}{}}$ 67
* 53	* 53	* 53
201	201	3350
335	3350	201
3551	3551	3551

Modified U.S. traditional algorithms

Examples:

1.	2.	3.
$\begin{array}{r} {\scriptstyle 3} \\ {\scriptstyle 2} \\ 67 \\ *\ \ 53 \\ \hline 201 \\ 335 \\ \hline 3551 \end{array}$	$\begin{array}{r} {\scriptstyle 3} \\ {\scriptstyle 2} \\ 67 \\ *\ \ 53 \\ \hline 201 \\ 3350 \\ \hline 3551 \end{array}$	$\begin{array}{r} {\scriptstyle 2} \\ {\scriptstyle 3} \\ 67 \\ *\ \ 53 \\ \hline 3350 \\ 201 \\ \hline 3551 \end{array}$

Modified U.S. traditional
algorithms

believe that real understanding includes both knowing what to do and knowing why it works. By these criteria, many adults' "understanding" of the traditional long multiplication algorithm is incomplete.

Example 2 solves the shift-over-a-place mystery by inserting a zero in the blank. This makes clear that for the second partial product, we are multiplying by 50 (five 10s) and not by 5. The reason for putting the 3 above the 6 is still unresolved; it's actually there for convenience in mentally adding to the product of 5 times 6, which is really 50 times 60. This version is a bit easier to understand than the traditional form.

Example 3 uses a left-to-right approach. Though it has its advantages, it is otherwise no different from the standard algorithm with 0s in place of the blanks.

Egyptian Multiplication

Over 4,000 years ago, the Egyptians developed an algorithm for multiplication that eliminates the need for all multiplication facts except for the 2s facts. The idea of doubling, which students find easy and fun, is used repeatedly. This algorithm was widely used well into the Middle Ages, and a variation, called the *Russian Peasant Method*, is still used today in Russia, Ethiopia, the Arab world, and the Near East. Here is how to use *Egyptian multiplication* to calculate 13 * 28:

1. In the first column, list the consecutive powers of 2 beginning with 1. Stop with the greatest power of 2 that is less than or equal to the first factor.
2. In the second column, write the second factor next to the 1, and then double that factor repeatedly, stopping with the last power of 2 in the first column. For example, 112 = 4 * 28.
3. Check off the powers of 2, including $2^0 = 1$, whose sum is the first factor. Start at the bottom with the greatest powers of 2 and work toward the lesser powers, always taking a power if it would not make the sum too large. *(8 + 4 + 1 = 13)*
4. Cross out the rows that are not checked off.
5. Add the numbers in the second column that are not crossed off. *(28 + 112 + 224 = 364)* This sum is the product of 13 and 28.

NOTE: Each number in the second column is the product of the number in the first column multiplied by the second factor 28.

Modern Notation		Egyptian Notation	
1st Column	**2nd Column**	**1st Column**	**2nd Column**
✔ 1	28	✔ I	IIII IIII ∩∩
~~2~~	~~56~~	II	IIII ∩∩∩ II ∩∩
✔ 4	112	✔ IIII	II ∩ 9
✔ 8	224	✔ IIII IIII	IIII ∩∩ 99
13	(364)		IIII ∩∩∩ ∩∩∩ 999

Source: Nelson, D., Joseph, G. G., and Williams, J. (1993). *Multicultural Mathematics.* Great Britain: Oxford University Pre

chapter 11

The Distributive Property of Multiplication over Addition explains why this method works.

$$13 * 28 = (1 + 4 + 8) * 28$$
$$= (1 * 28) + (4 * 28) + (8 * 28)$$
$$= 28 + 112 + 224$$
$$= 364$$

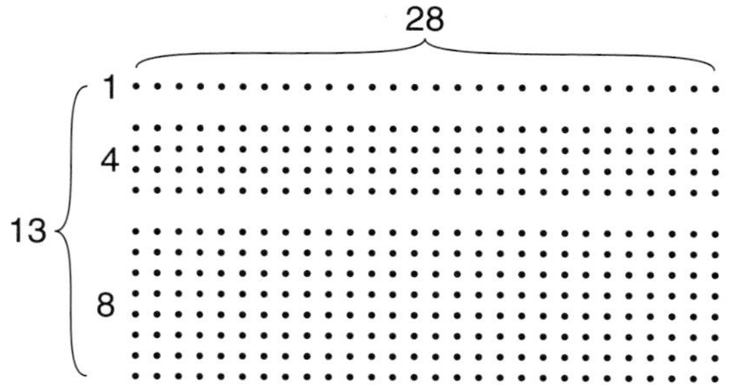

Multiplying Decimals

Everyday Mathematics students are encouraged to find their own algorithms for multiplying decimals in the same way they are asked to find algorithms for operations with whole numbers and fractions. The primary approach suggested in the program is to estimate the product, multiply as though the factors were whole numbers, and use the estimate to place the decimal point in the product.

Example: Evaluate 0.23 * 17.5.

Estimate: 0.23 * 17.5 is about twice as much as 0.1 * 17.5, or 1.75, or about 2. So the product is about 4.

Or, using fractions, 0.23 * 17.5 is about $\frac{1}{4}$ of 16 or $\frac{1}{5}$ of 20. Either of these estimates suggests a product of about 4.

Multiply as though the factors were whole numbers, ignoring the decimal points:

$$
\begin{array}{r}
175 \\
*\quad 23 \\
\hline
\end{array}
$$

20 * 100	2000
20 * 70	1400
20 * 5	100
3 * 100	300
3 * 70	210
3 * 5	+ 15
	4025

Use the estimate to place the decimal point: 4.025.

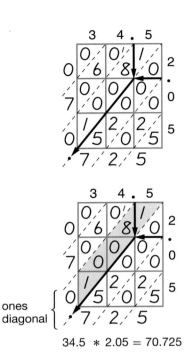

34.5 * 2.05 = 70.725

Several other approaches to multiplying decimals are also included in *Everyday Mathematics*.

- Use a calculator. Verify the size of the answer in the display (perhaps using one of the estimation techniques on page 131), because even experienced calculator users occasionally make mistakes. Also check for accuracy, because the calculator may round the product to fit the display.

- Multiply as if the factors were whole numbers to get a whole-number answer, then use a rule for placing the decimal point. The usual rule is to count the total number of places to the right of the decimal points in the factors, then put the decimal point that many places from the right of the whole-number answer.

- Adapt lattice multiplication for decimals. Place the decimal points of the factors as shown in the margin. Then locate the intersection of the horizontal and vertical lines next to the decimal points. Slide down the diagonal through the intersection to place the decimal point in the product.

Because of the way the lattice is arranged, the decimal points meet after the product of the digits in the ones place. In the example in the margin, 4 is in the ones place in 34.5, and 2 is in the ones place in 2.05. The diagonal with 8, the product of 4 and 2, is the ones diagonal. The decimal point goes just to the right of the ones place.

11.2.4 Division Algorithms

Students can benefit from mastering a paper-and-pencil division algorithm for several reasons. It supports their understanding of the concept of division, can be practically useful, meets societal expectations, and completes a set of paper-and-pencil algorithms that enables them to solve problems involving all the fundamental operations of arithmetic.

The practical needs of students to succeed on standardized tests may also require the teaching of paper-and-pencil division algorithms. Moreover, as discussed above and in Section 11.1.1, there are good reasons for teaching certain paper-and-pencil methods for division. Learning appropriate algorithms can help students to acquire useful insights into the operation of division without undue costs in time and effort. Toward these ends, *Fourth* through *Sixth Grade Everyday Mathematics* contain lessons aimed at helping students develop paper-and-pencil division algorithms that are both easier to learn than traditional long division and more instructive.

Focus Algorithm: Partial-Quotients Division

Equal-grouping division problems ask *How many of these are in that?* More symbolically, *a/b* asks *How many* bs *are in* a? One approach to solving such problems is to make a series of "at least, but less than" estimates of how many bs are in a. These interim estimates may be called *partial quotients*. At each step, check to see if you have taken as many bs from a as possible. If not, take some more. When you have taken all the bs there are in a, add the partial quotients and handle the remainder.

Example: How many groups of 12 are in 157?

Solve by calculating 157/12. One approach is shown here. The first estimate is that there are 10 [12s] in 157, so record 10 and subtract 10 [12s] from 157.

The next estimate is that there are 3 [12s] in the remaining 37. Record 3 and subtract 3 [12s] from 37.

$$
\begin{array}{r|r}
12\overline{)157} & \\
-\ 120 & 10 \\
\hline
37 & \\
-\ 36 & 3 \\
\hline
1 & 13 \\
\end{array}
$$

Only 1 remains, which is less than 12, so stop estimating. The final result is the sum of the estimates $10 + 3 = 13$ with a remainder of 1.

So 157/12 → 13 R1.

NOTE: Instead of an equal sign, *Everyday Mathematics* uses a right-facing arrow to write a quotient-and-remainder result of division. For example, 157/12 = 13 R1 is not a proper number sentence because the right-hand side (13 R1) is not actually a number. To give the result as an equation, write the remainder as a fraction $(157/12 = 13\frac{1}{12})$.

Of course you could have made different estimates than in the sample solution. The sample began with multiples of 10 because they are simple to work with, but there may be a great deal of mental work leading to that choice. For example:

- *There are at least 10 [12s] in 157 (10 * 12 = 120), but there are fewer than 20 (20 * 12 = 240). So I'll start with 10.*
- *How many 12s are in the remaining 37?* You might know the answer right away *(12 * 3 = 36)*, but a student might sneak up on it, saying *More than 1, more than 2, a little more than 3, but not as many as 4 . . . .*

Partial-quotients division is introduced in *Fourth Grade Everyday Mathematics* with 1- and 2-digit divisors. As shown below, making a list of multiples of the divisor can be helpful with "harder" multidigit divisors.

Example: Solve 758/28 = ?

$$
\begin{array}{ll}
1 * 28 = 28 & \\
2 * 28 = 56 & \\
3 * 28 = 84 & \\
4 * 28 = 112 & \\
5 * 28 = 140 & \\
8 * 28 = 224 & \\
10 * 28 = 280 & \\
\end{array}
$$

$$
\begin{array}{r|r}
28\overline{)758} & \\
-\ 560 & 20 \\
\hline
198 & \\
-\ 140 & 5 \\
\hline
58 & \\
-\ 56 & 2 \\
\hline
2 & 27 \\
\end{array}
$$

So 758/28 → 27 R2.

Algorithms   **133**

Column Division

Column division is a simplification of the traditional long-division algorithm. It is easier to learn and just as powerful, although perhaps a bit less efficient. However, if efficiency is an issue in solving division problems, then mental arithmetic or a calculator is usually preferable to any paper-and-pencil method.

In column division, vertical lines separate the digits in the dividend. To understand how the algorithm works, imagine sharing $683 among 5 people. Think about having 6 $100 bills, 8 $10 bills, and 3 $1 bills. Because there are 6 $100 bills, each person can get 1 $100 bill. There will be 1 $100 bill left over.

$$
\begin{array}{r|c|c}
1 & & \\
5)\ 6 & 8 & 3 \\
-5 & & \\
\hline
1 & &
\end{array}
$$

The leftover $100 bill cannot be shared 5 ways, so it gets traded for 10 $10 bills. Because there were 8 $10 bills already, that makes 18 $10 bills. Sharing the 18 $10 bills among 5 people is 3 each and 3 left over.

$$
\begin{array}{r|c|c}
1 & 3 & \\
5)\ 6 & \not{8} & 3 \\
-5 & 18 & \\
\not{1} & -15 & \\
\hline
& 3 &
\end{array}
$$

Trading the 3 leftover $10 bills for 30 $1 bills and adding them to the original 3 $1 bills makes 33 $1 bills. Sharing the 33 $1 bills among five people is 6 each with 3 left over.

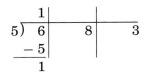

So, sharing $683 among 5 people works out to be $136 each with $3 left over, and 683/5 → 136 R3.

Column division can also be used with larger numbers. As with partial quotients, it can be helpful to start by making a table of multiples when the divisor has two or more digits. As in the previous example, the table of multiples can help with the harder divisions in the columns.

Example: Solve 5,467/28 = ?

$$1 * 28 = 28$$
$$2 * 28 = 56$$
$$3 * 28 = 84$$
$$4 * 28 = 112$$
$$5 * 28 = 140$$
$$8 * 28 = 224$$
$$10 * 28 = 280$$

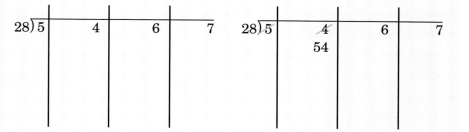

1. Set the problem up.

2. Trade 5 thousands for 50 hundreds.

3. Share 54 hundreds 28 ways.

4. Trade 26 hundreds for 260 tens.

5. Share the 266 tens 28 ways.

6. Trade the 14 tens for 140 ones.

7. Share the 147 ones 28 ways.

8. Write a number model.

5,467/28 → 195 R7
or
5,467/28 = $195\frac{7}{28}$

NOTE: In step 7 this problem solver didn't notice that 5 ∗ 28 = 140 in the table of multiples, so an extra share of 28 was needed.

Dividing Decimals

The authors of *Everyday Mathematics* believe that it is important for students to learn the basic meanings and uses of division, including division with decimals. The partial-quotients division algorithm can easily be adapted for all practical applications of decimal division. For arbitrary decimal quotients, the column-division method is both efficient and understandable.

The main approach to division with decimals in *Everyday Mathematics* is the same as for multiplication of decimals, that is, carry out the operation as though the numbers were whole numbers and use an estimate to place the decimal point in the answer. This approach works well for almost all decimal division problems students are likely to encounter in situations in which paper-and-pencil calculation is required or desirable. The method also reinforces important estimation skills and can be learned relatively quickly.

For more information, see Section 16.2: Approximation and Rounding.

Example 1: Solve 8.25/0.3 = ?

1. Divide, ignoring the decimal points.

$$
\begin{array}{r|r}
3\overline{)825} & \\
-\ 600 & 200 \\
\hline
225 & \\
-\ 210 & 70 \\
\hline
15 & \\
-\ 15 & 5 \\
\hline
0 & 275 \\
\end{array}
$$

2. Estimate the size of the quotient.

Because 8.25, which is greater than 1, is being divided by 0.3, which is less than 1, the answer must be greater than 8.25. Therefore, the quotient cannot be 2.75.

0.3 is almost $\frac{1}{3}$ and 8.25 is a little more than 8. If each of 8 pieces is divided into thirds, there will be 24 pieces, that is, $8 \div \frac{1}{3} = 24$.

So, it makes sense that 8.25/0.3 = 27.5.

If there is a remainder, it should be used to round the quotient to the nearest whole number before placing the decimal point.

Example 2: Solve 3.29/0.5 = ?

    1. Divide, ignoring the decimal points.

$$
\begin{array}{r|l}
5\overline{)329} & \\
-\ 300 & 60 \\
\hline
29 & \\
-\ 25 & 5 \\
\hline
4 & 65
\end{array}
$$

    2. Write the remainder as a fraction and round
       the quotient to the nearest whole number.

       From Step 1, 329/5 = $65\frac{4}{5}$. Rounded to the
       nearest whole number, this is 66.

    3. Estimate the size of the quotient and place the
       decimal point accordingly.

       3.29/0.5 is about 3 divided by $\frac{1}{2}$, or 6.

       So, correct to one decimal place, 3.29/0.5 = 6.6.

As long as the number of decimal places desired is specified at the
outset, this method can be used to rename fractions as decimals.

Example 3: Rename $\frac{5}{8}$ as a 3-place decimal.

    1. Because 3 decimal places are desired, rename
       5 as 5,000.

    2. Use partial quotients to find 5000/8.

$$
\begin{array}{r|l}
8\overline{)5000} & \\
-\ 4000 & 500 \\
\hline
1000 & \\
-\ 800 & 100 \\
\hline
200 & \\
-\ 200 & 25 \\
\hline
0 & 625
\end{array}
$$

    3. Because $\frac{5}{8}$ is more than 0.5 but less than 1.0,
       place the decimal point to make a number in this
       range: 0.625.

Column division can also be used to find quotients that have a decimal
part. Column division with decimals is an optional algorithm in
Everyday Mathematics, but you may want to show it to all students
if complicated paper-and-pencil divisions with decimals are required
by your state or district curriculum guidelines.

The money-sharing metaphor used in the description of whole-number
column division can be extended to decimal column division.

Example 4: Share $15 among 4 people.

1. Because 1 $10 bill cannot be shared 4 ways, trade it for 10 $1 bills.

```
    |    5̶
4)1̶  |
    |   15
```

2. Sharing the 15 $1 bills four ways is 3 $1 bills for each person with 3 $1 bills left over.

```
    |    3
4)1̶  |    5̶
    |   15
    | − 12
    |    3
```

3. Because the 3 $1 bills cannot be shared 4 ways, they can be traded for 30 dimes. Use decimal points to show that the amounts are now less than $1.

```
    |    3 |        |
4)1̶  |    5̶ |    0̶   |   0
    |   15 |   30   |
    | − 12 |        |
    |    3̶ |        |
```

4. Sharing 30 dimes 4 ways is 7 each with 2 left over. The 2 dimes are traded for 20 pennies. 20 pennies shared 4 ways is 5 each.

```
    |    3 |    7   |    5
4)1̶  |    5̶ |    0̶   |    0̶
    |   15 |   30   |   20
    | − 12 | − 28   | − 20
    |    3̶ |    2̶   |    0
```

So 15/4 = 3.75. This means that $15 shared 4 ways is $3.75 each.

Example 5: Solve 97.24/26 = ?

$1 * 26 = 26$

$2 * 26 = 52$

$3 * 26 = 78$

$4 * 26 = 104$

$5 * 26 = 130$

$8 * 26 = 208$

$10 * 26 = 260$

```
       |    3 |    7   |    4
26)9   |    7̶ |    2̶   |    4̶
       | ⁸9̶¹7 |   192  |  104
       | − 78 | − 182  | − 104
       |   19 |    10  |    0
```

So 97.24/26 = 3.74.

Column division with decimals can be carried out to an arbitrary number of decimal places. This can be used, for example, to show the conversion of a fraction to a repeating decimal.

Example 6: Rename $\frac{5}{11}$ as a decimal.

$$
\begin{array}{c|c|c|c|c|c|}
 & 4 & 5 & 4 & 5 & 4 & 5 \;\ldots \\
11\overline{)5.} & \cancel{0} & \cancel{0} & \cancel{0} & \cancel{0} & \cancel{0} & \cancel{0} \;\ldots \\
 & 50 & 60 & 50 & 60 & 50 & 60 \\
 & -44 & -55 & -44 & -55 & -44 & -55 \\
\hline
 & \cancel{6} & \cancel{5} & \cancel{6} & \cancel{5} & \cancel{6} & \cancel{5}
\end{array}
$$

So $\frac{5}{11} = 0.454545\ldots$.

U.S. Traditional Long Division

Beginning in *Fifth Grade Everyday Mathematics*, students are given the opportunity to learn U.S. traditional long division. To help understand this complicated algorithm, they are encouraged to imagine sharing play money where $1; $10; $100; and $1,000 bills model the place values of the dividend. The algorithm is to estimate how many of each bill are shared and record this in the quotient, subtract the total amount shared from the dividend, then repeat the process for the next smaller bill (i.e., the next place value to the right). Dollars left over after the $1s are shared are recorded as a remainder.

NOTE: Long division is sometimes called the "standard" division algorithm. In the 21st century, however, the standard approach to division in everyday life is to use a calculator.

Example 1: Share $957 equally among 5 people.

1. Set the problem up.

$5\overline{)957}$

2. Share the [$100]s.

$$
\begin{array}{r}
1 \quad\;\; \leftarrow \text{Each person gets 1 [$100].}\\
5\overline{)957}\\
\underline{-5}\quad\;\; \leftarrow \text{1 [$100] each for 5 people}\\
4 \quad\;\; \leftarrow \text{4 [$100]s are left.}
\end{array}
$$

3. Trade 4 [$100]s for 40 [$10]s. That makes 45 [$10]s in all.

$$
\begin{array}{r}
1\quad\;\;\\
5\overline{)957}\\
\underline{-5}\downarrow\quad\\
45 \quad \leftarrow \text{45 [$10]s are to be shared.}
\end{array}
$$

4. Share the $10s.

$$
\begin{array}{r}
19 \quad \leftarrow \text{Each person gets 9 [$10]s.}\\
5\overline{)957}\\
\underline{-5}\quad\;\;\\
45\quad\;\;\\
\underline{-45} \quad \leftarrow \text{9 [$10]s each for 5 people}\\
0 \quad \leftarrow \text{0 [$10]s are left.}
\end{array}
$$

5. Share the [$1]s.

$$
\begin{array}{r}
191 \quad \leftarrow \text{Each person gets}\\
5\overline{)957}\qquad \text{1 [$1].}\\
\underline{-5}\quad\;\;\;\\
45\quad\;\;\;\\
\underline{-45}\downarrow\;\;\\
07 \quad \leftarrow \text{7 [$1]s are to be shared.}\\
\underline{-5}\quad \leftarrow \text{1 [$1] each for 5 people}\\
2 \quad \leftarrow \text{2 [$1]s are left.}
\end{array}
$$

6. Write a number model.

$957 / 5 \rightarrow $191 R$2

Each person gets $191 with $2 left over.

NOTE: Some students may benefit from seeing long division on a computation grid that shows place value column names.

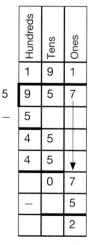

As in the column-division and partial-quotients algorithms, it can be helpful to start by making a table of multiples when the divisor has more than one digit.

Example 2: Share $681 equally among 21 people.

1 * 21 = 21	5 * 21 = 105
2 * 21 = 42	6 * 21 = 126
3 * 21 = 63	8 * 21 = 168
4 * 21 = 84	10 * 21 = 210

1. There are not enough [$100]s to share 21 ways, so trade 6 [$100]s for 60 [$10]s.

   Share the 68 [$10]s.

   ```
        3   ← Each person gets 3 [$10]s.
   21)681   ← 68 [$10]s to share.
      -63   ← 3 [$10]s * 21
        5   ← 5 [$10]s are left.
   ```

2. Trade the 5 [$10]s for 50 [$1]s.

   Share the 51 [$1]s.

   ```
        32   ← Each person gets
   21)681       2 [$1]s.
      -63↓
        51   ← 50 [$1]s + 1 [$1]
       -42   ← 2 [$1]s * 21
         9   ← 9 [$1]s are left.
   ```

So $681 / 21 → $32 R$9.

Each person gets $32 with $9 left over.

By dividing dollars and cents, the money model may help students see how long division can be used to divide decimals.

Example 3: Share $5.29 equally among 3 people.

1. Share the dollars.

   ```
        1   ← 1 dollar per person.
   3)5.29
     -3   ← 1 dollar * 3 people
      2   ← 2 dollars are left.
   ```

2. Trade the dollars for dimes. Share the dimes.

   ```
       1.7   ← 7 dimes per person.
   3)5.29       The decimal point
     -3↓         shows 70¢ = $0.70.
      2 2   ← 20 dimes + 2 dimes
     -2 1   ← 7 dimes * 3 people
        1   ← 1 dime is left.
   ```

3. Trade the dimes for pennies. Share the pennies.

   ```
       1.76   ← 6 pennies per person.
   3)5.29
     -3
      2 2
     -2 1↓
        19   ← 10 pennies + 9 pennies
       -18   ← 6 pennies * 3 people
         1   ← 1 penny is left.
   ```

So $5.29 / 3 → $1.76 R1¢.

Each person gets $1.76 with 1¢ left over.

Fifth and sixth grade students also use long division to show how rational fractions can be written as decimals, both terminating and repeating. This can help students understand the apparently terminating results given by calculators for repeating decimals.

Example 4: Rename $\frac{5}{8}$ as a decimal.

1. Write $\frac{5}{8}$ as a division problem. Write 5 with several 0s after the decimal point: 5.000. (You can always add more 0s if you need them.)

$$8\overline{)5.000}$$

2. Solve the division problem. Stop when the remainder is 0, or when you have enough precision for your purposes, or when you notice a repeating pattern.

$$
\begin{array}{r}
.625 \\
8\overline{)5.000} \\
-\,4\,8 \\
\hline
20 \\
-16 \\
\hline
40 \\
-40 \\
\hline
0
\end{array}
$$

This division problem divided evenly in three decimal places. So, $\frac{5}{8}$ = 0.625, a terminating decimal.

Example 5: Rename $\frac{7}{11}$ as a decimal.

1. Write $\frac{7}{11}$ as a division problem. Write 7 with several 0s after the decimal point: 7.000. (You can always add more 0s if you need them.)

$$11\overline{)7.000}$$

2. Solve the division problem. Stop when the remainder is 0, or when you have enough precision for your purposes, or when you notice a repeating pattern.

$$
\begin{array}{r}
.6363 \\
11\overline{)7.0000} \\
-6\,6 \\
\hline
40 \\
-33 \\
\hline
70 \\
-66 \\
\hline
40 \\
-33 \\
\hline
7
\end{array}
$$

The digits 6 and 3 in the quotient appear to repeat forever.

So, $\frac{7}{11}$ = 0.6363... = 0.$\overline{63}$, a repeating decimal.

NOTE: For the main *Everyday Mathematics* strategy for dividing by a decimal, see "Dividing Decimals" on page 136.

By building on the technique for rewriting fractions, students learn another strategy for dividing by a decimal.

Example 6: Solve 3.78/0.7 = ?

1. Think of the division problem as a fraction.

$$3.78/0.7 = \frac{3.78}{0.7}$$

2. Find an equivalent fraction with no decimal in the denominator.

$$\frac{3.78 * 10}{0.7 * 10} = \frac{37.8}{7}$$

3. Think of the equivalent fraction as a division problem.

$$\frac{37.8}{7} = 37.8/7$$

4. Solve the division problem.

$$
\begin{array}{r}
5.4 \\
7\overline{)37.8} \\
-\ 35 \\
\hline
2\ 8 \\
-\ 2\ 8 \\
\hline
0
\end{array}
$$

Because $\frac{37.8}{7}$ and $\frac{3.78}{0.7}$ are equivalent fractions, the division problems 37.8/7 and 3.78/0.7 are equivalent. So the answer to 37.8/7 is the same as the answer to 3.78/0.7.

So, 3.78/0.7 = 5.4

One of the hardest parts of U.S. traditional long division is accurately estimating the quotient at each step. Any wrong estimate, whether too high or too low, will cause the algorithm to fail, and an incorrect estimate must be erased and replaced. Using a table of easy multiples, as in Example 2 on page 139A, can help manage this difficulty. Another approach using partial-quotient estimates is shown in the margin.

$$
\begin{array}{r}
2\ \ 1 \\
688 \\
7\overline{)6225} \\
-42 \\
\hline
20 \\
-14 \\
\hline
62 \\
-56 \\
\hline
65 \\
-56 \\
\hline
9 \\
-7 \\
\hline
2
\end{array}
$$

Add the partial quotients to get 6225 / 7 → 889 R2.

A Note on Division by Zero

One often hears that dividing by zero is not defined or allowed. The reason for this is that dividing by zero does not produce a proper answer. Here are several ways to see why this is so:

- Any division problem can be rewritten as a missing-factor multiplication problem. For example, the problem $56/7 = n$ can be rewritten as $7 * n = 56$. The task then becomes to find the missing factor. In $7 * n = 56$, the missing factor is 8, which is the answer to the original division problem.

  When a division by zero is rewritten as a missing-factor multiplication problem, it becomes apparent that no answer will work. Consider, for example, $24/0 = n$. When the problem is rewritten as $0 * n = 24$, it is clear that no number can be multiplied by zero to get an answer of 24.

- When a series of division problems using the same dividend but smaller and smaller divisors is graphed, it becomes apparent that the closer the divisor is to zero, the greater the quotient becomes.

  For example, consider dividing 12 by a series of divisors: $12/6 = \mathbf{2}$, $12/4 = \mathbf{3}$, $12/3 = \mathbf{4}$, $12/2 = \mathbf{6}$, $12/1 = \mathbf{12}$.

  The quotient is clearly greater each time the divisor gets closer to zero. The effect becomes even more striking with divisors less than 1: $12 \div \frac{3}{4} = \mathbf{16}$, $12 \div \frac{1}{2} = \mathbf{24}$, $12 \div \frac{1}{4} = \mathbf{48}$, $12 \div \frac{1}{8} = \mathbf{96}$, $12 \div \frac{1}{16} = \mathbf{192}$. As the divisor approaches zero, the quotient "approaches infinity," that is, becomes large without limit. Because infinitely large quotients make no sense, division by zero is not allowed.

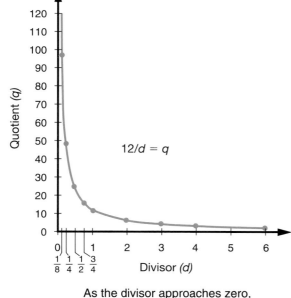

$12/d = q$

As the divisor approaches zero, the quotient approches infinity.

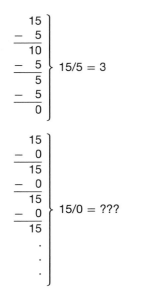

15/5 = 3

15/0 = ???

Repeated subtraction of 0 makes no sense.

NOTE: Fraction calculators make it possible to do arithmetic with fractions without tedious paper-and-pencil methods. Of course, the machines have their own pros and cons and require time for you and students to explore the techniques. But in the end, they can be very useful in helping students understand the concepts behind the algorithms in the following sections. For more information, see Section 11.4: Algorithms on Calculators.

- Just as multiplication can be seen as repeated addition of equal groups, division can be seen as repeated subtraction of equal groups. For example, $15/5 = n$ can be solved by finding out how many times 5 can be subtracted from 15. However, if the divisor is zero, the question becomes how many times zero can be subtracted from a given number. Clearly, there is no sensible answer.

- Division problems can also be written as fractions. For example, $8/4 = 2$ can be written as $\frac{8}{4} = 2$ and $3/4 = 0.75$ can be written $\frac{3}{4} = 0.75$. Just as division by zero is not allowed, having zero as the denominator of a fraction is not allowed.

The denominator of a fraction represents the number of parts into which a whole has been divided, but a whole cannot be divided into zero parts. For example, a pizza can be cut into fourths, or four equal parts; it can also be cut into halves, or two equal parts; or it could be left uncut, which means it has one part. But, there is no way to cut it so that it has zero parts. One whole pizza is one part before you start cutting it.

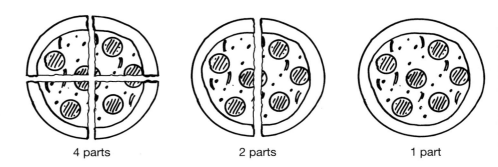

4 parts   2 parts   1 part

There is no way to cut a pizza so it has 0 parts.

▶ 11.3 Algorithms for Fractions

Decimal notation for rational numbers is increasingly important in the United States because of the growing acceptance of the metric system and the rapid spread of digital technology. Nevertheless, rational numbers written as fractions continue to be important both in everyday life and in mathematics beyond elementary school. Being able to add, subtract, multiply, divide, and compare fractions is useful in many practical real-world situations and is also necessary for success in algebra and higher mathematics, not to mention some high-stakes, standardized tests.

The overall approach to fractions in *Everyday Mathematics* is similar to that for whole numbers. In the beginning, the focus is on building a conceptual basis for understanding fractions. This work starts in *Kindergarten Everyday Mathematics*, considerably earlier than in most other programs, and continues throughout the primary grade program. Much of this early work is hands-on, using, for example, pattern blocks, clock faces, chips, and paper strips, and is closely connected to everyday uses of fractions.

During this period, and increasingly in third and fourth grades, students solve problems using their growing understanding of fractions rather than procedures they have been taught but may not understand. Much of this work continues to be hands-on, using concrete models for fractions, but pictorial and symbolic methods also appear. Often, students solve a problem in several ways, share their solutions, and compare and discuss the various approaches. During these discussions, you may highlight or introduce particularly effective or instructive methods. Important ideas introduced during this stage include the *unit whole,* or *ONE,* in fractions that name part of a whole, comparing fractions by size, and informal methods for adding and subtracting fractions and mixed numbers.

In fifth and sixth grades, students work extensively and systematically with algorithms for operations with fractions. Common-denominator approaches for addition, subtraction, and division are formally introduced—some students will have been using such methods already. Traditional topics are also treated, such as writing fractions in "simplest" form and operations with mixed numbers. In keeping with the *Everyday Mathematics* belief in multiple solution methods, students encounter several ways to solve most problems.

The following sections briefly discuss several symbolic methods for operations with fractions.

For more information on the unit whole, or ONE, see Section 9.3.2: Uses of Fractions.

11.3.1 Common Denominators

It is usually easier to operate on fractions with common denominators than on those without. *Everyday Mathematics* includes three main techniques for finding a common denominator.

Example: Rename $\frac{3}{4}$ and $\frac{1}{6}$ with a common denominator.

- *Use equivalent fractions.*

  List equivalent fractions for $\frac{3}{4}$ and $\frac{1}{6}$.

  $$\frac{3}{4} = \frac{6}{8} = \frac{9}{12} = \frac{12}{16} = \cdots$$

  $$\frac{1}{6} = \frac{2}{12} = \frac{3}{18} = \frac{4}{24} = \cdots$$

  Both $\frac{3}{4}$ and $\frac{1}{6}$ can be renamed as fractions with the common denominator 12.

  So $\frac{3}{4} = \frac{9}{12}$ and $\frac{1}{6} = \frac{2}{12}$.

- *Use multiplication.*

  Multiply the numerator and denominator of each fraction by the denominator of the other fraction.

  $$\frac{3*6}{4*6} = \frac{18}{24} \quad \text{and} \quad \frac{1*4}{6*4} = \frac{4}{24}$$

  This method gives a *quick common denominator,* works even if the denominators are variables, and so is commonly used in algebra manipulations.

- *Use the least common multiple.*

  Find the least common multiple of the denominators.

  The least common multiple of 4 and 6 is 12.

  Rename the fractions so that their denominator is the least common multiple.

  $$\frac{3}{4} * \frac{3}{3} = \frac{9}{12} \quad \text{and} \quad \frac{1}{6} * \frac{2}{2} = \frac{2}{12}$$

  This method gives what is known as the least common denominator. The *least common denominator* can be easier to use in complicated calculations.

11.3.2 Fraction Addition and Subtraction

To add or subtract fractions, students in *Fifth* and *Sixth Grade Everyday Mathematics* estimate answers and find quick common denominators by multiplying the denominators in a problem. Then they rewrite the original fractions using the quick common denominators, making it easy to add or subtract.

Examples:
$$\frac{1}{3} + \frac{5}{8} = \frac{1*8}{3*8} + \frac{5*3}{8*3} = \frac{8}{24} + \frac{15}{24} = \frac{23}{24}$$

$$\frac{2}{3} - \frac{5}{8} = \frac{2*8}{3*8} - \frac{5*3}{8*3} = \frac{16}{24} - \frac{15}{24} = \frac{1}{24}$$

This approach may be generalized for sixth graders in formulas, although students should not necessarily be expected to memorize or prove them. For any numbers a and c, and any nonzero numbers b and d:

$$\frac{a}{b} + \frac{c}{d} = \frac{(a*d) + (c*b)}{b*d}$$

$$\frac{a}{b} - \frac{c}{d} = \frac{(a*d) - (c*b)}{b*d}$$

11.3.3 Mixed-Number Addition and Subtraction

In *Everyday Mathematics,* there are two main approaches to adding and subtracting mixed numbers. One approach is to rename the mixed numbers as improper fractions and then add or subtract them in the same way as any other fractions.

chapter 11

Example 1: Evaluate $4\frac{1}{6} + 2\frac{2}{3}$.

1. Rename the mixed numbers as fractions.

$$4\frac{1}{6} = \frac{25}{6}$$

$$2\frac{2}{3} = \frac{8}{3}$$

2. Add the fractions.

$$\frac{25}{6} + \frac{8}{3} = \frac{25}{6} + \frac{16}{6} = \frac{41}{6}$$

3. Rename the result as a mixed number.

$$\frac{41}{6} = 6\frac{5}{6}$$

So, $4\frac{1}{6} + 2\frac{2}{3} = 6\frac{5}{6}$.

The other main *Everyday Mathematics* approach to adding and subtracting mixed numbers treats the whole-number and fraction parts separately, making trades as necessary.

Example 2: Evaluate $5\frac{1}{4} - 3\frac{2}{3}$.

1. Rename the fractions using a common denominator.

$$5\frac{1}{4} \quad \rightarrow \quad 5\frac{3}{12}$$
$$- 3\frac{2}{3} \quad \rightarrow \quad - 3\frac{8}{12}$$

2. Rename the first mixed number so that the numerator of the fraction part is greater than or equal to the numerator of the second mixed number.

$$5\frac{3}{12} \quad \rightarrow \quad 4\frac{15}{12}$$
$$- 3\frac{8}{12} \quad \rightarrow \quad - 3\frac{8}{12}$$

3. Subtract.
$$4\frac{15}{12}$$
$$- 3\frac{8}{12}$$
$$\overline{1\frac{7}{12}}$$

So, $5\frac{1}{4} - 3\frac{2}{3} = 1\frac{7}{12}$.

11.3.4 Fraction Multiplication

Even young children can solve problems like *What is $\frac{1}{2}$ of 6?* This is especially true with problems that arise in real-world fair-sharing situations. Solving many such "fraction-of-a-number" problems throughout the primary grades helps children build a foundation for work with multiplication of fractions in *Fourth* through *Sixth Grade Everyday Mathematics*.

In *Fifth Grade Everyday Mathematics*, students investigate an area model for fraction multiplication that allows them to find products of relatively "simple" fractions, that is, fractions that have small enough denominators to make drawing a divided rectangle a reasonable task.

Example: Evaluate $\frac{2}{4} * \frac{2}{5}$.

Draw a rectangular region and partition it as shown.

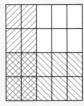

- $\frac{2}{5}$ of the region is shaded this way:

- $\frac{2}{4}$ of the region is shaded this way:

- $\frac{2}{4}$ of $\frac{2}{5}$ of the region is shaded this way:

So, $\frac{2}{4}$ of $\frac{2}{5}$ is $\frac{4}{20} = \frac{1}{5}$ of the whole region.

In symbols, $\frac{2}{4}$ of $\frac{2}{5}$ is $\frac{2}{4} * \frac{2}{5} = \frac{4}{20} = \frac{1}{5}$.

After seeing many problems solved in this way, students are likely to notice a pattern that can be generalized as a rule for multiplying fractions: *Multiply the numerators to get the product's numerator and multiply the denominators to get the product's denominator.* Some students may appreciate it as a formula, in which *a* and *c* can be any numbers and *b* and *d* can be any nonzero numbers:

$$\frac{a}{b} * \frac{c}{d} = \frac{a * c}{b * d}$$

Students later incorporate this rule into one for multiplying fractions and whole numbers, where the first step is to rewrite the whole number as itself over 1. As a formula, in which *a* and *b* can be any numbers, and *c* can be any nonzero number:

$$a * \frac{b}{c} = \frac{a}{1} * \frac{b}{c} = \frac{a * b}{1 * c} = \frac{a * b}{c}$$

These rules are practiced in *Sixth Grade Everyday Mathematics*.

11.3.5 Fraction Division

Situations that involve quotients of rational numbers in decimal form are fairly common in everyday life. However, the same kinds of situations involving quotients of rational numbers in fraction form are rare. Indeed, few adults ever need to divide fractions after they leave school. Therefore, the main goal of division of fractions in *Everyday Mathematics* is not to give students practical skills, but to:

- Complete the arithmetic system. Because whole numbers and decimals can be added, subtracted, multiplied, and divided, students should see that all these operations are possible with fractions as well.

- Anticipate future work with rational-number expressions in algebra courses.

"Quick Common Denominator" Fraction Division

The common denominator method for dividing fractions is less mysterious than the traditional "invert-and-multiply" rule described in the next section. Unfortunately, while it may make more sense than the latter rule, it is usually less efficient. The algorithm builds on the *quick common denominator* approach to adding and subtracting fractions. Once a common denominator is found, the quotient of the fractions is simply the quotient of the numerators.

For more information, see Section 11.3.2: Fraction Addition and Subtraction.

Example: Evaluate $\frac{3}{4} \div \frac{2}{5}$.

$$\frac{3}{4} \div \frac{2}{5} = \frac{15}{20} \div \frac{8}{20}$$

$$= \frac{15/8}{20/20}$$

$$= \frac{15/8}{1}$$

$$= \frac{15}{8}, \text{ or } 1\frac{7}{8}$$

You might point out to students that the 20ths behave like units of measure in a ratio. Say *15 twentieths divided by 8 twentieths is the ratio 15 to 8.*

That the common-denominator method for dividing fractions gives the same result as the more familiar invert-and-multiply method can be shown algebraically.

1. Rewrite the fractions to be divided with a common denominator. $\frac{a}{b} \div \frac{c}{d} = \frac{ad}{bd} \div \frac{cb}{db}$

2. Divide the numerators. $= ad \div cb$

3. Rewrite the division as a fraction. $= \frac{ad}{cb}$

This answer is the same as that obtained by the invert-and-multiply algorithm.

"Invert-and-Multiply" Fraction Division

Most adults were taught the "invert-and-multiply" rule to divide fractions. A significant advantage of this algorithm is that it is easy to use. A significant disadvantage is that few people understand why it works.

> **The Division of Fractions Property**
> To find the quotient of two fractions, multiply the first fraction by the reciprocal of the second fraction.

Example: Evaluate $\frac{4}{5} \div \frac{2}{3}$.

$$\frac{4}{5} \div \frac{2}{3} = \frac{4}{5} * \frac{3}{2}$$

$$= \frac{12}{10}$$

$$= 1\frac{2}{10}, \text{ or } 1\frac{1}{5}$$

chapter 11

Example: Evaluate $2\frac{3}{4} \div 1\frac{1}{3}$.

$$2\frac{3}{4} \div 1\frac{1}{3} = \frac{11}{4} \div \frac{4}{3}$$

$$= \frac{11}{4} * \frac{3}{4}$$

$$= \frac{33}{16}, \text{ or } 2\frac{1}{16}$$

The Division of Fractions Property is based on the following rules.

Rule 1: A fraction can have any number in its numerator and any number except zero in its denominator.

Examples:

27/55 can be written as the fraction $\frac{27}{55}$.

6.3/π can be written as $\frac{6.3}{\pi}$.

$\frac{2}{3} \div \frac{3}{4}$ can be written as $\dfrac{\frac{2}{3}}{\frac{3}{4}}$.

Rule 2: $\dfrac{a}{b} * \dfrac{c}{d} = \dfrac{a * c}{b * d}$

where a and c may be any numbers; b and d may be any nonzero numbers.

Examples:

$$\frac{5}{8} * \frac{3}{2} = \frac{5 * 3}{8 * 2} \qquad\qquad \frac{3}{5} * 7 = \frac{3}{5} * \frac{7}{1}$$

$$= \frac{15}{16} \qquad\qquad\qquad = \frac{3 * 7}{5 * 1}$$

$$\qquad\qquad\qquad\qquad\qquad = \frac{21}{5}, \text{ or } 4\frac{1}{5}$$

Rule 3: If the product of two numbers is 1, then the numbers are *reciprocals* of each other. A reciprocal of a fraction is the fraction written "upside down," with numerator and denominator exchanged.

Examples:

5 and $\frac{1}{5}$ are reciprocals because $5 * \frac{1}{5} = 1$.

$\frac{3}{4}$ and $\frac{4}{3}$ are reciprocals because $\frac{3}{4} * \frac{4}{3} = 1$.

$2\frac{3}{5}$ and $\frac{5}{13}$ are reciprocals because $2\frac{3}{5} = \frac{13}{5}$

and $\frac{13}{5} * \frac{5}{13} = 1$.

Rule 4: Multiplying the numerator and denominator of a fraction by the same number gives a fraction equal to the original fraction.

Example: $\dfrac{3}{5} = \dfrac{3 * 4}{5 * 4} = \dfrac{12}{20}$

Rule 5: Any number a divided by 1 is equal to a. That is,
$a \div 1 = \frac{a}{1} = a$.

Examples:

$$23 \div 1 = \frac{23}{1} = 23$$

$$46.3 \div 1 = \frac{46.3}{1} = 46.3$$

$$\frac{3}{8} \div 1 = \frac{\frac{3}{8}}{1} = \frac{3}{8}$$

Why the Division of Fractions Property works is shown in the following example.

Example: Evaluate $\frac{3}{4} \div \frac{2}{5}$.

1. Write the problem as a fraction. (Rule 1)

$$\frac{3}{4} \div \frac{2}{5} = \frac{\frac{3}{4}}{\frac{2}{5}}$$

2. Multiply the numerator and denominator of the fraction by the reciprocal of the denominator. (Rules 3 and 4)

$$\frac{\frac{3}{4}}{\frac{2}{5}} = \frac{\frac{3}{4} * \frac{5}{2}}{\frac{2}{5} * \frac{5}{2}}$$

3. Simplify the denominator. (Rule 3)

$$\frac{\frac{3}{4} * \frac{5}{2}}{\frac{2}{5} * \frac{5}{2}} = \frac{\frac{3}{4} * \frac{5}{2}}{1}$$

4. Divide by 1. (Rule 5)

$$\frac{\frac{3}{4} * \frac{5}{2}}{1} = \frac{3}{4} * \frac{5}{2}$$

5. Multiply. (Rule 2)

$$\frac{3}{4} * \frac{5}{2} = \frac{3 * 5}{4 * 2}$$

$$= \frac{15}{8}, \text{ or } 1\frac{7}{8}$$

You can see from Step 4 that $\frac{3}{4} \div \frac{2}{5} = \frac{3}{4} * \frac{5}{2}$; that is, the first fraction of the original problem is multiplied by the reciprocal of the second fraction of the problem.

▶ 11.4 Algorithms on Calculators

In a sense, using a calculator requires learning new algorithms, namely the *key sequences*, to get an anticipated result. Learning a new key sequence should be a topic of instruction, not something left for students to figure out for themselves. Therefore, when students encounter new keys and key sequences, spend a few minutes talking about the correct procedures for the model of calculator they have. Write the proper key sequences on the board and have students work through several sample problems.

For more information, see Section 3.1.1: Calculators.

Although the authors used the Texas Instruments TI-15 and Casio *fx*-55 calculators while writing *Fourth* through *Sixth Grade Everyday Mathematics,* many other calculators work just as well. Whatever the model, if all students have the same one, then the same key sequences work on every student's calculator, making it easier for you to manage activities. In particular, having one model of calculator ensures that they will all follow the same algorithm for the order of operations. Both of the scientific calculators above follow the algebraic order of operations.

For more information on the algebraic order of operations, see Section 10.2.3: The Order of Operations.

Key sequences in the *Teacher's Lesson Guide* and in the student materials are for both TI-15s and Casio *fx*-55s. In most cases, one or both of the key sequences also work with other calculators. If you have a different calculator, you should check that the given sequences work with your machines. In some cases, you may need to consult the owner's manual that came with your calculators.

Without specifically identifying the brands and models, the basic operations of the TI-15 and Casio *fx*-55 are described in the *Student Reference Books* for Grades 4 through 6. The TI is Calculator A; the Casio is Calculator B. The authors have consciously limited the discussion to features, or functions, that are common to both calculators and that they believe are appropriate for each grade level. If you wish to explore other functions with your students, please consult the owner's manual for ideas.

One important kind of algorithmic thinking in the world of computers and calculators is *programming*. Every program is an algorithm, whether it be as simple as the one that a calculator uses to add two numbers, or as complicated as the ones in a word processor. Programming computers is not a goal of *Everyday Mathematics,* but children do program their calculators to skip count in Kindergarten through third grade.

In Grades 4 through 6, students learn to use fraction calculators. The following sections present the information provided to students in the *Fourth* through *Sixth Grade Student Reference Books* on how to enter, rename and convert fractions and mixed numbers on both the TI-15 and Casio *fx*-55 calculators. Examples of operations with calculators are also included in the *Student Reference Books,* but are straightforward if you know the key sequences that follow.

11.4.1 Entering Fractions and Mixed Numbers

Most calculators that let you enter fractions use similar key sequences. For proper fractions, always start by entering the numerator. Then press a key to tell the calculator to begin writing a fraction.

Example: Enter $\frac{5}{8}$ as a fraction in your calculator.

TI-15	Key Sequence	Display
	5 [n] 8 [d] [Enter]	$\frac{5}{8} = \qquad \frac{5}{8}$

Casio *fx*-55	Key Sequence	Display
	5 [b/c] 8 [=]	$= \qquad \frac{5}{8}$

NOTE: Pressing [d] after you enter the denominator is optional.

To enter a mixed number, enter the whole number part and then press a key to tell the calculator what you did.

Example: Enter $73\frac{2}{5}$ as a fraction in your calculator.

TI-15	Key Sequence	Display
	73 [Unit] 2 [n] 5 [d] [Enter]	$73\frac{2}{5} = \qquad 73\frac{2}{5}$

Casio *fx*-55	Key Sequence	Display
	73 [a] 2 [b/c] 5 [=]	$= \qquad 73\frac{2}{5}$

Try entering a mixed number on your calculator.

The keys to convert between mixed numbers and improper fractions are similar on all fraction calculators.

Example: Convert $\frac{45}{7}$ to a mixed number with your calculator. Then change it back.

TI-15	Key Sequence	Display
	45 ⟦n⟧ 7 ⟦d⟧ ⟦Enter⟧	$\frac{45}{7} =$ $6\frac{3}{7}$
	⟦U$\frac{n}{d}$↔$\frac{n}{d}$⟧	$\frac{45}{7}$
	⟦U$\frac{n}{d}$↔$\frac{n}{d}$⟧	$6\frac{3}{7}$

Casio fx-55	Key Sequence	Display
	45 ⟦b/c⟧ 7 ⟦=⟧	$=$ $\frac{45}{7}$
	⟦$a\frac{b/c}{}$↔d/c⟧	$6\frac{3}{7}$
	⟦$a\frac{b/c}{}$↔d/c⟧	$=$ $\frac{45}{7}$

NOTE: Pressing ⟦Enter⟧ is *not* optional in this key sequence.

NOTE: Pressing ⟦=⟧ is optional in this key sequence.

Both ⟦U$\frac{n}{d}$↔$\frac{n}{d}$⟧ and ⟦$a\frac{b/c}{}$↔d/c⟧ toggle between mixed number and improper fraction notation.

11.4.2 Simplifying Fractions

Ordinarily, calculators do not simplify fractions on their own. The steps for simplifying fractions are similar for many calculators, but the order of the steps varies. So the instructions for simplifying on a TI and simplifying on a Casio are given separately in this section.

Simplifying Fractions on a TI-15

The TI lets you simplify a fraction in two ways. Each way divides the numerator and the denominator by a common factor. The first approach uses ⟦Simp⟧ to automatically divide by the smallest common factor, and ⟦Fac⟧ to display the factor. The message $\frac{N}{D} \rightarrow \frac{n}{d}$ in the display means that the fraction shown is not in simplest form.

Example: Convert $\frac{18}{24}$ to simplest form using smallest common factors.

Fac displays the common factor used to simplify a fraction.

TI-15	Key Sequence	Display
18 **n** 24 **d** **Simp** **Enter**		$\frac{18}{24} \blacktriangleright S \qquad \overset{\frac{N}{D} - \frac{n}{d}}{\frac{9}{12}}$
Fac		2
Fac **Simp** **Enter**		$\frac{9}{12} \blacktriangleright S \qquad \frac{3}{4}$
Fac		3

$$\frac{18}{24} = \frac{3}{4}$$

In the second approach to simplifying fractions on a TI, you tell the calculator what common factor to divide by. If you use the greatest common factor of the numerator and the denominator, you can simplify the fraction in one step.

Simp simplifies fractions.

Example: Convert $\frac{18}{24}$ to simplest form in one step by dividing the numerator and the denominator by their greatest common factor, 6.

TI-15	Key Sequence	Display
18 **n** 24 **d** **Simp** 6 **Enter**		$\frac{18}{24} \blacktriangleright S6 \qquad \frac{3}{4}$
Fac		6

$$\frac{18}{24} = \frac{3}{4}$$

NOTE: Pressing **Fac** toggles between the display of the factor and the display of the fraction.

Simplifying Fractions on a Casio *fx*-55

The Casio lets you simplify fractions in three different ways. Each way divides the numerator and the denominator by a common factor. The first approach uses $=$ to give the simplest form in one step. The word *Simp* in the display means that the fraction shown is not in simplest form.

chapter 11

Casio *fx*-55

[SIMP] simplifies a fraction by a common factor.

Press [=] [=] to write in simplest form.

NOTE: Each time you press [SIMP] in the smallest-common-factor approach, you briefly see the common factor, then the simplified fraction.
This can be done without pressing [=] first.

NOTE: If you enter a number that is not a common factor of the numerator and the denominator, you will get an error symbol "E" in the display with the unchanged fraction.

Example: Convert $\frac{18}{24}$ to simplest form in one step.

Casio *fx*-55	**Key Sequence**	**Display**
	18 [b/c] 24 [=]	Simp = $\frac{18}{24}$
	[=]	= $\frac{3}{4}$

$$\frac{18}{24} = \frac{3}{4}$$

If you enter a fraction that is already in simplest form, you will not see Simp on the display. The one-step approach does not tell you the common factor as the next two Casio approaches do using [SIMP].

Example: Convert $\frac{18}{24}$ to simplest form using smallest common factors.

Casio *fx*-55	**Key Sequence**	**Display**
	18 [b/c] 24 [=]	Simp = $\frac{18}{24}$
	[SIMP]	Simp 2 → Simp $\frac{9}{12}$
	[SIMP]	Simp 3 → Simp $\frac{3}{4}$

$$\frac{18}{24} = \frac{3}{4}$$

In the last approach to simplifying fractions with this type of calculator, you tell it what common factor to divide by. If you use the greatest common factor of the numerator and the denominator, you can simplify the fraction in one step.

Example: Convert $\frac{18}{24}$ to simplest form by dividing the numerator and the denominator by their greatest common factor, 6.

Casio *fx*-55	**Key Sequence**	**Display**
	18 [b/c] 24 [=]	Simp = $\frac{18}{24}$
	6 [SIMP]	Simp 6 → $\frac{3}{4}$

Try simplifying the fractions in the previous examples to see how your calculator works.

11.4.3 Fraction/Decimal/Percent Conversions

Calculators can be used to convert between fractions, decimals, and percents. Conversions of fractions to decimals and percents can be done on any calculator. For example, to rename $\frac{3}{5}$ as a decimal, simply enter 3 ÷ 5 =. The display will show 0.6. To rename a decimal as a percent, just multiply by 100.

Conversions of decimals and percents to fractions can only be done on calculators that have special keys for fractions. Such calculators also have keys to change a fraction to its decimal equivalent or a decimal to an equivalent fraction.

Example: Convert $\frac{3}{8}$ to a decimal and back to a fraction in simplest form.

TI-15	Key Sequence	Display
	3 [n] 8 [d] (Enter)	$\frac{3}{8} = \frac{3}{8}$
	(F↔D)	0.375
	(F↔D)	$^{\frac{N}{D} \to \frac{n}{d}}$ $\frac{375}{1000}$
	(Simp) (Enter)	$\frac{375}{1000} \blacktriangleright S$ $^{\frac{N}{D} \to \frac{n}{d}}$ $\frac{75}{200}$
	(Simp) (Enter)	$\frac{75}{200} \blacktriangleright S$ $^{\frac{N}{D} \to \frac{n}{d}}$ $\frac{15}{40}$
	(Simp) (Enter)	$\frac{15}{40} \blacktriangleright S$ $\frac{3}{8}$

Casio fx-55	Key Sequence	Display
	3 [b/c] 8	$\frac{3}{8}$
	(F↔D)	0.375
	(F↔D)	$\frac{3}{8}$

$\frac{3}{8} = 0.375$

See how your calculator changes fractions to decimals.

NOTE: (F↔D) toggles between fraction and decimal notation on both calculators.

The tables below show examples of various conversions. Although only one key sequence is shown for each conversion, there are often other key sequences that work as well.

Conversion	Starting Number	TI Key Sequence	Display
Fraction to decimal	$\frac{3}{5}$	3 [n] 5 [d] [Enter] [F↔D]	0.6
Decimal to fraction	0.125	.125 [Enter] [F↔D]	$\frac{N}{D} \rightarrow \frac{n}{d}$ $\frac{125}{1000}$
Decimal to percent	0.75	.75 [▶%] [Enter]	0.75▶% 75%
Percent to decimal	125%	125 [%] [Enter]	125%= 1.25
Fraction to percent	$\frac{5}{8}$	5 [n] 8 [d] [▶%] [Enter]	$\frac{5}{8}$ ▶% 62.5%
Percent to fraction	35%	35 [%] [Enter] [F↔D]	$\frac{N}{D} \rightarrow \frac{n}{d}$ $\frac{35}{100}$

Conversion	Starting Number	Casio Key Sequence	Display
Fraction to decimal	$\frac{3}{5}$	3 [b/c] 5 [F↔D]	0.6
Decimal to fraction	0.125	.125 [F↔D]	$\frac{1}{8}$
Decimal to percent	0.75	.75 [×] 100 [=]	= 75.
Percent to decimal	125%	1 [×] 125 [%]	1.25
Fraction to percent	$\frac{5}{8}$	5 [b/c] 8 [F↔D] [×] 100 [=]	= 62.5
Percent to fraction	35%	1 [×] 35 [%] [F↔D]	$\frac{7}{20}$

12 Data and Chance

Contents

Understanding statistics and probability is more important now than ever before. In a world inundated with numbers, citizens and consumers need to understand claims about data and probabilities in journalism and advertising. Workers need to know how to gather, display, and analyze data in order to work efficiently and effectively. Even many recreational activities such as fantasy sports leagues involve data and chance. Statistics and probability have become prominent in the elementary school curriculum, both because of their current importance and as a source of contexts for practicing arithmetic and other skills.

12.1 Probability

Everyday Mathematics authors believe that most students need to be exposed to concepts and skills many times in many different ways, often only briefly, before they are able to master them. The treatment of probability in the curriculum is a good example of this approach. Students play informal games and engage in activities involving the idea of fairness and the use of random-number generators such as cards, number cubes, and spinners. The first step toward a more formal treatment occurs in *Third Grade Everyday Mathematics.* Similar activities are presented early in *Fourth Grade Everyday Mathematics,* and probability ideas are extended and made more precise throughout the rest of the program. The *Probability Meter,* a number-line device for recording probabilities, is introduced in Grade 5.

12.1.1 Why Study Probability?

Most people are aware that our world is filled with uncertainties. Although there are some things that we can be sure of, for example, that the sun will rise tomorrow or that it will be hot this summer in Florida, we also know that there are degrees of uncertainty and that some things are more likely to happen than others. We know that there are also uncertain occurrences, such as weather patterns, that can be predicted with increasing accuracy. These qualitative ideas of probability—*impossible, possible, likely, certain,* and so on— are the basis for the mathematical treatment of probability in *Everyday Mathematics.*

Few people understand how to calculate the chance that something will take place. Yet many decisions in our personal lives, from the relatively trivial *Should I take an umbrella with me?* to the vitally important *Should I undergo surgery?* are based on probabilities. Probability is more useful in daily life than are most other branches of mathematics and fully deserves the greater prominence given to it in most contemporary elementary school mathematics curricula.

12.1.2 The Language of Chance

Because students should become comfortable talking about chance events as early as possible, *Everyday Mathematics* begins by focusing on vocabulary development. Some of the many terms introduced are *sure, certain, probably, 50-50, unlikely*, and *impossible*. These terms should not be taught formally. Through repeated use, students will gradually make them part of their vocabularies. Many students are familiar with terms like *forecast* and *predict,* but not with the term *probability.* Probability is a difficult word and need not be used at first.

All students have had experience comparing the chances of various outcomes of a random process. They understand everyday statements like *Rain is more likely than snow today.* They may also understand that getting a sum of 7 is more likely than getting a sum of 3 when two dice are rolled. Such informal comparisons are a good place to begin, because they provide a context in which the language of chance can be intuitively introduced. Discuss the fact that some things are certain to happen and other things are certain to not happen. The most interesting things are in between, neither certain nor impossible. Point out that if we think hard enough, we can often say which of these uncertain things are more likely to occur than others.

Randomness

Throughout *Everyday Mathematics,* many activities rely on spinning spinners, drawing from card decks, rolling dice, and flipping coins. All of these are procedures for generating random results, but *randomness* is not formally defined until fifth grade. This is because randomness is simple to describe with words such as *haphazard, unpredictable, without pattern,* and *chaotic,* but difficult to define formally and hard to verify in practice. Technically, a *random outcome* is an event selected from a set of outcomes, all of which have an equal probability of being selected. There are several reasons why randomness is hard to verify in practice.

First, there is the problem of assuring truly equal probabilities. Many variables affect this, such as the position of a spinner, weight distribution in a die, and thoroughness of the shuffle of a card deck. These problems affect classroom activities that rely on randomly generated numbers, but they are essentially beyond control. In *Everyday Mathematics,* random-number generators are trusted to provide numbers that are random enough to serve their purpose.

For more information, see Section 12.4.1: Random-Number Generators.

The second problem in verifying random results is an individual's perception of what such results should look like. Imagine a list of 1,000 randomly generated single-digit numbers. Somewhere in the list there are six consecutive 3s. Is this a problem? Most people would think so; it is counter to the notion that random means "all shook up." Six 3s in a row seems to be a pattern, and therefore the list is suspect. Similarly, if you flip a coin 8 times and get 8 HEADS, the coin seems suspect.

Results like these lead people to believe that previous outcomes can affect the next outcome. For instance, one might think *After 8 HEADS in a row, it seems that I should expect TAILS on the next flip, because I believe that on average, a fair coin will land TAILS half the time, and TAILS are now overdue.* The belief that a fair coin will land TAILS half the time is correct on average, in the long run. However, it is incorrect to think that the previous eight HEADS will affect the ninth toss, for which there is still a 50-50 chance of getting HEADS (or TAILS). If you see students acting as though past results affect the probability of future outcomes, you might ask them about their thoughts on the matter.

12.1.3 Making Predictions

In most of the probability activities in *Everyday Mathematics,* students make a prediction about the likelihood of a particular outcome of some random process such as rolling a die or flipping a coin. Then they check their predictions by performing an experiment that involves collecting, organizing, and interpreting data. Some activities call for students to compare the likelihood of several possible outcomes. Other activities ask students to estimate the chance that something will happen by assigning it a numerical value. For example, when a coin is tossed, the chance of its landing HEADS up is 1 out of 2, or $\frac{1}{2}$, because there are two ways the coin could land, one of which is HEADS up. When a single die is rolled, the chance of getting an even number is 3 out of 6, or $\frac{3}{6}$, because there are three even numbers {2, 4, 6} out of the six ways the die can land {1, 2, 3, 4, 5, 6}.

All outcomes are equally likely for some situations such as flipping a fair coin, rolling a fair die, and spinning a spinner that is divided into equal-size parts. In other situations, the outcomes are not equally likely. For example, when two 6-sided dice are rolled, a sum of 7 on the top faces is more likely than a sum of 4. In experiments with

Two 6-sided dice

For more information on rolling two dice, see Section 12.4.1: Random-Number Generators.

A *fair* spinner: The probability that a spin will land in any one of the three regions is $\frac{1}{3}$.

An *unfair* spinner: The probability that a spin will land in any one of the three regions is not $\frac{1}{3}$.

For more information on landmarks, see Section 12.2.4: Data Analysis.

unequally divided spinners, most students will probably conclude quickly that the spinner is more likely to land on the larger regions than on the smaller ones. Spinners are extremely useful for helping students to visualize the concept of chance.

Many random processes lend themselves to intuitive predictions because their outcomes follow very definite laws of chance. Coin tosses and spinner experiments are good examples of these. Other processes do not lend themselves to such precise analysis. Predicting the weather is much harder than predicting the outcome of a coin toss.

The Law of Large Numbers

In the long run, *Everyday Mathematics* aims to help students understand that the more often they repeat an experiment, the more reliable their predictions will be. For example, if a coin is tossed 10 times, it is possible, but not certain, that it will land HEADS up about half the time. If you try it, you may be surprised at how often you obtain a 7-3 or 8-2 split. But if the coin is tossed 100 times, it is more likely to land nearer to a 50-50 split, as the occurrences of HEADS and TAILS tend to "even out" with more tosses.

Students have a variety of experiences throughout *Everyday Mathematics* that illustrate this important idea, known to mathematicians as the *law of large numbers.* For example, in *Third Grade Everyday Mathematics,* children participate in a block-drawing experiment. Children are asked to figure out how many blocks of different colors are hidden in a bag by examining the results of repeatedly drawing a block from the bag. The more times they draw a block, the more likely it is that they will make the correct guess.

Similarly, in *Fifth Grade Everyday Mathematics,* pairs of students each take small samples from a bowl of multicolored candy and count how many of each color they have. The class then pools the results from each pair to form one large sample, thereby concluding that a large sample produces a better estimate of the color distribution than does a small sample.

▶ 12.2 Data Collection, Organization, and Analysis

Students' initial data explorations should be informal, allowing them to collaborate with you and with one another to decide on methods of collecting, representing, and explaining their data. As students gain experience using common displays such as bar and line graphs and appropriate statistical landmarks such as median and range, they can answer questions and communicate their findings to others.

In *Everyday Mathematics,* work with data provides a context and motivation for the development of numerical skills that are often developed artificially or in isolation in traditional programs. For example, a number of data lessons are coordinated with the World Tour section in Grade 4 and the American Tour section in Grade 5. Much of the data that students collect and use in these lessons involve rates and percents, for example, currency exchange rates, cars per 1,000 persons, and percent of urban population. These real-world applications support and enrich other lessons concerned with fractions, decimals, and percents.

In *Everyday Mathematics,* data activities are designed so that students are involved in all aspects of data collection and analysis. For this reason, many data activities span several days and lessons. For example, in fifth grade, students are instructed to investigate whether a card game called *Finish First* is fair. In one lesson, students learn how to play the game and are introduced to the problem of figuring out if it is fair. In subsequent lessons, they collect data by playing the game many times over the course of several days. They record their data individually and collectively on tally charts and on a class bar graph, which is updated daily. In a later lesson, students analyze the data to determine whether the game is fair (it is not) and how it could be made fair. The *Finish First* game and activities also relate to probability.

For more information, see Section 12.1: Probability.

Many of the data activities in *Everyday Mathematics* are integrated with other topics in mathematics and other curricular areas. In addition to the many and varied data activities that are included in the *Teacher's Lesson Guide,* many opportunities for working with data will also arise naturally in the course of classroom life.

12.2.1 Formulating a Question

Ordinarily, data are collected and analyzed to describe a situation and/or to make predictions. The process almost always begins with a question. When we want to know something, a good strategy is to gather information. Then we look at the information—the *data*—in various ways to determine whether we found what we wanted to know.

There are two important reasons to take time to formulate a question for data exploration. The first is motivational. Data-collection activities are usually more meaningful to students if they are connected to a real-life problem or involve situations that students really care about. *Everyday Mathematics* presents many problem situations that require data collection and analysis. You are encouraged to personalize them and to add your own.

An example of personalization comes from a fifth-grade class. To raise funds for new library books, the students decided to hold a cookie sale for younger children in their school. To plan which kinds of cookies to bake and in what amounts, the fifth graders asked a sample of children, one class per grade level, how many and what type of cookies they would buy. They tallied and graphed their findings and used them to estimate how many cookies to bake and which kinds would be most popular. Although they could not determine exactly how to stock their sale, the survey data still helped them plan wisely.

A second reason to take time to formulate a question for data exploration is to clarify the essential information that can lead to an answer. In the cookie-sale survey, for example, it was important to know which kinds of cookies were preferred, but it was not important to know whether cookies were more popular than ice cream or whether the cookies would be eaten at school or at home. As another example, if students are collecting data to find out who runs the fastest, does hair color matter? Does distance matter? What about footwear or clothing? Even if the questions sometimes seem silly, it is important to ask them to help students develop habits of thinking about the possible effects various factors may have on the data they collect.

12.2.2 Collecting and Recording Data

Everyday Mathematics uses many sources of data and a variety of collection procedures, such as the following:

- Counting and measuring in the classroom;
- Observing and measuring at home;
- Taking surveys at school, including surveys of other classes;
- Collecting data from such sources as TV, newspapers, magazines, encyclopedias, and the Internet.

In *Kindergarten* through *Third Grade Everyday Mathematics,* the most common data are counts, and the usual goal is to examine the frequency of various occurrences. *How many . . . ?* is the classic beginning to the questions that are formulated by young children. In Grades 4 through 6, data may involve fractions, decimals, and negative numbers. Students in Grades 4 and 5 use the World Tour and American Tour sections, respectively, of their *Student Reference Books* as sources of data. Students in Grades 4 through 6 use other data from their reference books. Data are recorded on journal pages, on the Class Data Pad, and in bulletin-board displays.

Data analysis begins as the data are collected. If the information is not recorded in an organized table or chart, students will likely end up with an indecipherable heap of numbers instead of useful information. *Everyday Mathematics* provides various tools to help with the initial collection and organization of data, including journal pages, masters, and suggestions for what to add to the Class Data Pad and bulletin-board displays.

Sampling

Beginning in *Third Grade Everyday Mathematics,* students explore sampling when collecting and analyzing data. A *sample* is a relatively small part of a group chosen to represent the larger group being studied. The larger group is the *population.* The population might be all of the students in a school, all of the people in a state, all adults of voting age in a country, or any other large group that has been designated for study. Often, the collection of data from every member of the population is impossible; therefore, a representative sample of the population is surveyed.

For more information about randomness, see Section 12.1.2: The Language of Chance.

An important aspect of certain samples is that they are random. A *random sample* is taken from a population in a way that gives all members of the population the same chance of being selected. Large samples give more precise estimates of the population's characteristics than do small samples.

12.2.3 Organizing and Displaying Data

The tools in *Everyday Mathematics* provide some organization during data collection, but it is also important for students to design their own ways of recording and displaying data. Organization can help you "see the data *better*," while reorganizing it can help you "see the data *differently*," in a way that may better suit your needs. Students are encouraged to make and observe a wide variety of data displays.

Two simple methods for organizing data are:

* To arrange the data in order from the least value to the greatest;
* To sort the data by one or more characteristics.

When the data come from students' characteristics, this can be done concretely in the classroom. For example, you could order students' age data by having them line up by age. Or you could organize students by gender and then handedness. Direct all boys to move to the north wall of the room and all girls to the south wall; then have all right-handers move to the east wall and all left-handers to the west wall.

Several types of data displays are described in the following sections. Do not insist that all displays be neat and nicely labeled, especially tally tables or line plots. If students sketch many plots quickly, they can "see" the data in several different ways. After they analyze the data, ask students to report on their findings in some way. You may then require that tables and graphs in a report be neat and nicely labeled.

In *Sixth Grade Everyday Mathematics,* students have the option to use a spreadsheet program that allows them to draw line plots, bar graphs, and other displays.

For more information, see Section 3.1.3: Spreadsheets.

Data Tables

Tables are one of the most basic formats for the display of data. Newspapers, reference books, scientific articles, Web sites, and some publications are filled with data tables. Tables have specific uses, such as tally tables, lists, and the in/out tables used in "What's My Rule?" activities. Tables of numbers, arithmetic facts, and statistics such as the two shown here are also used extensively to help students improve their mental-arithmetic skills.

World's Largest Urban Agglomerations Projected 2015 Populations	
City, Country	**Population**
Tokyo, Japan	36,214,000
Bombay (Mumbai), India	22,645,000
Delhi, India	20,946,000
Mexico City, Mexico	20,647,000
Sao Paulo, Brazil	19,963,000
New York City, U.S.	19,717,000
Jakarta, Indonesia	17,498,000

Source: World Almanac, 2005

NBA Eastern Conference Standings				
7 March, 2005	**W**	**L**	**PCT**	**GB**
Miami	45	16	0.738	0.0
Detroit	36	22	0.621	7.5
Boston	31	29	0.517	13.5
Washington	33	25	0.569	10.5
Cleveland	31	27	0.534	12.5
Orlando	31	27	0.534	12.5
Chicago	29	27	0.518	13.5
Philadelphia	29	30	0.492	15.0
Indiana	29	30	0.492	15.0
New Jersey	26	34	0.433	18.5
Toronto	25	34	0.424	19.0
New York	25	34	0.424	19.0
Milwaukee	24	33	0.421	19.0
Charlotte	12	45	0.211	31.0
Atlanta	10	48	0.172	33.5

Source: www.nba.com

chapter 12

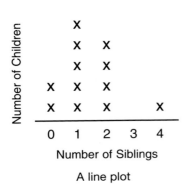

Number of Children

0 1 2 3 4
Number of Siblings

A line plot

NOTE: Line plots are also called *sketch graphs, dot plots,* or *pictographs* when the tally marks are pictures. Bar graphs are sometimes called *bar charts.*

Line Plots and Bar Graphs

Line plots are used extensively to organize and display data. A *line plot* is a sketch of data in which checks, Xs, stick-on notes, or other marks above a labeled line show the frequency of each value. A line plot can be thought of as a rough sketch of a bar graph.

Bar graphs are introduced in second grade and are used throughout the rest of *Everyday Mathematics.* Bar graphs are excellent for displaying *how much* or *how many* and can be drawn vertically or horizontally like the ones below. Students need to be aware of the important parts of a graph, including the title, labels for axes, and the scales for numbering the axes.

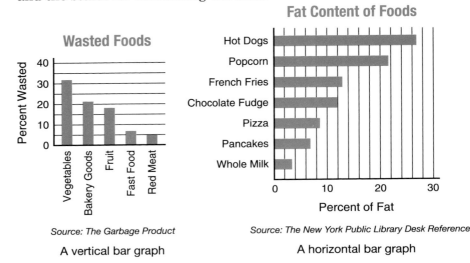

Wasted Foods

Percent Wasted

Source: The Garbage Product

A vertical bar graph

Fat Content of Foods

Percent of Fat

Source: The New York Public Library Desk Reference

A horizontal bar graph

Bar graphs are useful for comparing counts, or *frequencies,* of data. Sometimes the data are *categorical,* such as the food types in the "Wasted Foods" graph. Usually, each category is assigned its own bar in a graph so frequencies or other information about the categories can be compared. But you could combine categories to get a different picture of the data. For example, you could make a new category called "probably healthy foods" that combines vegetables, fruit, and red meat, and another category called "questionably healthy foods" that combines bakery goods and fast food. A graph with two bars could then compare waste based on healthiness of foods.

For *noncategorical* data, such as measurements, there are likely to be so many distinct data values that they need to be collected into intervals or else there would be too many bars on the graph. A *histogram* is a fancy name for a bar graph of noncategorical data. To make a histogram, you decide on a fixed interval, or scale, and count all of the values in each interval. For example, to display a histogram of the heights of all the students in your school, you might decide to group them by 4-inch intervals: 30–33 inches, 34–37 inches, and so on. Once you have determined a scale, it is displayed on a number line as one of the axes of the graph.

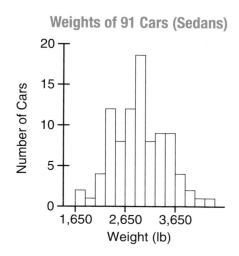

Weights of 91 Cars (Sedans)

A histogram of car weights: Scale 200 pounds. Eighteen cars weighed between 2,850 and 3,050 pounds.

Sometimes the scale of a histogram is called a *bin* or *bin width*. This fits with the view of the graph as a collection of equal-width bins into which the data are sorted. In any bar graph, if the scale used on the axis displaying the counts or frequencies is too small or too large, the "look" of the data can be distorted, as in the "Favorite Flavors of Ice Cream" bar graphs below.

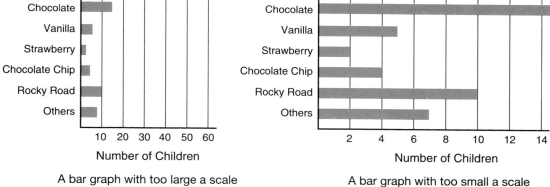

A bar graph with too large a scale   A bar graph with too small a scale

Computer or graphic-calculator programs may distinguish between bar graphs and histograms. The main reason is that, before you enter the data, you usually need to tell the program whether it is categorical or noncategorical. Better programs then let you manipulate the scales of both the frequency counts and the bar widths of histograms. If you have access to such a program it is a wonderful way to show students how easily the "look" of a graph can affect the way the data are perceived.

In *Fourth* through *Sixth Grade Everyday Mathematics*, students are introduced to side-by-side and stacked bar graphs. *Side-by-side bar graphs* display related data in adjacent bars, and *stacked bar graphs*

chapter 12

display related data by subdividing a single bar to represent parts of a total. These graphs are especially good for making comparisons among data, because the information is displayed close together rather than separated.

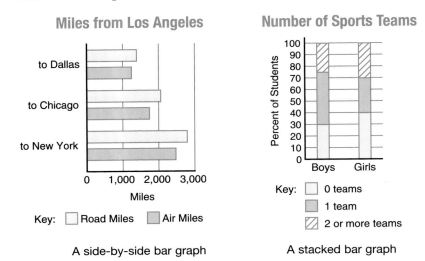

A side-by-side bar graph   A stacked bar graph

Line Graphs

Line graphs are good applications of ordered pairs, which are introduced in *Third Grade Everyday Mathematics*. These graphs are particularly good for showing how data change over time, and time is often one of the variables used and labeled. Drawing and analyzing line graphs gives students good practice in working with the coordinate plane.

Circle Graphs

Circle graphs, also known as *pie graphs* or *pie charts,* are used to compare parts of a whole. The circle represents the whole set of data. Categories in the data set are represented by pie-shaped pieces *(sectors)* of the circle and its interior. The measures of the angles of the sectors are calculated by finding the fraction or percent that each is of the whole circle, 360°.

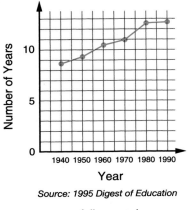

Median Number of Years of School Completed by Peoples Age 25 or Over in the United States

Source: 1995 Digest of Education

A line graph

Areas of the Continents (mi²)

North America
9,400,000

Antarctica
5,400,000

Africa
11,700,000

Asia
17,400,000

Europe
3,800,000

South America
6,900,000

Australia
3,300,000

In Grade 5, students use a *Percent Circle* to construct circle graphs because it eliminates the need to calculate the number of degrees in a sector. In Grade 6, students also use protractors to make circle graphs. Although a Percent Circle is simpler to use, the activity is more an application of a student's skill at taking percents of numbers, in this case, percents of the 360° in a circle.

Stem-and-Leaf Plots

A *stem-and-leaf plot* resembles a line plot because it displays the individual pieces of the whole data set. A stem-and-leaf plot separates the digits of the numerical data into two columns, "stems" and "leaves," and differs from a line plot by showing sorted data values within each "bar," or stem. A stem-and-leaf plot is helpful for finding the mode and median of a data set. There are three basic steps to creating a plot.

1. *Locate the maximum and minimum values of the data and number the stems by a sensible interval between those values.* For example, the table of toaster prices in the margin lists a maximum price of $90 and a minimum price of $14. Because the greatest place value is tens, the stem values are the tens digits in the prices. The stem column is numbered from 1 to 9. (See Figure 1.)

2. *Place the leaves next to the corresponding stems.* The leaves in this plot are the digits in the ones place in the prices. The price of the Salton TO-6 is $40. A "0" is placed next to the "4" on the stem, indicating a value of $40. (See Figure 1.) The remaining leaves are placed to complete the plot. (See Figure 2.)

3. *Sort the leaves on each stem.* The finished stem-and-leaf plot for the toaster data is in Figure 3. Now it is easy to find the mode, which is the stem with the most leaves, $40. The median is the value of the middle leaf. You can count up from the bottom or down from the top. This data set has two middle prices of $39 and $40, so the median price is $(39 + 40)/2 = \$39.50$.

As with a line plot, bars can be drawn around the leaves so that the plot looks like a bar graph.

Stems (10s)	Leaves (1s)
9	
8	
7	
6	
5	
4	0
3	
2	
1	

Figure 1

Stems (10s)	Leaves (1s)
9	0
8	
7	
6	
5	0
4	0 5 0 7 5 0 8
3	8 9 2
2	5 5 7
1	8 8 4

Figure 2

Stems (10s)	Leaves (1s)
9	0
8	
7	
6	
5	0
4	0 0 0 5 5 7 8
3	2 8 9
2	5 5 7
1	4 8 8

Figure 3

For tips on managing students' construction of circle graphs, see Section 3.2.5: Measuring Tools.

Toaster Prices	
Brand and Model	**Price**
Salton TO-6	$40
Rowenta TO-38A	45
Toastmaster 740	38
Rival Wide Slot 9150	40
Proctor-Silex T-2830	47
Wide Mouth ET-9	45
Oster 3211-18A	40
Tefal 8443-40	50
Toastmaster 735A	25
Farberware 292	39
Proctor-Silex T33 OW	32
Panasonic NT-131	18
Conair Cuisine CT260	25
Sunbeam 20030	90
Kenmore 4808	18
Black & Decker T-215	27
Toastmaster B705A	14
Black & Decker T-235	48

Source: *Consumer Reports*, June 1990

NOTE: Aside from the costs of toasters in the example, you might spend several interesting minutes with students trying to interpret the model numbers.

chapter 12

Step Graphs

In *Sixth Grade Everyday Mathematics,* students use *step graphs* to represent situations in which changes occur in "jumps" rather than gradually. A step graph is a variation of a bar graph that is useful when the variable represented on the *x*-axis is a *continuous* quantity such as time. The variable displayed on the *y*-axis is *discrete,* jumping from one value to another. The different *y* values form the steps. The step graph in Figure A shows how the minimum hourly wage changed from 1938 to 1974. The number of years at a given wage varied, so the steps have different widths.

At an *x* value for which the *y* value jumps, the graph needs to indicate which *y* value goes with the *x* value. One way is to place a solid dot at the end of the step that belongs with the *x* value, and either *no* dot at the other end, as in Figure A, or an *open* dot, as in Figure B.

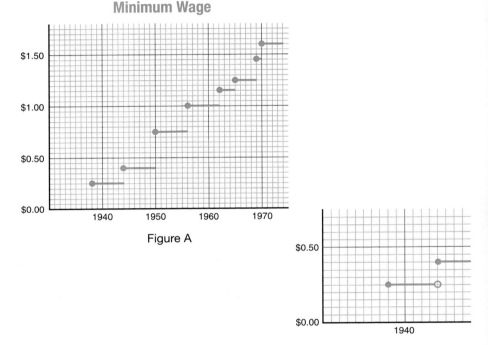

Figure A

Figure B

Venn Diagrams

Euler circles are used to model relationships among sets of things. A circle represents each set, and its *elements* are inside the circle. Three simple relationships of sets are described below.

Disjoint sets

Overlapping sets

A subset

- *Disjoint sets* have no common elements. For example, the sets {1, 2, 3} and {4, 5} are disjoint and are modeled by the first diagram in the margin.
- *Overlapping sets* share at least one element. For example, {1, 2, 3} overlaps {2, 4, 5} because they share the value 2, as shown in the second diagram.
- One set is a *subset* of another if it shares all its elements with another set. For example, {2, 3} is a subset of {1, 2, 3}, as shown in the third diagram.

The *intersection* of two or more sets is the set of elements found in *all* of the sets. In the previous examples, the intersection of the disjoint sets is empty. The intersection of the overlapping set is {2}. The intersection in the subset example is the same as the subset, {2, 3}.

An intersection helps answer questions about what is in one set *and* in one or more other sets. For the overlapping sets, the value 2 in the intersection answers the question *What numbers are in {1, 2, 3} and in {2, 4, 5}?*

The *union* of two or more sets is the set of elements found in *any* of the sets. For both the disjoint and overlapping sets, the union is {1, 2, 3, 4, 5}. The union in the subset example is {1, 2, 3}.

A union helps answer questions about what is in one set *or* in one or more other sets. For the overlapping sets, the values 1, 2, 3, 4, and 5 in the union answer the question *What numbers are in {1, 2, 3} or in {2, 4, 5}?*

Swiss mathematician Leonhard Euler developed Euler circles in the 1700s, and English logician John Venn improved on them more than 100 years later. Venn drew a rectangle around all the circles in a model to represent the *universal set U,* as shown in the margin. The universal set contains all the elements that make sense in a given problem situation, whether or not they are in a set of interest. Venn diagrams allow you to talk about elements not in any set represented by a circle. For example, if the universal set *U* is the set of all counting numbers:

- In the disjoint and overlapping examples in the margin, the region outside both circles, but inside the rectangle, represents all counting numbers greater than 5.
- In the subset example, the region outside the larger circle and inside the rectangle represents all counting numbers greater than 3.

The set of elements outside an Euler circle and inside the universal rectangle is called the *complement* of the set in the circle. A complement helps answer questions about what is *not* in one or more sets. For the overlapping sets of the example, the complement *counting numbers greater than 5* answers the question *What counting numbers are* not *in {1, 2, 3} or in {2, 4, 5}?*

Students in *Sixth Grade Everyday Mathematics* use Venn diagrams. Along with helping to analyze sets of data, Venn diagrams are useful tools in *set theory,* which students may study in secondary school. Among other things, set theory is useful in:

- Arithmetic to compare the number of whole numbers with the number of rational numbers;
- Algebra to define functions;
- Geometry to define sets of points or lines;
- Probability to compare successful occurrences of an event to all possible occurrences.

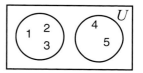

A Venn diagram showing disjoint sets

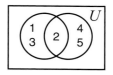

A Venn diagram showing overlapping sets

A Venn diagram showing a subset

12.2.4 Data Analysis

To many people, data analysis is synonymous with statistics. In *Everyday Mathematics*, however, this is not the case. For our purposes, *data analysis* means the examination and explanation of data. A good data analysis for a first grader can be summed up in a single well-phrased comment, such as *More than half the people in class are girls.* Statistics may be completely irrelevant in such an analysis. A *statistic* is simply a number used to describe some characteristic of one or more data sets and may not necessarily shed any particular light on the situation being examined.

One of the most common statistics is the *average,* or *mean,* of a set of data. Finding the mean requires adding a set of numbers and then dividing, tasks too difficult for most young students. Yet a lack of arithmetic skills should not bar students from data analysis of a more general nature. *Everyday Mathematics* provides activities for students to study two general attributes of data at increasingly sophisticated levels: useful *landmarks* within a data set and the *spread and pattern* of the set as a whole.

Landmarks of Data Sets

Once data have been organized, take every opportunity to have students discuss things they notice about the data. The following terms are commonly used to describe features of *ordered,* or *sorted,* data. These statistics are called *landmarks* in a data set because they show important features of the data.

- *Maximum* – the *largest* data value observed;
- *Minimum* – the *smallest* data value observed;
- *Range* – the *difference* between the maximum and minimum values;
- *Mode* – the *values observed most often;* the most popular or frequent data value or values;
- *Median* – the *middle data value* or, if there is an even number of values, the number halfway between the two middle data values;
- *Mean* or *average* – the sum of the values in a data set divided by the number of values in the set.

Students can use landmarks as reference points when they discuss other features of the data, just as cartographers use landmarks as reference points when they discuss the lay of the land on maps.

Note that finding a median may require averaging the two values nearest the middle. This is probably the first use of average that students encounter other than as a descriptive term for data found in newspapers, TV, and other media. Students often develop the idea of an average in the context of finding a median. The question *What do we do if there is no single middle value?* leads to an important discussion about what is a fair value between two others. One approach to finding that fair value is to point to a spot on a number line. Another is to guess a value and check if its differences from the two nearest values are equal. Some students may develop the common algorithm of averaging on their own.

NOTE: Some data sets may have no landmarks other than the mode. For example, a survey of hair color would not lead to a largest or average color, but just the most popular color among the people who are surveyed.

Spread and Pattern of Data Sets

Encourage students to talk about the spread and pattern, or distribution, of the data in tables or graphs. Terms such as *clump, hole, bump, way-out number,* and *all-alone number* are fine for describing how data values are arranged in a table or along a number line. Sometimes these characteristics can spark interesting explorations. Data that are clumped too closely together may suggest the need to ask a more discriminating question or to change the scale in a display.

The range of a data set can be useful in comparing the spreads of different sets of similar data. However, taken by itself it can hide the clumps or holes or singularities that make a data set really interesting.

In *Kindergarten* through *Third Grade Everyday Mathematics,* children discuss landmarks, spread, and patterns of *raw* data, that is, data as they are recorded, and of *sorted* data, or data that are numerically ordered or grouped by categories. Children also discuss their data *qualitatively* without using landmarks such as median or range, noting where the data bunch together or spread out. Exploring reasons for the *shape* of the data can lead to a better understanding of the data set in question and the data analysis process in general. Formal treatment of averages and other statistics begins in Grades 4 through 6. In Grade 6, students learn to play *Landmark Shark,* a game that provides practice in finding the range, mode, median, and mean of data sets.

Remember that a typical reason for analyzing data is to solve a problem, make a prediction, or arrive at a decision. It isn't wise to finish a data lesson before students have had an opportunity to summarize, discuss, report, or reach some sort of conclusion. Think of data analysis as a process with several stages: gathering the data, displaying the data, analyzing the data, and looking back. In some ways, the last step—to achieve closure—is most important.

Box-and-Whiskers Plots

Line plots, stem-and-leaf plots, and bar graphs all display the spread and pattern of a data set. In *Sixth Grade Everyday Mathematics,* students learn to make a more sophisticated display called a *box-and-whiskers plot,* or *box plot* for short. These plots show the spread of a data set using 5 landmarks: the *minimum, median,* and *maximum* described in an earlier section and the *lower* and *upper quartiles.*

NOTE: For more about minimum, median, and maximum, see "Landmarks of Data Sets" on page 168.

Quartiles are values that split an ordered set of data into four sections, each containing about a quarter of the data. Because it splits a data set in half, the median is also called the *middle quartile.* The *lower quartile* is the middle value of the data below the median. Similarly, the *upper quartile* is the middle value of the data above the median. In *Everyday Mathematics,* any data values equal to the median are excluded when finding the upper and lower quartiles. For this reason, each quartile may not contain exactly one quarter of the data. The lower quartile, median, and upper quartile are also called the first (Q1), second (Q2), and third (Q3) quartiles, respectively.

Calories in Chicken Snacks	
Chicken Snack	**Calories**
Brand A Chicken Nuggets	250
Brand A Chicken Strips	630
Brand B Chicken Tenders	250
Brand B Chicken Fries	260
Brand C Chicken Nuggets	230
Brand D Chicken Tenders	630
Brand D Popcorn Chicken	531
Brand E Chicken Strips	630
Brand F Chicken Strips	1,270
Brand G Popcorn Chicken	550
Brand H Chicken Strips	710
Brand I Chicken Rings	340

For actual brand names and products, see *source: http://www.acaloriecounter.com/fast-food.php*, November, 2007.

NOTE: There are several computer and web-based applications for drawing box plots.

Students are taught five basic steps for creating a box plot.

1. *Order the data and find the minimum, maximum, and median.* For example, the chicken snack data shown in the table in the margin has a minimum of 230 calories, a maximum of 1,270 calories, and a median of 540.5 calories.

2. *Find the lower and upper quartiles.* For the chicken snack data, the lower quartile $Q1 = 255$ calories and the upper quartile $Q3 = 630$ calories.

3. *Draw a number line with a convenient scale and long enough to include the 5 landmarks found in Steps 1 and 2.* The range of chicken snack data is $1,270 - 230 = 1,040$, or about 1,000. So we choose a scale of 100.

4. *Draw tick marks above the number line to mark the 5 landmarks.*

5. *Draw the box and whiskers.* Connect the tick marks at $Q1$ and $Q3$ with horizontal lines to form the box. Draw one whisker from the minimum tick mark to the $Q1$ box end. Draw the other whisker from the $Q3$ box end to the maximum tick mark.

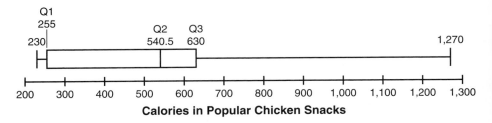

Calories in Popular Chicken Snacks

Without having to display every data value, a box plot elegantly summarizes the spread and pattern of a data set and allows the viewer to make generalizations. For example, although the chicken snacks vary over a wide range of calories, at least three quarters of them contain 630 calories or less, and the middle half of them (between the lower and upper quartiles) differ by only $630 - 255 = 375$ calories.

For any data set, this difference $Q3 - Q1$ is called the *interquartile range* (IQR). The interquartile range also refers to the interval between the lower and upper quartiles. So, for example, you can say that both of Brand D's snacks are in the interquartile range.

Box plots are commonly used to compare two or more data sets, or different categories of data within one set. For example, the side-by-side box plots below show how beef burgers compare to the chicken snacks.

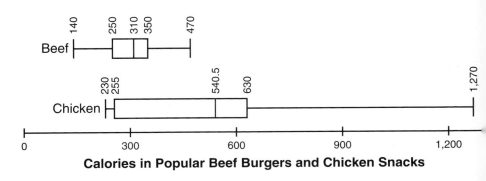

Calories in Popular Beef Burgers and Chicken Snacks

From the plots, it is easy to see the following:

- There is a much wider range of calories in chicken snacks than beef burgers.
- There are more calories in typical chicken snacks than typical beef burgers.
- The beef burger with the highest number of calories has fewer calories than half of the chicken snacks.

Mean Absolute Deviation (M.A.D.)

Range is a simple measure of the spread of a data set found by subtracting the minimum data value from the maximum data value, the *extremes* of the set. With a little more effort, you can find the *interquartile range,* a measure of the spread of the middle half of the data, as described in the previous section. With even more effort, you can calculate a measure of spread that accounts for how *every* data value compares to an average data value for the set.

The *mean absolute deviation* (m.a.d.) is the average distance between individual data values and the mean of those values. The difference of a data value and the mean is called the *deviation* of that value from the mean. To calculate the m.a.d.:

1. *Find the mean of the data values.* For example, column B of the spreadsheet in the margin contains the chicken snack calorie data from the previous section. The mean for this data, rounded to the nearest calorie, is 523, which is entered into column C.

2. *Find the deviation of each data value from the mean data value.* Column D shows these values for the chicken snack data, found by subtracting column C values from column B values.

3. *Find the absolute deviations.* Column E shows these absolute values of the deviations in column D.

4. *Find the mean of the absolute deviations.* In column E, this mean absolute deviation, to the nearest calorie, is 215.

Compared to the 215 m.a.d. for chicken snacks, the beef burger data used to make the box plot on the previous page has m.a.d = 62 calories. This shows that there is much less spread, or variation, in calories among beef burgers than among chicken snacks.

12.2.5 Mystery Plots

In the *mystery-plots* routine, fifth and sixth grade students match plots with the data that could have led to those plots. The routine requires students to act as consumers and critics of data and data displays, rather than as producers. It helps students begin to develop judgment, common sense, and a healthy skepticism regarding data and claims "based" on the data that they encounter daily.

> **NOTE:** Probably the most famous of this third type of measure of spread is *standard deviation*, which is beyond the scope of *Everyday Mathematics*.

◇	A	B Total Calories	C Mean Calories	D Deviation	E Absolute Deviation
1					
2		250	523	-273	273
3		630	523	107	107
4		250	523	-273	273
5		260	523	-263	263
6		230	523	-293	293
7		630	523	107	107
8		531	523	8	8
9		630	523	107	107
10		1,270	523	747	747
11		550	523	27	27
12		710	523	187	187
13		340	523	-183	183
14	Mean	523		0	215

> **NOTE:** The *median absolute deviation*, unfortunately also abbreviated *m.a.d.*, is the median of the distance between individual data values and the median of the data set.

chapter 12

▶ 12.3 Using Data and Probability

Everyday Mathematics is committed to developing mathematics through applications, and virtually any number drawn from an application is a piece of data. In *Fourth* through *Sixth Grade Everyday Mathematics,* students continue to collect, organize, and analyze data, and to explore probability. In Grades 4 and 5, most of the data analysis occurs within the context of the World Tour and American Tour, respectively. In Grade 6, students use data analysis and probability to explore contexts found in their *Student Reference Books* and presented in individual lessons.

You probably do not need specific suggestions for data sets as much as you need suggestions for applications in other subjects. Students are naturally interested in surveying topics like favorite colors, favorite foods, pets, and handedness. You know better than anyone else what interests your students, so use your best ideas and theirs. The goal is to have students understand data exploration as a *sensible process.* Can they ask sensible questions? Can they make sense of graphs? Can they make sensible graphs? If so, then they are intelligent users of data and probability.

▶ 12.4 Data and Chance Tools and Techniques

Along with measurement tools for collecting data discussed in Section 14.11 and the tables and graphs for representing data described in Section 12.2.3, random-number generators play an important role throughout all grades of *Everyday Mathematics,* especially in the context of games. In Grade 5, a Probability Meter is introduced, and in Grade 6, students use tree diagrams to explore situations with dependent events.

12.4.1 Random-Number Generators

Everyday Mathematics uses a variety of devices to generate random outcomes. These tools are integral to the success of many games. Often these devices do not generate perfectly random outcomes, but they are good enough for most purposes. Several tools for helping students generate random outcomes are listed below.

Calculator Random-Number Keys

Some scientific calculators have one or more keys for generating random numbers. See your owner's manual if have one you'd like to use. The Casio *fx*-55 has a random-number key RAN#. This key, and most like it, generate a decimal greater than or equal to 0 and less than 1. You can then multiply the number by an appropriate factor and truncate (ignore) the decimal part. For example, to generate numbers from 0 through 9, multiply by 10 and truncate. If a calculator generates 0.659, you would get 10 * 0.659 = 6.59, which rounds down to 6.

NOTE: Calculator random numbers are more correctly called "pseudo-random" numbers. The machine needs an algorithm to carry out any calculation, so it uses one for generating numbers. However, most pseudo-random algorithms are sophisticated enough for *Everyday Mathematics* and most other educational uses. Statistically, it can be shown that the numbers resulting from using a calculator random-number generator are as unpredictable as anyone might practically need and certainly as unpredictable as those generated by any of the other methods discussed in this section.

Dice

Use a regular die to generate the numbers 1 through 6. Use a polyhedral die (with 12 or 20 sides) to extend the range of numbers to be generated. Note that rolling more than one die and adding the resulting numbers of dots produces a nonuniform distribution of possible outcomes. For example, if you roll two standard dice, the 36 possible ways for them to land are shown below. Only one of the 36 has a sum of 2 (two 1s), but six of the 36 have a sum of 7 {[1,6], [2,5], [3,4], [4,3], [5,2], and [6,1]}. Therefore, the chance of rolling a sum of 7 is much greater than the chance of rolling a sum of 2. This is what is meant by a "nonuniform distribution." Shaking a die in a cup may lead to slightly more random results than throwing the die by hand.

					6+1					
				5+1	5+2	6+2				
			4+1	4+2	4+3	5+3	6+3			
		3+1	3+2	3+3	3+4	4+4	5+4	6+4		
	2+1	2+2	2+3	2+4	2+5	3+5	4+5	5+5	6+5	
1+1	1+2	1+3	1+4	1+5	1+6	2+6	3+6	4+6	5+6	6+6
2	3	4	5	6	7	8	9	10	11	12

Sums of two dice

Egg Cartons

Label each egg-carton cup with a number. For example, you might label the cups 0 through 11. Place one or more pennies, beans, or centimeter cubes inside the carton, close the lid, shake the carton, and then open it to see in which cups the objects have landed. Randomness depends on how thoroughly the carton is shaken. This is probably the least random method of the list.

The Everything Math Deck

This deck of cards consists of four sets of number cards 0 through 10 and one set of number cards 11 through 20. Fractions are on the reverse side of the 0 through 10 cards. You can limit the range of numbers to be generated simply by removing some of the cards from the deck. For a uniform distribution of numbers 0 through 20, for example, use only one set of 0 through 10 cards and the set of 11 through 20 cards. To use the cards, simply shuffle and draw. The better the shuffle, the more unpredictable the draw will be.

Spinners

Spinners are used throughout *Everyday Mathematics,* usually in games. They are extremely useful for helping students visualize the idea of chance. There are many commercially available spinners, although it is not necessary to purchase them. Students can use a pencil and paper clip with a spinner mat as shown in the margin. Use either a large (about 2-inch) or a standard (about 1-inch) paper clip for the part that spins. The larger size is preferred because it spins more easily. Make a mark, as a pointer, at one end of the paper clip using a permanent felt-tip marker.

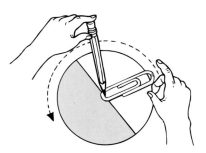

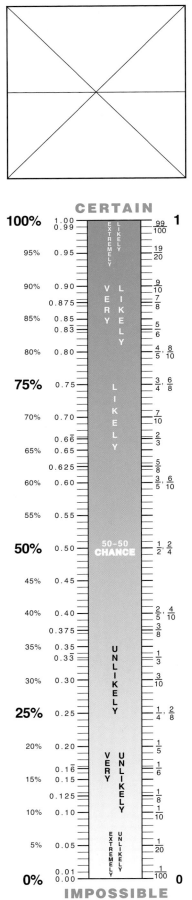

The spinning mat may be drawn on cardstock or paper. Sometimes a mat is supplied as a master or journal page. If you make your own mat, start with a circle or square large enough to accomodate the paper clip. Mark the center of the circle, choose the number and sizes of the regions, and then measure and draw the appropriate angles. For example, the central angles of six equal regions would each measure 360°/6 = 60°. You can use shapes other than circles for the spinner, and the regions do not have to be the same size, as in the square mat in the margin.

Before spinning, tape the mat to a level surface. You need only two small pieces of tape, one at the top and one at the bottom. To spin, place the tip of a pen or pencil on the center of the circle and within the paper clip as shown in the diagram on page 171. Flick the paper clip about halfway between the center of the circle and the tip of the paper clip, as flicking the paper clip near the pointer end will generate less of a spin.

Standard Playing Cards

Use the 2 through 9 cards, the aces for 1s, and the queens for 0s. Draw one card to get a 1 in 10 chance for each one of the digits 0 through 9. Draw two cards to make 2-digit numbers, three cards for 3-digit numbers, and so on. If more than one card is drawn, you will need to decide whether to replace it before another card is drawn. If the first card is replaced in the deck and the deck is reshuffled, the probability will remain the same for each draw. If the card is not replaced, the chance of drawing that digit decreases.

12.4.2 Probability Meter

Everyday Mathematics uses a Probability Meter to show probabilities expressed as fractions, decimals, and percents. It is part of a number line from 0 to 1 that is divided into 100 equal parts. The unit interval for regularly-spaced tick marks is $\frac{1}{100}$ (or 0.01 or 1%) of the Probability Meter. Other interesting fractions, decimals, and percents are also shown. In the interior of the Probability Meter are phrases such as *50-50 chance, unlikely, impossible,* and *extremely likely* that correspond to the numerical figures on the meter.

The Probability Meter is introduced in *Fifth Grade Everyday Mathematics* and is used thereafter to help students develop their understanding of the language of chance by correlating their use of informal phrases with precise locations on the meter. It is used in various lessons to record probabilities and to compare probabilities expressed as fractions, decimals, and percents. The Probability Meter can also be used as a reference for equivalent names for rational numbers.

12.4.3 Tree Diagrams

In *Sixth Grade Everyday Mathematics,* students investigate situations in which a sequence of events has subsequent events that depend on the outcomes of previous events. In other words, the events are *not independent. Tree diagrams* are models to help visualize such situations. For example, Figure 1 shows a maze through which 60 people are going to walk. Each person makes two decisions during the journey—which path to take at the first junction, and which to take at the second. The problem is to determine how many people are expected to end up in Room A and how many in Room B.

To model this situation, you can draw a *tree diagram* like the one in Figure 2. The rectangles represent the junctions in the maze where people make a decision. The number in the rectangle is the number of people expected to be at that point in the maze if decisions are made randomly. All 60 people arrive at the first junction, where half are expected to go to the right and half to the left. This leaves 30 people expected to arrive at the next two junctions, and so on.

The numbers in the last row of boxes of the tree diagram represent the number of people expected to reach Rooms A and B by each of the possible paths. In all, 10 + 15 = 25 people are expected to end up in Room A and 10 + 10 + 15 = 35 in Room B.

Tree diagrams are a first step toward using *probability trees*. The probability tree in Figure 3 is for the maze problem above. In a probability tree, the *vertices,* or *nodes,* represent events. In Figure 3, the vertices represent choices of paths. Each *branch* between vertices is labeled with the probability of a particular outcome. In the example, the probability that someone will take either path from the first junction is $\frac{1}{2}$.

The last row of fractions in the tree gives the probability of taking each of the five possible paths. For example, the probability that someone will take the left-most path is $\frac{1}{6}$. These path probabilities can also be calculated using the tree diagram. Ten of 60, or $\frac{1}{6}$, of the people are expected to take the left-most path to Room B; 15 of 60, or $\frac{1}{4}$, of them are expected to take the right-most path to Room B.

To generalize, the probability tree indicates that $\frac{1}{2}$ of any number of people are expected to take the first left branch, and $\frac{1}{3}$ of that $\frac{1}{2}$ are likely to take the next left branch. So $\frac{1}{3}$ of $\frac{1}{2}$, or $\frac{1}{3} * \frac{1}{2} = \frac{1}{6}$, of the people are expected to take the left-most path. This calculation is the same for each path—the probability that a person will take a path is the product of the probabilities of taking each branch on the path.

Given any number of people entering the maze, the values in the last row of the probability tree let you predict how many of them will wind up at the end of any path. The sum of the probabilities in the last row is 1, meaning all people entering the maze will get to the end of some path.

Students in *Sixth Grade Everyday Mathematics* use probability trees to investigate maze problems, coin-flipping problems, and the probabilities of winning games of chance. They also use trees to help criticize the fairness of games and to design fair games of their own.

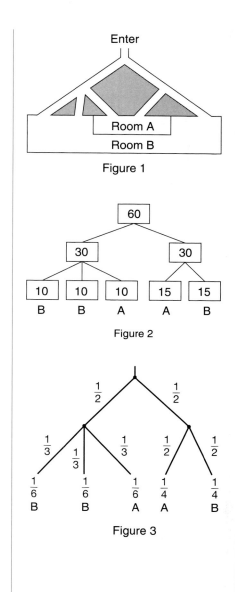

Figure 1

Figure 2

Figure 3

NOTE: In 1657, Dutch mathematician Christian Huygens introduced probability trees in the first published book on probability theory.

13 Geometry

Geometry, the study of visual patterns of objects in space, is a natural and deeply intuitive part of mathematics for children. From birth, children need to make sense of forms and shapes, such as a mother's face, their own bodies, shapes that move, shapes that don't, curved things, and sharp things. Then, with a wealth of informal knowledge about spatial objects, they come to school. The teacher's role is first to acknowledge and value what children already know and then to help them "notice" what they see and to organize their perceptions into a meaningful system.

The word *geometry* derives from Greek words for "earth" and "measure," which gives a clue about the first geometric activity of humans. The earliest records of geometric thinking, from the Egyptians, Babylonians, and Chinese, confirm that it centered on solving practical problems, such as laying out fields, finding areas and volumes, and constructing houses and temples.

The Greeks are credited with formalizing geometry. In high school, most of us encountered the geometry of Euclid with its axioms and theorems. And, for many, this was a mystifying experience. This was due in part to the inappropriate structure and content of many of these geometry courses—a situation that is slowly changing as new approaches to secondary school geometry instruction are being developed. But, an equally compelling reason is that many students have little or no formal experience with geometry prior to their high school courses. The *Everyday Mathematics* curriculum places significant emphasis on this part of mathematics beginning in Kindergarten.

Students investigate geometry through many hands-on experiences, including manipulating pattern blocks; building shapes with straws; tracing, cutting out, and folding shapes; forming figures on geoboards; and constructing figures with compasses, straightedges, and protractors.

–Adapted from *Everyday Teaching for Everyday Mathematics*™ by Sheila Sconiers

This chapter first describes common 1-, 2-, and 3-dimensional objects. Next, it discusses some operations on these objects and some relationships that the objects have with one another. Then it briefly discusses tessellations, topology, and geometric constructions. The chapter concludes with an outline of the approach used in *Everyday Mathematics* for teaching geometry.

▶ 13.1 Dimension

Dimension is a tricky word. One meaning refers to the size of an object, as in the dimensions of a room or of a piece of paper; another meaning, the one implicit in terms like *3-dimensional,* refers to how much information is required to specify an exact location. For example, a checkerboard is *2-dimensional* because two pieces of information can specify a particular square: its row and its column. A line is *1-dimensional* because a point on it can be located using one number, its distance from an origin. An opera house is *3-dimensional* because a seat in it can be determined using a row number, a seat number, and a floor level.

We live in 3-dimensional space, *3-D space.* The objects that constitute our physical experience are all 3-dimensional. Objects in other dimensions, such as lines, triangles, and circles, are abstractions that do not physically exist in the way that dogs, cellular telephones, and pencils exist. Even the checkerboard, which was called 2-dimensional a moment ago, is really 3-dimensional; it has length, width, and depth. The 2-dimensional surface of the checkerboard is an abstraction.

Many 1- and 2-dimensional abstractions are so useful in the 3-dimensional world that we name them and study their properties. You can model them with wood or plastic, with drawings, and with

NOTE: Both *3-D* and *3D* are widely used shorthand for 3-dimensional. If you ever search the Web for information about 3-D objects, try both.

NOTE: Although the objects of geometry are presented here from less complicated to more complicated, students encounter them in the opposite order in *Everyday Mathematics,* a more developmentally appropriate order in which 1- and 2-dimensional objects are introduced informally as parts of 3-D objects. For example, a line segment is modeled by an edge of a box and a rectangle by four adjoining edges of a box. For more information on developmental stages in the learning of geometry, see Section 13.12.1: The van Hiele Levels.

● ● ● ·

Models of points

NOTE: *Synthetic* geometry is the study of geometric objects without concern for their position on a line, in a plane, or in space. *Analytic* geometry is the study of geometric objects on a number line, coordinate plane, or 3-D coordinate grid.

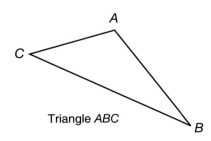

Triangle *ABC*

For more on coordinate geometry, see Section 15.3: Coordinate Systems.

special manipulatives. But the models are always 3-dimensional, not the "real" thing. Even a drawing made with ink has length, width, and depth.

The following sections discuss objects in dimensions 0 through 3 and describe how students examine them in *Everyday Mathematics* activities.

▶ 13.2 Points

Point is an undefined term in geometry, so no one can say exactly what it is. Nevertheless, most people have some idea of what a point is and what it is not. A point cannot be broken into pieces; it is one indivisible thing and so it has 0 dimensions. Because a point has no parts, no information is needed to specify which part of a point is being referred to; it cannot be measured.

You can model a point by drawing a *dot* on a piece of paper. If you get a finer pen and draw a smaller dot, then you have a better model of a point. But no matter how small you make your dot and no matter how fine your pen's tip, you still cannot draw a true point. Even the smallest dot of ink has length, width, and depth, and therefore, it is not a point.

Another way to think about a point is as a *location,* or an exact position. On a map or other reference frame, a point marks where something is. For example, there is a point on a number line that is exactly 3 units from the origin. In fact, there are two such points, one at +3 and one at −3. In *Kindergarten Everyday Mathematics,* children use points as locations when they follow maps and count steps to get from one classroom to another. Children also locate points on number lines beginning in Kindergarten. *Length* is the distance between two points, so children imagine points as locations on objects every time they measure a height, width, or depth. Points on maps are used to estimate distances, and children learn about map scale beginning in Grade 3.

Sometimes a location is considered a point, but its position is not important. For example, the vertices (corners) of a polygon are the points where two sides meet, but unless the polygon is on a coordinate system, the position of a vertex is of little interest. Yet the fact that the point is a vertex *is* interesting, because the vertex often receives a name and that name contributes to a name for the whole polygon. On geometric objects, points are usually named with capital letters such as point *A,* point *B,* and so on. Naming geometric figures using the names of points begins in Grade 2, for example, "triangle *ABC.*"

In analytic geometry, points correspond to numbers on a number line, ordered pairs of numbers on a coordinate plane, and ordered triples of numbers in coordinate space. Graphing ordered pairs begins in third grade. Applications of ordered pairs, such as latitude and longitude, appear in Grades 4 through 6. The idea of a function as a set of ordered pairs can be visualized by plotting the pairs on a coordinate graph.

There are other uses and models of points not discussed here. The aim is simply to give you some ways to think about points and to help you realize how often they are used in the 3-dimensional world.

▶ 13.3 Lines, Segments, and Rays

Line is another undefined term, but, again, one for which most people have good intuition. You can model a line with a pen and ink, by folding a piece of paper, or by pulling a piece of string taut.

A *line* is made up of infinitely many points extending forever in opposite directions. "Forever" is an important word here; it means that a line has no ends. If you started marking off unit intervals on a line, you would never finish, no matter how many intervals you marked. One-dimensional figures on a line are called *linear figures*. Zero-dimensional points make up 1-dimensional figures.

A line is 1-dimensional in that one number is enough to specify any point on a line relative to an origin. One-dimensional objects on a line have length, but no width or depth.

A drawing of a line has arrowheads on its "ends" to indicate that it does not stop. A line is named using any two points on it, as in line *AB* in the margin. Shorthand for "line *AB*" is $\overleftrightarrow{AB}$.

Now think about any two points on a line. No matter how close together they are, there are infinitely many points on the line between them. Mathematicians say lines are *dense*, meaning that between any two points on a line there is always another point. The fact that each point on a line can be associated with a number is a key to understanding why our real-number system does not run dry. Just as there is always a point between any two points on a line, there is always a number between any two numbers.

A *line segment*, or *segment* for short, is a part of a line between and including two different *endpoints*. Although you cannot measure the length of a line, a segment has a finite length that you can approximate. A segment is labeled using any two points on it, as in line segment *CD* in the margin. Shorthand for "line segment *CD*" is $\overline{CD}$.

A *ray* is a part of a line with only one endpoint and all the points on the line to one side of the point. For this reason, rays are sometimes called *half-lines*. Like a line, a ray has no measure. A drawing of a ray has an arrowhead at the "end" opposite its endpoint. A ray is labeled using the name of the endpoint and another point on it, as in ray *EF* in the margin. Shorthand for "ray *EF*" is $\overrightarrow{EF}$.

Everyday Mathematics is consistent about using arrowheads in drawings of lines and rays. Encourage students to use them as well. However, it is not important for them to use the shorthand names for lines, segments, and rays.

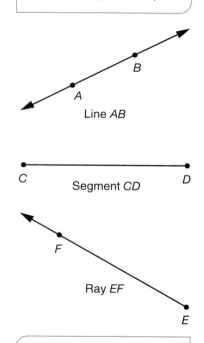

NOTE: In formal Euclidean geometry, *line* is an undefined term. The informal definition used in *Everyday Mathematics* builds on a common intuition that lines go on forever in a fixed direction. In that spirit, the shortest segment between any two points on a line determines the line's direction, or the way it is oriented in a plane or space.

Line *AB*

Segment *CD*

Ray *EF*

NOTE: Computer geometry packages such as the *Geometer's Sketchpad*® and *Cabri Geometry*™ do not place arrowheads on lines. It is not practical to draw arrowheads in these packages because you can "grab" lines and rays with a cursor and move them around. What you see, then, are models for rays and lines that extend to the edge of the screen and, in your mind's eye, beyond.

► 13.4 Planes and Plane Figures

Plane is yet another undefined geometric term for which most people have some intuition. A tabletop, a smooth floor, and the surface of a calm body of water all suggest planes.

A *plane* extends forever in every direction in two dimensions. There are infinitely many points and infinitely many lines in a plane. Two-dimensional objects that are entirely contained in a plane are called *plane figures* or *planar figures*. Just as 0-dimensional points make up 1-dimensional objects like lines, both 0-dimensional and 1-dimensional objects make up plane figures.

A plane is 2-dimensional in that two numbers can specify any point in a plane relative to an origin. Two-dimensional objects in a plane have length and width, but no depth. Like a line, a plane cannot be measured.

The next three sections discuss some of the common planar figures that students explore in *Everyday Mathematics:* angles, polygons, and circles.

13.4.1 Angles and Rotations

In mathematics, an *angle* consists of two rays that have the same endpoint, called the *vertex* of the angle. The rays are called the *sides* of the angle. An angle usually takes the name of its vertex, as in angle *A* below. Sometimes the name of an angle contains three points—a point on one ray, the vertex, and a point on the other ray, as in angle *BAC* below. And sometimes an angle is named with a number in the region between the rays, as in angles 1 and 2 below. Shorthand for "angle *A*" is ∠*A*.

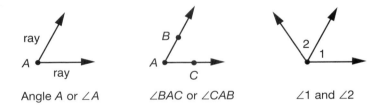

Angle *A* or ∠*A*   ∠*BAC* or ∠*CAB*   ∠1 and ∠2

Sometimes it is convenient to think of the sides of an angle as line segments, for example, "the angles of a square," but strictly speaking, the sides of an angle are rays, each continuing without end. In *Everyday Mathematics,* angles are often modeled using segments because they are introduced in Grade 1 as features of solids and in Grades 2 and 3 as features of polygons. In Grades 4 through 6, angles are studied as features of polygons and polyhedrons.

It is often useful to think of an angle as being formed by starting with the two rays or segments pointing in the same direction and then rotating one ray or segment around the common endpoint. In first grade, children model angles in this manner by bending a straw and rotating one of the sides around the bend.

chapter 13

Angles are most commonly measured in *degrees*. One complete rotation, a full circle, measures 360 degrees. Shorthand for "360 degrees" is 360°. If a child begins with both parts of a bent straw together and then rotates one of the parts 1 quarter of the way around the bend, the resulting figure models an angle of 360°/4 = 90°. If the rotation continues another 1 quarter of the way around the bend, the straw is straight and models an angle of 180°. A further 1-quarter rotation models an angle of 270°. A final 1-quarter rotation returns the straw to its starting position, an angle of 360°, which looks like an angle of 0°.

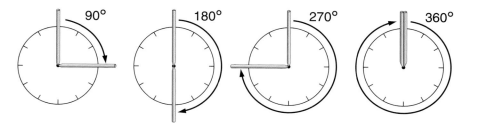

An analog clock also shows angles. At 12 o'clock, the overlapping hands model an angle of 0° or 360°; at 3 o'clock, an angle of 90° or 270°; at 6 o'clock, an angle of 180°; and at 9 o'clock an angle of 270° or 90°.

Angles are categorized according to their measures as follows:

- An *acute* angle measures less than 90°.
- A *right* angle measures 90°.
- An *obtuse* angle measures between 90° and 180°.
- A *straight* angle measures 180°.
- A *reflex* angle measures between 180° and 360°.

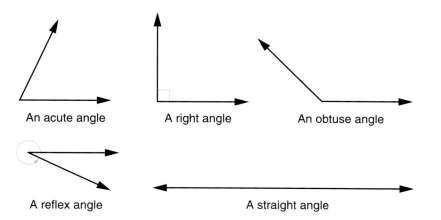

An acute angle   A right angle   An obtuse angle

A reflex angle   A straight angle

Children in Grades 1 through 3 are not expected to learn the categories of angles, but they manipulate angles of each category. Students in Grades 4 through 6 examine angles more closely as they measure

NOTE: The region between the rays of an angle is not part of the angle. If the angle measures between 0° and 180°, the region is called the *interior of the angle*. However, people commonly refer to both the angle proper and its interior as "the angle," and you should not hold students responsible for knowing the difference.

Number of Angles	Name
3	triangle
4	quadrangle or quadrilateral
5	pentagon
6	hexagon
7	heptagon
8	octagon
9	nonagon
10	decagon
12	dodecagon

Names for polygons

NOTE: Unlike quadrangles, which are also called quadrilaterals, triangles are not usually called "trilaterals."

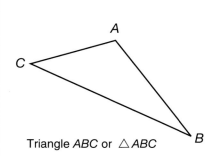

Triangle *ABC* or △*ABC*

angles with protractors, construct angles with a compass and straightedge, and learn about categories and relationships of angles.

13.4.2 Polygons (*n*-gons)

A *polygon* is a 2-dimensional figure formed by three or more line segments that meet only at their endpoints to make a closed path. The sides may not cross one another. The segments are the *sides* of the polygon. The endpoints are *vertices,* or *corners.* Each pair of adjacent sides defines an interior *angle of the polygon.*

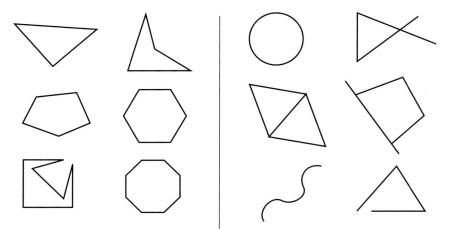

Polygons   Not polygons

The term *polygon* comes from the Greek *polu-,* "many," and *-gonon,* "angled." Polygons are named according to the number of angles (or sides or vertices) they have. A 12-gon is a polygon with 12 sides. In general, an n-*gon* is a polygon with *n* sides.

A dodecagon, or 12-gon

A few *n*-gons have their own names, as shown in the table in the margin. Children in Grade 3 classify triangles and quadrilaterals by special features such as parallel sides, right angles, and sides or angles of equal measure. In *Fourth* through *Sixth Grade Everyday Mathematics,* the exploration of polygons is extended to include transformations of polygons by reflections, rotations, and translations (flips, turns, and slides), and classifications of polygons as regular, convex, and concave. Polygons are also studied in the coordinate plane as part of analytic, or coordinate, geometry.

Triangles

A *triangle* is a 3-sided polygon. A triangle is usually named for its three vertices as in triangle *ABC.* Shorthand for "triangle *ABC*" is △*ABC*.

Triangles may be classified in three ways according to side lengths.

- A *scalene triangle* has no two sides with the same length.

A scalene triangle

- An *isosceles triangle* has two sides of equal length. This makes two of the angles equal in measure.
- An *equilateral triangle* has all three sides of equal length. This makes all the angles equal in measure (60° each), so an equilateral triangle is also an *equiangular triangle*. Every equilateral triangle is also an isosceles triangle.

An isosceles triangle

An equilateral triangle

A triangle may also be classified according to its angles.

- An acute triangle has every angle measure less than 90°.
- A right triangle has a right angle.
- An obtuse triangle has an angle with measure greater than 90°.

An acute triangle   A right triangle   An obtuse triangle

Any triangle can be given two names, one for its sides and the other for its angles. Some examples are shown below.

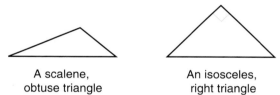

A scalene, obtuse triangle   An isosceles, right triangle   An equilateral, or equiangular, triangle

Over the course of Kindergarten through Grade 3, children learn some of the triangle categories, label vertices, write and read names for triangles, and write and read names for their sides. In Grades 4 through 6, students find areas of triangles, use triangles in tessellations, and represent triangles analytically by graphing them in the coordinate plane. In Grade 6, they learn about one of the most profound discoveries in the history of mathematics, the Pythagorean theorem.

The Pythagorean Theorem

In a right triangle, the side opposite the right angle is called the *hypotenuse* of the triangle. The other two sides are called *legs*. In any right triangle, like the one in the margin, if a and b are the lengths of the legs and c is the length of the hypotenuse, then $a^2 + b^2 = c^2$. This very useful and celebrated property of right triangles is called the *Pythagorean theorem*. The following passage is from the Grade 6 *Student Reference Book*.

> Nobody knows when this relationship was first discovered. The Babylonians, Egyptians, and Chinese knew of it before the Greeks. But Pythagoras, a Greek philosopher born about 572 B.C., was the first person to prove that the relationship is true for any right triangle. It is called a *theorem* because it is a statement that has been proved.

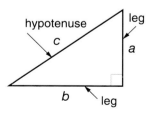

hypotenuse   leg
c a
b leg

A Chinese proof of the Pythagorean theorem (written about A.D. 40) is shown below. Two identical squares, each with sides of length $a + b$, are partitioned in different ways.

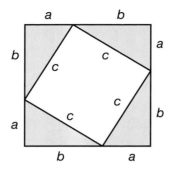

The large square contains four identical right triangles and one square whose area is $c * c = c^2$.

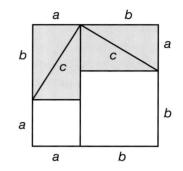

The large square contains four identical right triangles and two squares whose areas are a^2 and b^2.

The four right triangles inside each square all have the same area. Therefore, the area of the large square (c^2) inside the first square must be equal to the total area of the two smaller squares ($a^2 + b^2$) that are inside the second square; that is, c^2 must equal $a^2 + b^2$.

The famous mathematical problem solver George Polya (1990) preferred the slightly different version of the second square shown in the margin. He liked the position of the triangles because it highlighted the squares of the legs of the triangle.

In 1940, E. S. Loomis (1968) catalogued 370 different proofs of the Pythagorean theorem, including one in 1876 by the 20th President of the United States, James A. Garfield. There may well be more to add to Loomis's list by now.

References on the Pythagorean theorem

Loomis, E. S. (1968). *The Pythagorean Proposition.* Reston, VA: National Council of Teachers of Mathematics.

Polya, G. (1990). *Mathematics and Plausible Reasoning, Volume 1: Induction and Analogy in Mathematics.* Princeton, NJ: Princeton University Press.

Quadrangles (Quadrilaterals)

A *quadrangle,* or *quadrilateral,* is a 4-sided polygon. *Diagonals* of a quadrangle are line segments connecting opposite vertices. Some quadrangles have special features and names.

- A *trapezoid* is a quadrangle with exactly one pair of parallel sides. In an *isosceles trapezoid,* the two nonparallel sides are the same length.

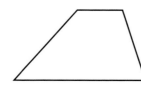

A trapezoid   An isosceles trapezoid

For an application of the Pythagorean theorem to find distances, see Section 15.3.2: 2- and 3-Dimensional Coordinate Systems.

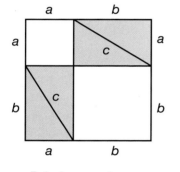
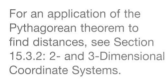

Polya's second square

chapter 13

- A *kite* is a quadrilateral with two adjacent sides of one length and two other sides of a different length. The diagonals of a kite are perpendicular.

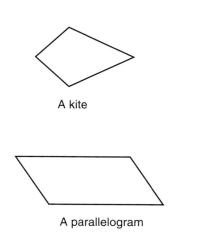

A kite

- A *parallelogram* is a quadrangle with two pairs of parallel sides. Both parallelograms and kites have pairs of equal-length sides, but in kites the equal-length sides are adjacent, not opposite. The diagonals of a parallelogram intersect at their midpoints, or *bisect* each other.

A parallelogram

- A *rhombus* is a parallelogram with all sides the same length. The diagonals of a rhombus bisect each other and are perpendicular.

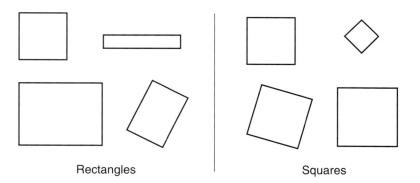

Rhombuses

- A *rectangle* is a parallelogram in which all angles are right angles. Diagonals of a rectangle are equal in length.

- A *square* is a rectangle with all sides the same length. It is also a rhombus with four right angles. Diagonals of a square are equal in length, bisect each other, and intersect at right angles.

Rectangles   Squares

Some definitions depend on previously defined quadrangles. For example, a rectangle is first a parallelogram, then a parallelogram with right angles. This means that all the features and properties of parallelograms are also features and properties of rectangles, along with new ones specific to rectangles.

The diagram on the next page shows the *Everyday Mathematics hierarchy of quadrangles*. Pick any quadrangle in the hierarchy. It has all the properties of any quadrangle on a path leading to it. For example, a square is a rectangle, a rhombus, a parallelogram, and a quadrangle.

NOTE: If students have trouble identifying equal-length sides in polygons, you and they can mark the sides with hash marks as shown below. Equal-length sides have equal numbers of hash marks.

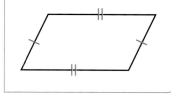

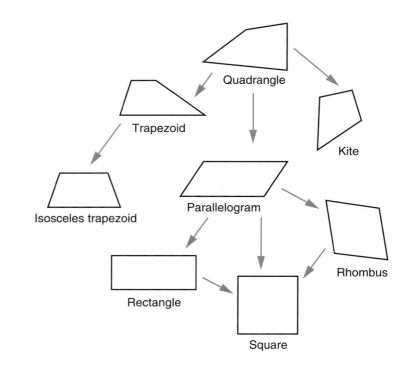

In Grade 3, children find areas of rectangles and squares. In Grades 5 and 6, students learn to formulate clear definitions of quadrangles, find areas of parallelograms, and use quadrilaterals in tessellations and transformations. Features of quadrangles are also important to student investigations into surface areas and volumes of solids.

Other Features of Polygons

Although children in Kindergarten through Grade 3 explore polygons with the following features, defining them at that time is not especially helpful. In Grades 4 through 6, the terminology becomes more useful, especially in compass-and-straightedge constructions and when talking about tessellations.

- A *regular polygon* is a polygon in which all sides are the same length and all angles have the same measure. If a polygon is regular, it is possible to draw a circle that passes through all its vertices. Equilateral triangles and squares are regular polygons.

- A *convex polygon* is a polygon on which no two points can be connected with a line segment that passes outside the polygon. Each angle of a convex polygon measures less than 180°.

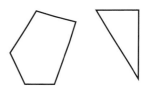

Convex polygons

- A *concave,* or *nonconvex, polygon* is a polygon that is not convex. At least one line segment drawn to connect points on two different sides contains at least one point that is outside the polygon. At least one angle of a concave polygon has a measure greater than 180°.

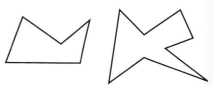

Concave, or nonconvex, polygons

Most students have little difficulty distinguishing convex and nonconvex polygons, but they may give crude explanations such as *The hexagon is not convex because these two sides bend in*. Try to use more precise definitions yourself, but do not insist that students master them.

13.4.3 Circles and Pi (π)

A *circle* consists of all the points in a plane that are the same distance from a given point in the plane called the *center* of the circle. Many physical objects have circular shapes, although none are likely to be perfectly circular. Features of a circle include the following:

- A *radius* is a segment connecting the center of a circle and any point on the circle. The radius is also the length of that segment.
- A *chord* is a segment with endpoints on a circle.
- A *diameter* is a chord through the center of a circle. The diameter is also the length of such a chord. The diameter of a circle is twice its radius.
- The *circumference* is the distance around a circle, or its perimeter.

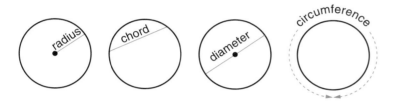

Another way to think of a circle is as a regular *n*-gon where *n* is infinitely large. For example, start with a square, not a very good approximation of a circle, but a start. Next, double the number of sides of the square to obtain a regular octagon; this is closer to a circle. Then double the number of sides again to obtain a regular 16-gon; this is closer still. Doubling a few more times would give a figure that could be distinguished from a circle only with a magnifying glass. Double infinitely many times and the result would actually be a circle.

Pi is the ratio of the circumference of a circle to its diameter. This ratio, represented by the Greek letter π, is the same for all circles. If *C* is the circumference and *d* is the diameter of a circle, then:

$$\frac{C}{d} = \pi \qquad \text{or} \qquad C = \pi d$$

In third grade, children begin an inquiry into the relationship between the diameter and the circumference of a circle. They roll food cans to find circumferences, measure across the tops of the cans to find diameters, and display the results in a table. From these results, they discover that the circumference of a circle is consistently about 3 times its diameter. This is a first approximation of π, and a pretty good approximation at that.

Pi is also the ratio of the area *A* of a circle to the square of its radius *r*:

$$\frac{A}{r^2} = \pi \qquad \text{or} \qquad A = \pi r^2$$

Pi is an irrational number; its decimal does not repeat and never ends. Two common approximations for pi are 3.14 and $\frac{22}{7}$.

NOTE: As with angles and polygons, the interior of a circle is not part of the circle itself. Sometimes the circle and its interior are together called a *disk*, or a *circular region*. A *sector* is part of a disk outlined by two radii and an *arc* of the circle connecting the endpoints of the radii. As with the other figures, do not expect students to make this distinction.

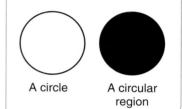

A circle   A circular region

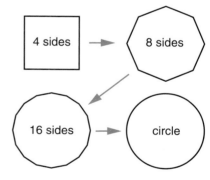

NOTE: Another definition of the *circumference* of a circle is the limit of the perimeter of a regular *n*-gon as *n* gets infinitely large.

For more information, see Section 9.5: Irrational Numbers.

chapter 13

Mountains of Pi

The earliest known reference to π occurs in an Egyptian papyrus scroll written around 1650 B.C. by a scribe named Ahmes. He found the area of a circle using a rough approximation of π. Around 200 B.C., Archimedes of Syracuse (in Sicily, then a Greek colony) found that π is between $3\frac{10}{71}$ and $3\frac{1}{7}$. Little more was learned about π until the 17th century, when new formulas were discovered. Ludolph van Ceulen, a German mathematician, spent most of his life calculating π to 35 decimal places. Now most inexpensive calculators display π to 7 or 9 decimal places.

Today, investigations of π often involve powerful computers. Such calculations have been a standard task for each new generation of computers. In 1949, π was calculated to 37,000 places on ENIAC, one of the first computers. Later, π was computed to 100,000 digits on an IBM 7090 computer and in 1981 to 2 million digits on an NEC supercomputer. In the next few years, these calculations were extended to 17.5 million digits, then 34 million, then past 200 million, and then in 1989 to more than 1 billion digits. As of December 2002, the laboratory of Dr. Yasumasa Kanada of the University of Tokyo held the world record of 1.2411 *trillion* digits.

The article "The Mountains of Pi" by Richard Preston relates the fascinating history of π and why it has captivated mathematicians for thousands of years. According to the article:

> The decimal for pi goes on forever, so the number cannot be written with complete accuracy: 3.14159265358979323846264338327950288419 7 . . . is only an approximation . . . . No apparent pattern emerges in the succession of digits . . . . They do not repeat periodically, seeming to pop up by blind chance, lacking any perceivable order, rule, reason, or design . . . .

NOTE: Preston, R. (1992). "The Mountains of Pi." *The New Yorker,* March 2, 1992, pp. 36–67.

"The Mountains of Pi" tells the story of two mathematicians, David and Gregory Chudnovsky, who calculated π to more than 2 billion digits on a computer of their own design, which they built in Gregory's apartment using mail-order parts. Calculating π to so many digits not only tests the power of new supercomputers, but also continues the search for patterns in the digits—a search that, so far, has yielded no results. As the article states:

> [The Chudnovskys] wonder whether the digits contain a hidden rule, as yet unseen architecture, close to the mind of God . . . . If we were to explore the digits of π far enough, they might resolve into a breathtaking numerical pattern . . . and it might mean something . . . . On the other hand, the digits of π may ramble forever . . . .

▶ 13.5 Space and 3-D Figures

Space is one more undefined geometric term about which people have plenty of intuition. Space is the 3-dimensional, or 3-D, world we live in. Everything around us is space.

Space extends forever in 3 dimensions. There are infinitely many points, infinitely many lines, and infinitely many planes in space. *Spatial figures* are objects in space, and they come in infinitely many shapes, sizes, and orientations.

Having good *spatial sense* means you can mentally manipulate 1-, 2-, and 3-dimensional objects in space and describe their orientations. Spatial sense is important in constructing 3-D objects, in representing 3-D objects in 2 dimensions by drawing on paper or on a computer screen, and in interpreting drawings of 3-D objects. Video games often demand a well-developed spatial sense of the latter kind, at least if you want to win.

13.5.1 "Solid" Figures

The items listed below are models for familiar 3-D mathematical shapes. The items in the left column are "hollow." The items in the right column are "filled up."

empty box with lid	brick
basketball	baseball
empty ice-cream cone	filled ice-cream cone
empty food can	rolling pin

All these objects are solid in the sense that they can be felt when touched. All concrete models of 3-dimensional figures are solid in this sense. For example, a cube can be modeled by a construction made of drinking straws, by an empty box, or by a die. All three models are solid, but each highlights a different mathematical aspect of cubes. The drinking-straw model emphasizes a cube's edges, the box emphasizes the surfaces of a cube, and the die emphasizes a cube and its interior.

To be consistent with definitions in 0, 1, and 2 dimensions, *Everyday Mathematics* defines a *geometric solid* as all the points on the surface of a 3-dimensional figure. According to this definition, a geometric solid is actually just the "skin" of a 3-dimensional object. Common 3-dimensional figures such as cones, pyramids, spheres, cubes, cylinders, and prisms do not include the points in their interior. That's why the objects listed in the left column above are better models for a prism, sphere, cone, and cylinder, respectively, than the objects in the right column.

Yet perhaps even more so than for plane figures, people commonly think of solids as solid through and through. So, just as with the difference between a polygon and a polygonal region, do not expect students to distinguish between the proper definition of a cone versus the solid and its interior. When eventually the distinction becomes mathematically relevant, it can be made and understood easily enough.

13.5.2 Polyhedrons

A *polyhedron* is a closed 3-dimensional figure formed by *polygons* and their interiors and having no holes. The word polyhedron comes from

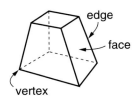

edge

face

vertex

An irregular polyhedron

For more information, see Section 13.6.2: Congruence and Similarity.

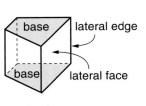

base   lateral edge

base   lateral face

A prism

For more information, see Section 13.7.1: Reflections, Rotations, and Translations.

A crystal

Greek words meaning "many bases" or "many seats." Polyhedrons include cubes, pyramids, prisms, and many other shapes. Features of polyhedrons include the following:

- *Faces* are the polygonal regions that make up a polyhedron. Although faces are always regions, they are often called by the name of the polygon defining the region. For example, it's common for a face that is a triangular region to be simply called a triangle.

- An *edge* of a polyhedron is a line segment where two faces meet.

- A *vertex,* or *corner,* of a polyhedron is a point where three or more edges meet.

In a *regular polyhedron,* all the faces are congruent, that is, the same shape and the same size; and the same number of faces join at the same angles at each vertex. Although there are infinitely many regular polygons, there are only five regular polyhedrons, which are illustrated below. The regular polyhedrons are also known as the *Platonic solids.*

A tetrahedron (4 equilateral triangles)

A cube (6 squares)

An octahedron (8 equilateral triangles)

A dodecahedron (12 regular pentagons)

An icosahedron (20 equilateral triangles)

Prisms

A *prism* is a polyhedron with two congruent and parallel polygonal regions for *bases.* The bases are connected by line segments with endpoints on corresponding edges of the bases. These segments form parallelograms and their interiors called *lateral faces.* Lateral faces intersect at *lateral edges.*

A prism can also be defined using transformations. Start with a polygonal base in one plane and translate (slide) this preimage to a parallel plane to get its image (the other base). The line segments that are the sides of the preimage generate lateral faces of the solid as they slide to the image, and the vertices of the preimage generate the lateral edges.

Prisms are usually named according to the shape of their bases. If a prism has a triangular region for a base, it is called a triangular prism. If a prism has a pentagonal region for a base, it is called a pentagonal prism. Emerald crystals often take the form of hexagonal prisms.

In a *right prism,* all the lateral faces are rectangles. This means that the lateral edges are perpendicular to the bases. If a prism is not a right prism, it is a *slanted* or *oblique prism.*

height

A slanted (oblique) prism

The *height,* or *altitude,* of a prism is the perpendicular distance between the planes containing the bases.

Pyramids

A *pyramid* is a polyhedron consisting of a polygonal region for a *base,* a point (*apex*) not in the plane of the base, and all of the line segments with one endpoint at the apex and the other on an edge of the base. The *lateral edges* of a pyramid are the segments from the vertices of the base to the apex. The lateral edges form triangles, and the triangular regions are the *lateral faces* of the pyramid.

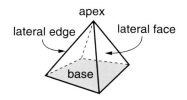

apex
lateral edge   lateral face
base

A pyramid

A pyramid can also be defined by transformations. Start with a polygonal base, an apex not in the plane of the base, and a line segment with one endpoint at the apex and the other endpoint on an edge of the base. Keep the endpoint at the apex fixed and slide the other endpoint around the edges of the base until it returns to the starting point. The line segments generate the lateral faces of the pyramid.

In a *right pyramid,* a line segment with endpoints at the apex and the center of the base is perpendicular to the base. If it is not a right pyramid, it is a *slanted* or *oblique pyramid.*

Like a prism, a pyramid is usually named according to the shape of its base. The famous Pyramids at Giza, Egypt, are square, right pyramids. A triangular-based pyramid is also known as a *tetrahedron.*

All prisms and pyramids are polyhedrons, but not all polyhedrons are prisms or pyramids. For example, three of the five regular polyhedrons shown on page 188 are neither pyramids nor prisms.

13.5.3 Solids with Curved Surfaces

All the faces of a polyhedron are flat. Three interesting geometric solids with curved surfaces are spheres (entirely curved), cylinders (two flat surfaces and one curved surface), and cones (one flat surface and one curved surface).

Spheres

A *sphere* consists of all the points in space at an equal distance, the *radius,* from a given point, its *center.* A sphere is modeled by a basketball.

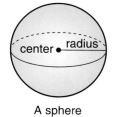

center • radius

A sphere

Cylinders

A *cylinder* is a geometric solid with two congruent, parallel circular regions for bases and a face formed by all the segments with an endpoint on each circle. These segments are parallel to a segment with endpoints at the centers of the circles. Food cans with top and bottom on, but no food inside, are models of cylinders.

A cylinder may be defined in terms of transformations. Start with a circular base in one plane and generate a translation, or slide, image in a parallel plane to form the other base. All the segments with endpoints on the edges of the bases form the curved face of the cylinder.

In a *right cylinder*, a line segment with endpoints at the centers of the bases is perpendicular to the base. If it is not a *right cylinder*, it is a *slanted* or *oblique cylinder.* Most cylinders in everyday life are right rather than slanted.

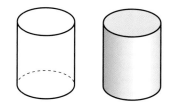

Cylinders

NOTE: A cylinder resembles a prism in every way except that the former has circular bases and the latter has polygonal bases.

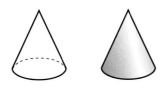

Cones

NOTE: A cone resembles a pyramid in every way except that the former has a circular base and the latter has a polygonal base.

The *height,* or *altitude,* of a cylinder is the perpendicular distance between the planes containing its bases.

Cones

A *cone* is a geometric solid with a circular *base,* a point *(apex)* not in the plane of the base, and all of the line segments with one endpoint at the apex and the other endpoint on the edge of the base. Together, these line segments form the *lateral face* of the cone.

In a *right cone,* a line segment with endpoints at the apex and the center of the base is perpendicular to the base. If it is not a right cone, it is a *slanted* or *oblique cone.*

The *height,* or *altitude,* of a cone is the perpendicular distance from the apex to the plane of its base.

In *Kindergarten* through *Fourth Grade Everyday Mathematics,* students explore geometric solids by manipulating blocks available in most classrooms, paper models constructed from blackline masters, and a variety of real-life materials such as shoeboxes and tin cans. More formal definitions such as those above are introduced in Grades 5 and 6.

13.5.4 Connecting 2-D and 3-D

A goal of the geometry strand at all levels of *Everyday Mathematics* is to help students see connections between 2-dimensional figures, such as polygons and curves, and the corresponding polyhedrons and curved surfaces in three dimensions. Students work toward this goal by building 3-dimensional models using materials such as straws, twist-ties, and paper. Beginning in first grade, these constructions help children develop good connections between 1-dimensional line segments, 2-dimensional polygons, and 3-dimensional figures having polygonal regions as faces.

In Grade 5, students cut out 2-dimensional patterns of prisms and pyramids to fold and tape together. These models are then used to compare and contrast the properties of vertices, edges, and faces of the solids they represent. Later, students use patterns to help them understand links between surface area and volume.

A Note about 2-Dimensional Drawings of 3-Dimensional Figures

This section briefly explains the conventions used for most of the geometric drawings in *Everyday Mathematics.* It is not intended to be a drawing tutorial, but rather a summary of various approaches, highlighting the one used in most geometry textbooks.

An artist needs to pick a point of view when drawing a 3-D object on paper or any other 2-D surface such as a computer monitor. The three main points of view, or *projections,* are *orthogonal, nonorthogonal,* and *perspective.*

Orthogonal Views

An *orthogonal* point of view looks at a 3-dimensional object head on. It generally ignores depth and simply draws the 2-dimensional part of the object that is in full view. Children's drawings are typically orthogonal; a drawing of a house is only face-on with no perspective or angles as in the margin. A drawing of a die would be a square or rectangle showing the top face because that's the one that counts.

Orthogonal views are useful in engineering and architecture. Blueprints often have three orthogonal views, a front, top, and side view, all drawn to the same scale so that a builder can get accurate measurements of the object to be built.

An orthogonal view

Semioblique orthogonal views show both front and side views as if seen head on, but attached to each other to indicate the "wrap-around." Many artists in the middle ages used this technique, along with modern so-called "primitive" artists such as Grandma Moses, who painted pictures similar to the one below.

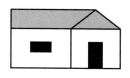

A semioblique orthogonal view

Nonorthogonal Views

Nonorthogonal views of 3-dimensional objects attempt to show the third dimension, depth, that may be hidden in a head-on view of an object. The depth of the object is shown using lines drawn at an angle to the front of the object, and all these depth lines are parallel. These views are common in mathematics, science, engineering, and other textbooks that aim to show the technical aspects of 3-dimensional objects. Three types of nonorthogonal views, *oblique, axonometric,* and *isometric,* are briefly described below.

Oblique 2-dimensional views of 3-D objects show a life-size or similar view of the front of the object, with the sides angled away from the front to show the object's depth. Sometimes the lengths of the sides are proportional to the front, but more often they are shorter to mimic the depth perception of the human eye.

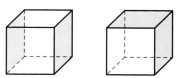

Oblique views of a cube

NOTE: In computer applications, oblique views are commonly called *dimetric* views.

Oblique views are the most common views in geometry textbooks and in *Everyday Mathematics.* For example, the oblique drawings in the margin highlight parallel and perpendicular sides of a cube. Note that shading of faces and the inclusion or omission of dashed lines to indicate hidden edges can reveal more or less about the 3-dimensional features of the object being drawn. The dashed edges are always parallel to corresponding visible edges.

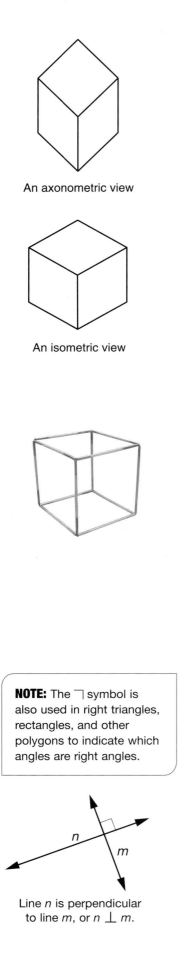

An axonometric view

An isometric view

Line n is perpendicular to line m, or $n \perp m$.

Axonometric 2-dimensional views of 3-D objects show a life-size or similar view of the top of an object, usually rotated 45° degrees, with the sides angled away to show the object's height. As in oblique views, lengths of the vertical edges are at the discretion of the artist; shorter ones mimic human perception better than proportional ones.

Axonometric views are used in architectural drawings showing the insides of buildings with the roofs removed. People want the true dimensions of the floor plan, and shorter walls make it easier to see objects placed in rooms.

Isometric 2-dimensional views of 3-D objects preserve all distances in the object. For example, each edge of the isometric drawing of the cube at left measures 1.5 cm. The view is also symmetric so that all the faces are rhombuses.

Isometric means "equal distance," and isometric drawings are common in technical manuals for machine parts, car manuals, and so on. The drawing orients the sides to each other so an observer can picture the whole object, while the actual measures, or similar ones, can help an observer determine if a replacement part might actually fit into a space.

Perspective Views

A 2-dimensional view of a 3-D object in *perspective* does not attempt to display actual or similar measurements of the object. Instead, perspective views are intended to mimic how objects look to a human eye. Although there is much geometry to be found in perspective views, along with other advanced mathematics such as trigonometry, such views are not as useful as orthogonal and nonorthogonal views in showing the features of abstract geometric objects. This is not to say that perspective views have no purpose in *Everyday Mathematics*. The photograph in the margin of a straw-and-twist-tie cube does a nice job of showing what a finished model would look like. In this context, it does not matter too much that none of the parallel edges appear to be parallel in the 2-dimensional image.

▶ **13.6 Geometric Relations**

Just as numbers can be related to one another in various ways, for example, $5 > 2$, $\frac{6}{2} = 3$, and $5 \neq 3$, geometric objects can likewise be related to one another. For example, if two figures are exactly the same size and shape, we say they are *congruent*. In the following sections, we discuss several interesting geometric relations.

13.6.1 Perpendicular and Parallel

Two lines in a plane either cross or do not cross. Lines that cross each other are said to *intersect*. When two lines intersect, they form several angles. When the angles formed are right angles, the lines are *perpendicular*. The symbol ⌐ is often included in a drawing of perpendicular lines to indicate a right angle. The symbol $\perp$ means *is perpendicular to*.

Lines in a plane that never cross are *parallel*. Parallel lines are always the same perpendicular distance apart, as shown below for parallel lines *AC* and *DF*. Many objects in our everyday world suggest parallel lines: window gratings, highway-lane markings, and lines on notebook paper. The symbol ∥ means *is parallel to*.

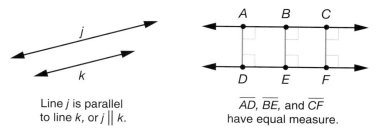

Line *j* is parallel to line *k*, or *j* ∥ *k*.

$\overline{AD}$, $\overline{BE}$, and $\overline{CF}$ have equal measure.

Skew lines are neither intersecting nor parallel. For example, an east-west line on the floor of a room and a north-south line on the ceiling are skew. Skew lines cannot be in the same plane.

Planes, or figures in planes such as line segments and squares, can also be parallel or intersecting. If two planes intersect at right angles, they are perpendicular, and two squares, one in each of those planes, are also perpendicular. Opposite faces of a cube are parallel; adjacent faces are perpendicular.

Beginning in first grade, children are introduced to the ideas of parallel and perpendicular through the exploration of solids, their faces, and their edges. Drawing and naming parallel and perpendicular line segments begins in second grade.

13.6.2 Congruence and Similarity

Congruent figures are exactly the same size and shape. They can be as simple as line segments or as complicated as polyhedrons. The symbol ≅ means *is congruent to*. In drawings, corresponding sides of congruent figures are often identified by small slashes called hash marks, as shown in congruent triangles *EFG* and *HIJ* below.

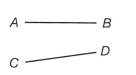

$\overline{AB} \cong \overline{CD}$
Congruent segments

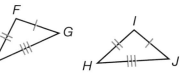

△*EFG* ≅ △*HIJ*
Congruent polygons

Congruent polyhedrons

Congruent figures do not have to be oriented the same way to be congruent. They may be rotated, flipped, or otherwise arranged, as shown in the drawings above. Isometric transformation images are congruent.

Skew lines can be modeled with two pencils.

Parallel faces of a cube

Perpendicular faces of a cube

NOTE: Hash marks are sometimes called *hatch marks* or *tick marks*, as on a number line. Cabinetmakers use hash marks to indicate where two pieces of wood are to be joined.

NOTE: In theory, even two rocket motors could be congruent; the same blueprints could be used to build both. But as in most real life applications of geometry, the motors could not be exactly the same, as each would have nicks and marks the other would not. Only abstract geometric objects can be congruent.

For more information on isometric transformations, see Section 13.7.1: Reflections, Rotations, and Translations.

chapter 13

For more information, see Section 13.7.2: Size-Change Transformations.

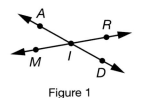

Figure 1

Similar figures are the same shape but not necessarily the same size. For example, any two squares are similar, as are any two equilateral triangles, or the two polyhedrons in the drawing below.

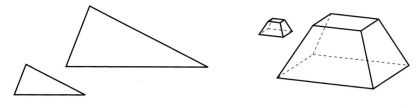

Similar triangles   Similar polyhedrons

Corresponding angles of similar polygons are congruent and corresponding side lengths are proportional. In the diagram, △*CAT* is similar to △*DOG*, with the following relations:

$$\angle C \cong \angle D, \qquad \angle A \cong \angle O, \qquad \angle T \cong \angle G;$$

$$\frac{\text{length of } \overline{CA}}{\text{length of } \overline{DO}} = \frac{\text{length of } \overline{AT}}{\text{length of } \overline{OG}} = \frac{\text{length of } \overline{TC}}{\text{length of } \overline{GD}}$$

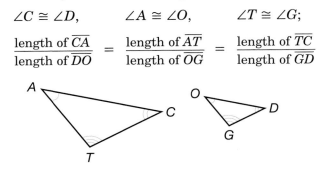

Size-change images are similar to each other, with the size-change factor giving the proportionality of lengths. A size-change factor is a ratio comparison of the lengths of the sides of the size-change images. If the ratio is equal to 1, then the objects are congruent as well as similar.

Fifth graders are informally introduced to similarity when they explore how copy machines enlarge and reduce figures and when they measure the effect of these size-change transformations on perimeter and area. Because perimeters on each image are measured in linear units, their ratio is the size-change factor. Because areas of each image are measured in square units, their ratio is the square of the size-change factor.

As part of their work to link the concepts of ratio, scale, and size change, students in *Sixth Grade Everyday Mathematics* explore similar polygons using drawing and measuring tools. They also solve problems involving similar polygons and other applications of ratios.

13.6.3 Relations and Orientations of Angles

Beginning in *Fifth Grade Everyday Mathematics,* students learn names for pairs of angles. For example, any pair of intersecting lines forms two sets of *vertical,* or *opposite, angles.* Vertical angles share no sides, only a vertex. In this context, vertical has nothing to do with vertical in relation to the horizon. The word here means that the angles are across from each other through the common vertex. In Figure 1, ∠*AIM* and ∠*RID* are vertical angles, as are ∠*MID* and ∠*AIR.* Vertical angles are congruent.

Adjacent angles share an endpoint and a ray. There are four pairs of adjacent angles in Figure 1:

$$\angle MID \text{ and } \angle AIM \qquad \angle AIM \text{ and } \angle AIR$$

$$\angle AIR \text{ and } \angle RID \qquad \angle RID \text{ and } \angle MID$$

Because the noncommon rays of each pair form a line, the sum of the angle measures in each pair is 180°. Whether they are adjacent or not, any two angles whose measures add to 180° are called *supplementary angles*. Figure 2 shows that adjacent angles do not have to be supplementary. Figure 3 shows a pair of nonadjacent supplements.

Figure 4 shows a pair of adjacent angles ∠1 and ∠2 whose noncommon sides form a right angle. This means that the measure of ∠1 + the measure of ∠2 = 90°. Adjacent or not, two angles whose measures add to 90° are called *complementary angles*.

Students in *Sixth Grade Everyday Mathematics* explore the relationships among angles formed when a line called a transversal intersects two parallel lines. These relationships are traditionally studied in secondary school geometry, when students *prove* that certain pairs of angles are congruent or supplementary. Sixth-grade students do not prove anything but are encouraged to measure the angles and make conjectures about them.

The following relationships can be proved for any pair of parallel lines cut by a transversal. In Figure 5, lines *l* and *m* are parallel, line *t* is the transversal, and the angles are numbered as shown.

- Pairs of vertical angles are ∠1 and ∠3; ∠2 and ∠4; ∠5 and ∠7; ∠6 and ∠8. Vertical angles are congruent.
- Pairs of *corresponding angles* are ∠1 and ∠5; ∠2 and ∠6; ∠3 and ∠7; ∠4 and ∠8. Corresponding angles are congruent.
- Pairs of *alternate interior angles* are ∠3 and ∠5; ∠4 and ∠6. Alternate interior angles are congruent.
- Pairs of *alternate exterior angles* are ∠2 and ∠8; ∠1 and ∠7. Alternate exterior angles are congruent.
- Each of the eight pairs of adjacent angles are supplementary.
- Pairs of *interior angles on one side of the transversal* are ∠3 and ∠6; ∠4 and ∠5. Interior angles on one side of the transversal are supplementary.

13.6.4 Other Geometric Relations

Students explore many other relationships between figures in *Everyday Mathematics*. Terms that describe how things are oriented to each other in a plane or space have geometric ties, such as those listed on the next page.

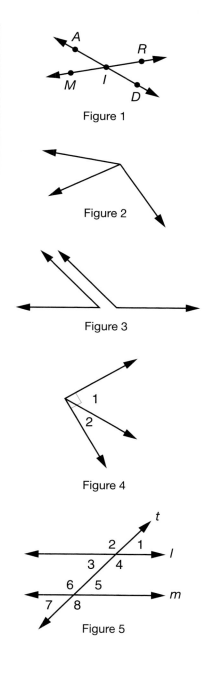

Figure 1

Figure 2

Figure 3

Figure 4

Figure 5

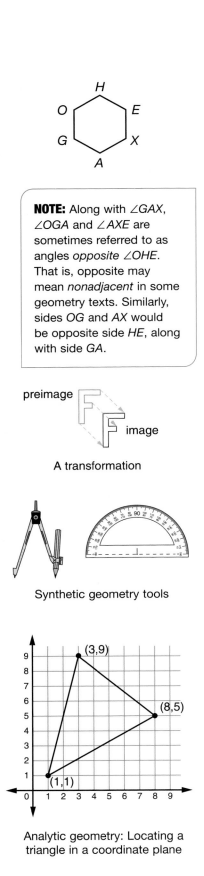

NOTE: Along with ∠*GAX*, ∠*OGA* and ∠*AXE* are sometimes referred to as angles *opposite* ∠*OHE*. That is, opposite may mean *nonadjacent* in some geometry texts. Similarly, sides *OG* and *AX* would be opposite side *HE*, along with side *GA*.

preimage

image

A transformation

Synthetic geometry tools

Analytic geometry: Locating a triangle in a coordinate plane

Inside/Outside

The distinction between *inside* and *outside* is obvious to even the youngest children. In precise geometric terms, however, the distinction is a bit complicated. That is, a plane figure has an inside, or *interior*, if it separates the plane into two parts, one bounded, the other not. The bounded part is the inside; the rest, excluding the figure itself, is the outside. Polygons and circles have insides. Lines and angles do not have insides; although they divide the plane into two parts, neither of the parts is bounded. A 3-dimensional figure has an inside if it separates space into two parts, one bounded, the other not.

The inside of a plane figure is not part of the figure itself. If you refer to the inside of a 2-dimensional figure, call it a *region*. This topic comes up when you want to know how much of a plane is inside a figure, that is, the area of the figure's interior region.

Consecutive/Opposite

Consecutive and *opposite* describe how parts of an object are oriented to one another. If the parts share something such as a side, they are consecutive. If they are across from each other in some sense, they are opposite, as in opposite angles. This meaning of opposite is not the same as the meaning of "antonym." In hexagon *HEXAGO* in the margin, angles *OHE* and *HEX* are consecutive. Angles *OHE* and *GAX* are opposite. Side *HE* is adjacent to sides *OH* and *EX* and opposite side *GA*.

▶ 13.7 Transformations

A *transformation* is an operation on a figure that produces a new figure. The original figure is called the *preimage;* the figure produced by the transformation is called the *image*. The transformations usually studied in elementary school mathematics produce images that have either the same shape as the preimages or both the same size and the same shape as the preimages. In *Everyday Mathematics,* students explore reflections, rotations, translations, and size changes.

Transformations can be studied using tools such as compasses, straightedges, protractors, and transparent mirrors. This method of study, *synthetic geometry,* was developed by the Greek geometer Euclid around 300 B.C. Transformations can also be studied using *analytic,* or *coordinate, geometry.* Computer programs enable a user to draw and manipulate figures on a monitor by storing points on shapes as coordinate pairs and by using functions, matrices, and algebra to relate points to each other geometrically. The transformations of figures discussed on the next page are produced using simple arithmetic on the coordinates of points. In *Sixth Grade Everyday Mathematics,* students explore translations in the coordinate plane.

13.7.1 Reflections, Rotations, and Translations

An *isometry* is a transformation in which a preimage and image are congruent. In *Everyday Mathematics*, students investigate three isometries: reflections (flips), rotations (turns), and translations (slides).

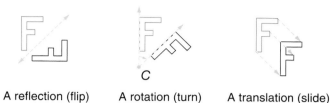

A reflection (flip)   A rotation (turn)   A translation (slide)

Reflections (Flips)

Two points A and A' are *reflection images* of each other over a *line of reflection* if line segment AA' is perpendicular to the line of reflection and is bisected (cut in half) by the line of reflection. If all the points in one figure are reflection images of all the points in another figure, the figures are reflection images. The images are congruent, but their orientation is reversed or flipped.

In Kindergarten through Grade 3, children explore reflections of objects through lines of symmetry. Activities with transparent mirrors in *Fourth Grade Everyday Mathematics* help students discover the properties of perpendicularity and equidistance in reflections. A good student description of a reflected figure is *Its image is in the same place on the other side of the mirror, only reversed.*

In Grades 4 through 6, students draw reflection images and find reflection lines for given images. They explore uses of reflections in frieze patterns and quilt designs. In both art forms, designs are repeatedly flipped to produce decorative strips and regions. Students are introduced to the analytic geometry of reflections by reflecting the positive number line over zero. The coordinates of the reflection images of points are negative numbers, the opposites of the positive numbers. For example, the reflection image of a point (x,y) over the y-axis is $(-x,y)$. Similarly, the reflection image over the x-axis is $(x,-y)$.

Rotations (Turns)

A point P' is a *rotation image* of a point P around a *center of rotation* C if P' is on the circle with center C and radius CP. For a specific rotation, you would pick both the center of rotation and an angle of rotation. If all the points in one figure are rotation images of all the points in another figure around the same center of rotation and with the same angle of rotation, the figures are rotation images. The images are congruent, but their orientation is turned.

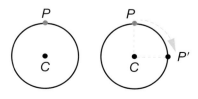

A rotation image of P around
center of rotation C

A rotation by $45°$
clockwise around point C

NOTE: Sometimes the line of reflection is called a *mirror,* or *mirror line.*

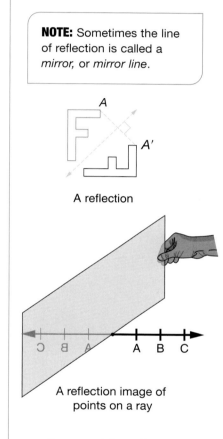

A reflection

A reflection image of
points on a ray

For more information, see Section 13.8.1: Line Symmetry.

chapter 13

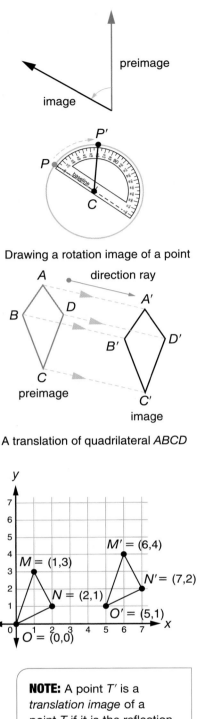

Drawing a rotation image of a point

A translation of quadrilateral *ABCD*

NOTE: A point *T'* is a *translation image* of a point *T* if it is the reflection image of *T* through two parallel lines. This definition of a translation is not very intuitive to most people, even adults. Because of this difficulty, *Everyday Mathematics* expects students to give only informal descriptions of translations as slides of objects in a plane or through space.

In *Kindergarten* through *Third Grade Everyday Mathematics,* children informally explore rotations when they model angles with drinking straws. Children form angles by bending a straw in half and rotating one half away from the other half. In the language of transformations, the final position of the rotated half is the image of its original position or preimage. So an angle is a preimage ray together with its image after a rotation.

A simple way to draw the image of one point rotated around another is to use a protractor. Place the center of the protractor at the center of rotation *C*. Mark a preimage point *P* at the zero mark on the protractor where the base and curved part of the protractor meet. A rotation image of *P* is any point *P'* on the curve of the protractor. The magnitude or measure of the rotation is the measure of angle *PCP'*.

Beginning in *Third Grade Everyday Mathematics,* students explore angles in depth. In Grades 4 through 6, they use half-circle and full-circle protractors to continue this exploration. Fourth graders take an informal look at rotation symmetry in figures in the contexts of frieze patterns and quilt making.

In analytic geometry, producing most rotations requires trigonometry, which is beyond the scope of this manual.

Translations (Slides)

A figure is a *translation* image of another figure if every point in the image is at the same distance in the same direction from its corresponding point in the preimage. A ray can be drawn to indicate the direction of the translation.

Translations are simple to define in coordinate geometry. First, define a preimage figure by giving coordinates of important points on the figure. For example, the coordinates of the vertices of $\triangle ONM$ are (0,0), (2,1), and (1,3). To draw a translation image of $\triangle ONM$ five units to the right and 1 unit up, simply add 5 to each *x*-coordinate and 1 to each *y*-coordinate in the preimage. So the coordinates of the vertices of the image, $\triangle O'N'M'$, are (5,1), (7,2), and (6,4). The translation is on a slant, as shown in the diagram.

If a number is added to only the *x*-coordinates and the results are plotted, the image is a *horizontal* translation. If a number is added to only the *y*-coordinates, the result is a *vertical* translation. In general, the translation image of point (*x,y*) by *h* horizontal units and *v* vertical units is $(x + h, y + v)$. If *h* or *v* is negative, the translation is left or down, respectively.

Everyday Mathematics students are not expected to be able to formally define a translation. In Grades 4 and 5, they examine translations informally by making frieze patterns and tessellations, respectively. Translations are important parts of such artistic designs. In Grade 6, students explore translations in the coordinate plane.

13.7.2 Size-Change Transformations

In a *similarity transformation,* the image of a figure stays the same shape but does not necessarily stay the same size. The name comes from the fact that the image is *similar* to the preimage.

Size Changes (Stretches and Shrinks)

A *size-change transformation* is defined by a *center of similarity P* and a *size-change factor k.* For example, if $k = 2$, then the image will be 2 times as large as the preimage. A point A' is a *size-change image* of A if it is on ray PA and the length of segment PA' is k times the length of segment PA.

If all the points on one figure are size-change images of all the points on another figure through the same center of similarity and with the same size-change factor, then the figures are *size-change images.*

Like translations, size changes are easy to define in coordinate geometry. First, define a preimage figure by giving coordinates of important points on the figure. For example, point A has coordinates $(1,3)$. To draw its size-change image by a factor 2, simply multiply each coordinate by 2, giving $A' = (2,6)$, as shown in the graph.

A coordinate size change is the basis of how computer programs zoom in and out on objects. A positive size-change factor zooms in or out. A negative size-change factor zooms in or out and also reflects the object through the origin, producing an image that looks similar to a 180° rotation of the object around the origin followed by a positive size change.

Students in *Fifth Grade Everyday Mathematics* explore size changes, but they do not learn any of the terminology discussed above. Sixth-grade students learn the terminology as they review reductions and enlargements and then apply size changes to map scales and in other applications. Sixth graders then tie together their understanding of ratios, scales, and size changes by studying properties of similar polygons.

▶ 13.8 Symmetry

A figure is *symmetric* if you can transform it and the image looks exactly like the original. For example, a butterfly has reflection symmetry, or line symmetry, because you can fold it and the two halves (wings) align perfectly. A starfish has rotation symmetry because you can turn one arm to where the next one was and it looks the same. A strip of wallpaper border has translation symmetry if a tracing of one part slides over and exactly matches another part of the pattern.

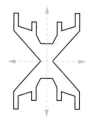
Line symmetry

Rotation symmetry

Translation symmetry

For more information, see Section 13.10: Tessellations.

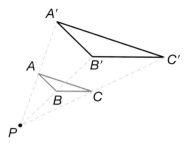

A size-change through P by a factor of 2 (length of $\overline{PA'}$ = 2 times length of $\overline{PA}$)

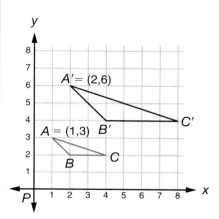

NOTE: *A size-change factor* is sometimes called a *scale factor,* because the image is at a different scale than the preimage.

For more information, see Section 13.6.2: Congruence and Similarity.

For more information, see Section 13.7.1: Reflections, Rotations, and Translations.

chapter 13

13.8.1 Line Symmetry

A figure has *line symmetry* if there is a line that divides it into two halves that are reflection images of each other. They are the exact size and shape, but have opposite orientation. The line is called a *line of symmetry* of the figure, but no part of it is necessarily part of the figure. The two halves look exactly the same but face in opposite directions.

To check a figure for line symmetry, fold, or imagine folding, the figure on a line. If the halves match, the fold is a line of symmetry. An isosceles trapezoid has one line of symmetry. Figures may have more than one line of symmetry. A square has four lines of symmetry. A circle has infinitely many lines of symmetry through its center.

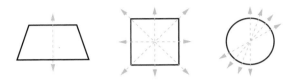

A solid figure has *bilateral symmetry* if there is a *plane* that divides it into two haves that are reflection images of each other in space. For example, each half of a human face is the mirror image of the other half, more or less. Other living things have this sort of bilateral symmetry, as do many human-made objects such as car grilles and traffic lights. Verifying bilateral symmetry is trickier than verifying line symmetry because it is very difficult to fold solid figures.

13.8.2 Rotation and Point Symmetries

Sometimes people think a figure has line symmetry when it doesn't. They may think, for example, that there is a way to fold the parallelogram at left so that the two halves match.

Parallelograms that are not rectangles do not have line symmetry, but they do have *rotation symmetry*. If a parallelogram is given a half-turn around its center (where the diagonals bisect), it will look unchanged. Other figures take less turning to show rotation symmetry. For example, a regular pentagon looks the same after 1 fifth of a full turn around its center.

To test for rotation symmetry, turn, or imagine turning, a figure around a point. If it coincides with itself before a full rotation of 360°, then it has rotation symmetry. The number of times a figure coincides with its preimage during one full rotation is called its *order of rotation symmetry*. The pentagon in the margin has order-5 rotation symmetry.

A figure can have both rotation and line symmetry. For example, a regular pentagon has order-5 rotation symmetry and five lines of symmetry, one through each vertex perpendicular to the opposite side.

A figure has *point symmetry* if it is a reflection image of itself through a *center of symmetry* C. A line through C and any point M on the figure intersects the figure again at reflection image M', where the length of segment MC equals the length of segment $M'C$. In a sense, reflecting a figure through a point turns it inside out.

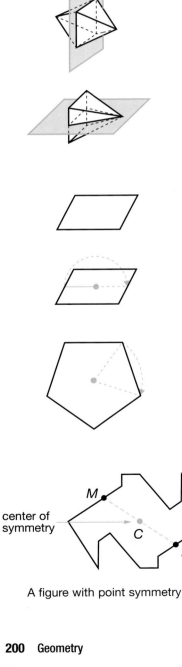

center of symmetry

A figure with point symmetry

Point symmetry can also be viewed as a special case of rotation symmetry. A figure has point symmetry if it is the rotation image of itself through 180°.

Other Symmetries

Line symmetry and rotation symmetry are not the only kinds of symmetry. Some *tessellations,* or tilings of a plane, involve symmetry based on translations, just as line symmetry is based on reflections and rotation symmetry is based on rotations.

In *Kindergarten* through *Third Grade Everyday Mathematics,* the focus is on line symmetry, but children may notice other symmetries when they are working with pattern blocks or looking for mathematics in their world. Many corporate logos, for example, have line symmetry or rotation symmetry. In fourth grade, students explore line symmetry with transparent mirrors and rotation symmetry in a quilting project. Fifth graders investigate rotation symmetry in tessellations. Point and rotation symmetry are explored further in Grade 6.

▶ 13.9 Coordinate Geometry

Coordinate geometry integrates reference frames and geometry. The simplest coordinate geometry is a number line on which every point has a real number coordinate that measures the distance of the point from a zero point, or origin. For example, the point plotted on the number line in the margin has coordinate −2.5.

Two perpendicular number lines, called *axes,* that intersect at right angles at their zero points form a rectangular coordinate system, or *coordinate plane.* Any point in the plane can be located relative to each axis with an ordered pair of coordinates. By convention, the position relative to the horizontal axis comes first. For example, the point on the coordinate plane in the margin has coordinates (3,2).

The ancient Egyptians and Romans used rectangular coordinates to survey fields. In the early 17th century, the French philosopher and mathematician René Descartes (1596–1650) made significant advances in coordinate geometry. Today, rectangular coordinates are often called *Cartesian coordinates* in his honor.

Since the time of Descartes, coordinate geometry has been a powerful tool for advances in many areas of mathematics. In *Everyday Mathematics,* the serious study of coordinate geometry begins in fourth grade. Before that, work with coordinate geometry is restricted mostly to number lines.

▶ 13.10 Tessellations

A *tessellation* is a pattern formed by repeated use of polygons or other figures to cover a surface without gaps or overlaps. The Latin root of the noun *tessellation* and the verb *tessellate* is *tessella,* referring to small, square stones used to create mosaics. Real-life examples of tessellations include honeycombs and checkerboards.

For more information, see Section 13.10: Tessellations.

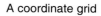

A number line

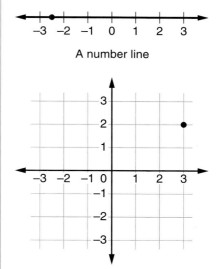

A coordinate grid

chapter 13

In a tessellation formed from polygons, the sides of the polygons coincide as the triangles marked "yes" do in Figure 1. A point where vertices of the polygons meet is called a *vertex point* of the tessellation, as in Figure 2. For there to be no gaps or overlaps as in Figure 3, the sum of the measures of the angles around every vertex point of a tessellation must be 360°.

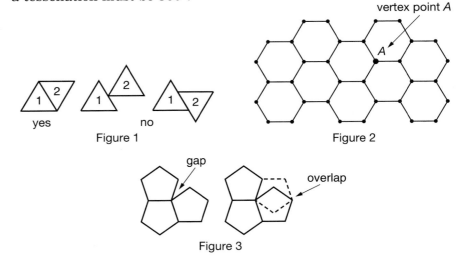

Figure 1

Figure 2

Figure 3

In order for a *regular* polygon to tessellate the plane, the polygon's interior angles must fit snugly around each vertex point, and this means that the measure of each interior angle must exactly divide 360°.

Consider the simplest regular polygon, an equilateral triangle. Each angle of an equilateral triangle measures 60°. Because $\frac{360°}{60°} = 6$, an equilateral triangle tessellates the plane, with six such triangles meeting at each vertex point.

In general, if the measure of one interior angle of a regular polygon exactly divides 360°, the polygon will tessellate the plane. One way to find this measure is to:

- Draw diagonals from one vertex to all the other nonadjacent vertices. This dissects the polygon into triangles.
- Use the fact that the sum of the angle measures of any triangle is 180° to calculate the sum total of the measures of all the angles in the polygon. For example, for three triangles this total is 3 * 180° = 540°.
- Divide the sum of the angle measures in the polygon by the number of angles in the polygon to get the measure of one interior angle.

For example, to find the number of degrees in each angle of a regular pentagon, draw the two diagonals from any vertex as in Figure 4. The resulting figure consists of three triangles, each with angle measures totaling 180°, so the total of the angle measures of the pentagon is 3 * 180° = 540°. Because the measures of all the angles of a regular pentagon are equal, each angle in the pentagon measures $\frac{540°}{5} = 108°$.

Figure 4

The following chart applies this method to calculate the measure of an interior angle of each regular n-gon up to $n = 10$.

Regular Polygon (n-gon)		Number of sides n	Total Interior Angle Measure (number of triangles $*$ 180°)	Measure of Each Interior Angle
Triangle		3	$1 * 180° = 180°$	$\dfrac{180°}{3} = 60°$
Square		4	$2 * 180° = 360°$	$\dfrac{360°}{4} = 90°$
Pentagon		5	$3 * 180° = 540°$	$\dfrac{540°}{5} = 108°$
Hexagon		6	$4 * 180° = 720°$	$\dfrac{720°}{6} = 120°$
Heptagon		7	$5 * 180° = 900°$	$\dfrac{900°}{7} = 128\frac{4}{7}°$
Octagon		8	$6 * 180° = 1,080°$	$\dfrac{1,080°}{8} = 135°$
Nonagon		9	$7 * 180° = 1,260°$	$\dfrac{1,260°}{9} = 140°$
Decagon		10	$8 * 180° = 1,440°$	$\dfrac{1,440°}{10} = 144°$

Note that the number of triangles formed by drawing the diagonals from one vertex (the first factor in the third column) is always 2 less than the number of sides n. So, in general, the number of triangles is $(n - 2)$ and the total interior angle measure is $(n - 2) * 180°$. All angles have equal measure in a regular n-gon, so dividing this total by n gives a formula for the measure of an interior angle.

$$\text{Measure of an angle in a regular } n\text{-gon} = \frac{(n - 2) * 180°}{n}$$

A regular dodecagon has 12 sides. By the formula, each of its interior angles has measure

$$\frac{(12 - 2) * 180°}{12} = \frac{10 * 180°}{12} = 150°.$$

Because 150° does not exactly divide 360°, a regular dodecagon does not tessellate the plane.

Of the n-gons in the chart, only equilateral triangles, squares, and regular hexagons have interior angle measures that are factors of 360°. It turns out that they are the *only* regular polygons of any number of sides that tessellate the plane. The drawing in the margin shows how a regular pentagon does *not* tessellate.

13.10.1 Classifying Tessellations

Three main categories of tessellations are *pure, semipure,* and *demiregular* tessellations.

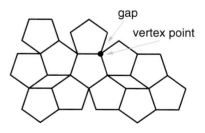

gap

vertex point

A regular pentagon does not tessellate.

Pure Tessellations

A *pure,* or *same-tile, tessellation* consists of the same figure repeated over and over. Pure tessellations made with regular polygons are called *regular tessellations.* Figure 1 shows the three regular tessellations and their mathematical code names, which list the number of sides of the polygons that meet at each vertex point.

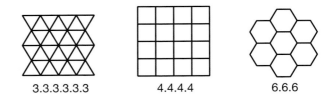

3.3.3.3.3.3   4.4.4.4   6.6.6

Figure 1: Names of the regular tessellations

Examples of *irregular* pure tessellations are shown in Figure 2.

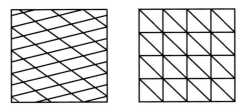

Figure 2: Irregular pure tessellations

Semipure Tessellations

Semipure tessellations consist of at least two different kinds of polygons arranged in the same way around each vertex point. Again, the sum of the angle measures at each vertex point must equal 360°. Consider the tessellation in the margin, in which three equilateral triangles and two squares meet at each vertex point. The sum of measures of the angles around each vertex point is $3 * 60° + 2 * 90° = 360°$.

A *semiregular tessellation* is semipure with all regular polygons, and the angles around any vertex point are in the same order and respectively congruent to the angles around any other vertex point. There are eight semiregular tessellations, made up of the following sets of regular polygons. In the code names in parentheses, the numbers indicate the numbers of sides of the polygons that meet at each vertex point. The order of the numbers indicates the orientations of the polygons. Drawings of these semiregular tessellations are on the next page.

- Four triangles and a hexagon (3.3.3.3.6)
- Three triangles and two squares (3.3.3.4.4)
- Triangle, square, hexagon, square (3.4.6.4)
- Square and two octagons (4.8.8)
- Triangle, hexagon, triangle, hexagon (3.6.3.6)
- Two triangles, square, triangle, square (3.3.4.3.4)
- Triangle, two dodecagons (3.12.12)
- Square, hexagon, dodecagon (4.6.12)

A semipure tessellation named 3.3.3.4.4

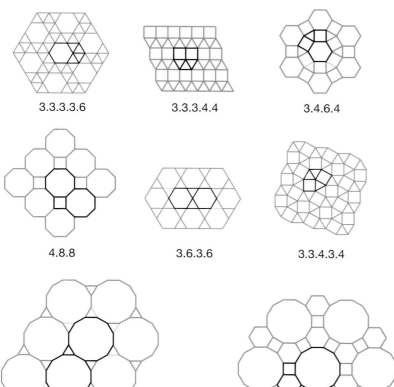

3.3.3.3.6

3.3.3.4.4

3.4.6.4

4.8.8

3.6.3.6

3.3.4.3.4

3.12.12

4.6.12

Demiregular Tessellations

Demiregular tessellations are made with regular polygons, but the arrangements of angles around vertex points are not all the same. The figure in the margin is a demiregular tessellation with two different arrangements, 3.4.6.4 around vertex point *A* and 3.4.4.6 around vertex point *B*.

Tessellations appeared as early as 4000 B.C. in Sumerian art. Persians and Romans decorated buildings with colorful mosaic tessellations. Islamic designs with tessellations can be found in the Alhambra, a Moorish palace built around A.D. 1300 in Granada, Spain.

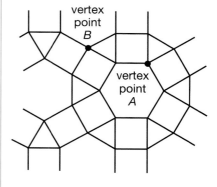

The name of this demiregular tessellation is 3.4.6.4/3.4.4.6.

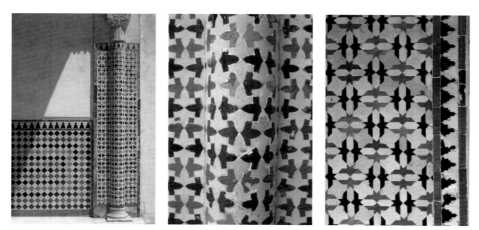

An Escher-type translation

An Escher-type reflection

An Escher-type rotation

For more information, see Section 13.7.1: Reflections, Rotations, and Translations.

M. C. Escher, an artist born in 1898 in the Netherlands, was interested in the process of filling space with snugly fitting pieces. He was inspired by the decorations at the Alhambra. One of Escher's goals was to discover how shapes could fill a plane in a systematic manner. He concluded that geometric translations, rotations, reflections, and combinations of them could reproduce exact shapes. Each snugly fitting piece in Escher's tessellations evolves from one of these six geometric shapes: parallelogram, rectangle, square, triangle, 60° rhombus, and regular hexagon.

Students encounter pure and regular tessellations in *Fifth Grade Everyday Mathematics.* Sixth graders investigate semiregular tessellations and get a taste of constructing Escher-type translation tessellations, in which one side of a polygon with an even number of sides is somehow manipulated and the result is translated onto the opposite side. Different manipulations can be done with each pair of opposite sides, as the example below shows. The procedure works for square and regular hexagon tessellations and certain irregular variations, such as parallelogram tessellations.

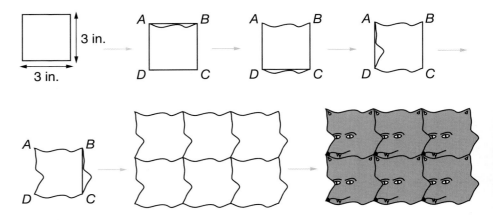

How to create a translation tessellation

▶ 13.11 Topology

Late in Grade 6, students are introduced to topology, a flourishing branch of mathematics with roots in classical geometry and *analysis,* or the study of functions. *Topology* is the study of unchanging properties of sets of points that undergo bending, stretching, squeezing, and other types of transformational mayhem. Because of this, topology is sometimes called "rubber-sheet geometry." If you imagine an object made of a rubber sheet and then imagine all the shapes you could stretch and squish the object into without ripping, tearing, or puncturing it, you are thinking about topological transformations.

Two objects are said to be topologically equivalent if one can be transformed into the other via topological transformations. A die and a baseball, for example, are topologically equivalent to each other and to a bowling ball. The "holes" in a bowling ball aren't really holes because they don't go all the way through; they are really just dents that can be smoothed out. A sphere and a doughnut are not topologically equivalent because of the hole in the doughnut. A doughnut and a coffee cup, however, are topologically equivalent, as both have exactly one hole. The illustration below shows how you might imagine the transformation of a coffee cup into a doughnut.

To a topologist, in fact, holes are among the more interesting features of geometric shapes. The *genus* of a shape is the number of holes it contains. For example, a hockey puck has genus 0 because it has no holes, a coffee cup has genus 1, and the Geometry Template has genus 64. Geometric features such as parallel and perpendicular lines, angle measures, and areas are not so interesting to topologists. None of these features remain unchanged under topological transformations.

13.12 Teaching Geometry

Children in *Kindergarten Everyday Mathematics* play with models of shapes, manipulate pattern blocks, cut shapes out of paper, and look for shapes in their everyday environment. This informal approach is intended to let students' curiosity lead them toward recognizing features of polygons and other geometric figures. Vocabulary is introduced as necessary in order to identify groups of shapes by name. Informally, many common shapes that young students recognize are embedded in solids. For example, a square is a face on a cube, a rectangle is a face on a box, and a circle is the rim of a can.

The approach of using concrete manipulations leading to the recognition of key features and the naming of objects continues throughout the grades. Children in Grade 3 reach a point when they know the names of most common polygons. They are also able to informally classify triangles and quadrilaterals by describing such characteristics as parallel sides, equal-length sides, right angles, and equal-size angles. In Grade 4, students explore properties of angles, polygons, and solids; classify quadrilaterals using a hierarchical scheme similar to the one in Section 13.4.2; and begin to work with compass-and-straightedge constructions and transformations.

Work with classification and definition continues in *Fifth Grade Everyday Mathematics*. Students also explore tessellations; the effects of similarity transformations on area, perimeter, and angles; and transformations on the coordinate grid. In sixth grade, students classify tessellations, explore cross sections of geometric solids, and investigate the relationships among the angles formed when parallel lines are crossed by a transversal. As in the primary grades, students in Grades 4 through 6 use a variety of geometric tools and concrete models. In later grades, however, the focus increasingly shifts from merely identifying and naming shapes to informal reasoning and the analysis of geometric properties and relationships.

NOTE: A mathematical model of a doughnut shape is called a *torus*.

NOTE: Recent computer software for manipulating images mimics the rubber-sheet geometry of topology. Such software lets the user stretch, squish, twist, and otherwise mangle, or *morph,* an image on the screen. This technique is often seen in movies and on television where things not only appear to change shape but babies wink and animals seem to speak, and vice versa.

NOTE: Although the square and rectangle in the examples are technically the *edges* of the faces of the cube and box, respectively, it is not necessary to oblige younger students to make this distinction.

chapter 13

13.12.1 The van Hiele Levels

The *Everyday Mathematics* curriculum is based on research that has been carried out by the authors and others over several decades. In geometry, some of the most important research was done in the late 1950s by two Dutch researchers, Dina and Pierre van Hiele.

The van Hieles identified five stages in the development of geometric understanding. During the first stage, students approach shapes holistically. A triangle is a triangle because its overall shape is like other objects that are also called triangles. At this stage, shapes are not broken down into parts; line segments, vertices, and angles of the triangle are not considered separately. Instead, the child grasps the whole figure at once. At this visualization stage, students can benefit from hands-on work with pattern blocks, geometric solids, geoboards, straws and connectors, and real objects from their everyday environment.

During the second stage of geometric understanding, students begin to notice the individual elements that make up geometric figures. They see that a triangle has three sides and three corners; they see that a square has four sides all the same length and four right angles. At this stage, students continue hands-on work and begin to compare, measure, sort, and describe shapes. They can also begin to learn the names for the parts of geometric figures: side, angle, face, edge, and so on.

In the third stage of geometric understanding, students begin to move beyond the analysis of single shapes and start thinking about relationships among different shapes. They can, for example, understand that squares are rectangles because they meet the minimal requirements of four sides and four right angles. Students also begin to understand hierarchical classification schemes like the one for quadrilaterals in Section 13.4.2. They also begin formulating simple chains of reasoning. If the context is not too abstract, students at this stage can work with definitions of geometric objects and properties. This is also the stage of informal proof, which is the highest level expected of students in elementary school geometry.

Beyond the informal proof stage, the van Hieles identified two further levels. One is the level of deductive reasoning, the level at which high school geometry is traditionally taught. The highest level is the formal axiomatic geometry of professional mathematicians, a level most of us would not even recognize as geometry.

13.12.2 Solid versus Plane Geometry

Which is less abstract, a cube or a square? In a purely mathematical sense, both are equally abstract. But in a practical sense, a cube is less abstract than a square. Good, concrete models for cubes are commonplace; a sugar cube, a die, or a lump of clay pressed into shape are all excellent representations of a cube. A square, on the other hand, is not so easily modeled. The face of a cube is a model for a square region, not a square. You can use straws to build a model of the square, but everyday objects that are good models of squares, circles, triangles, and other plane figures are hard to find.

So, odd as it may sound, solid geometry is more concrete than plane geometry. For this reason, *Everyday Mathematics* includes work with spheres, prisms, cylinders, and other 3-dimensional figures much sooner than in a traditional curriculum.

▶ 13.13 Geometry Tools and Techniques

The study of geometry in *Everyday Mathematics* involves many hands-on experiences, such as manipulating pattern blocks and attribute blocks, tracing shapes from templates, working with geoboards, cutting out shapes, folding shapes, drawing shapes with straightedges or compasses, constructing shapes out of straws, and constructing 3-dimensional figures from 2-dimensional nets (flat figures that can be folded to form closed, 3-dimensional solids). The following sections highlight some of the most widely used tools.

13.13.1 Compass-and-Straightedge Constructions

Around 300 B.C., a Greek named Euclid wrote his famous work *The Elements*. In it, he presented the basis for what we now call *Euclidean Geometry,* which is the geometry traditionally taught in high school geometry courses. According to mathematics historian Howard Eves (1983, pp. 70–71),

> With the unique exception of the Bible, no work has been more widely used, studied, or edited, and for over two millennia it has dominated all teaching of geometry. More than a thousand editions of the work have appeared since the first printed one in 1482. Its content and its form have made a tremendous impact on the development of both the subject matter and the logical foundations of mathematics.

For a complete reference to Eves' book, see page 77.

Actually, more than half of *The Elements* is about number theory and algebra. It is his organization of the study of geometry, however, that has made Euclid legendary.

Perhaps Euclid's most important contribution was his *axiomatic method* of doing mathematics. This method requires that anything to be proved must be deduced logically from previously proven results called *theorems* or from "self-evident" truths called *axioms.* Euclid identified a number of axioms, such as the following:

- Things that are equal to the same thing are also equal to one another.
- The whole is greater than the part.
- A straight-line segment can be drawn joining any two points.
- All right angles are congruent.

Axioms are ideas that cannot be proved, but that have to be accepted to get started doing mathematics. Over the millennia, other axioms have been added or substituted for some of Euclid's, but the axiomatic method he pioneered is still the basis of mathematical proof today.

The logical approach of the axiomatic method is not appropriate for elementary school students. Elementary school geometry is better treated as an inductive science than as formal axiomatic mathematics.

chapter 13

For more information on stages of geometric understanding, see Section 13.12.1: The van Hiele Levels.

Axiomatic geometry is more appropriate for high school or college students, in part because of the time needed to reach the proof stage of geometric understanding.

However, one aspect of Euclid's geometry is appropriate for elementary school students. Many of Euclid's geometric proofs can be illustrated by compass-and-straightedge constructions that produce specific geometric objects. In a sense, each construction is a step-by-step algorithm that proves a geometric theorem.

The *Student Reference Books* for Grades 4 through 6 include selected classic compass-and-straightedge constructions. For example, the following algorithm from sixth grade describes how to copy a triangle with a compass and a straightedge.

Copying a Triangle

Step 1: Draw a triangle ABC. Draw a line segment that is longer than $\overline{AB}$, and label an endpoint A' (read as "A prime"). Place the compass anchor at point A and pencil point at point B. Without changing your compass opening, place the compass anchor on A' and draw an arc that crosses the segment. Label the point where the arc crosses the segment B'.

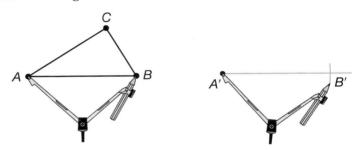

Step 2: Place the compass anchor at A and the pencil point at C. Without changing your compass opening, place the compass anchor on A' and draw an arc.

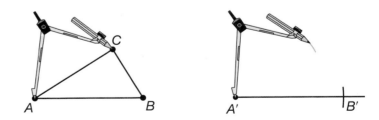

Step 3: Place the compass anchor at B and the pencil point at C. Without changing your compass opening, place the compass anchor on B' and draw another arc. Label the point where the arcs intersect C' and move on to Step 4.

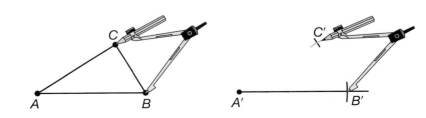

Step 4: Draw $\overline{A'C'}$ and $\overline{B'C'}$.

Triangles *ABC* and *A'B'C'* are congruent; that is, they are the same size and same shape.

As geometry computer software becomes available in elementary schools, algorithms for drawing and manipulating figures will necessarily become important new topics. Two such computer programs, the *Geometer's Sketchpad* and *Cabri Geometry*, each have ways for students to define their own algorithms. These are called *custom tools* or *scripts* in the *Sketchpad* and *macros* in *Cabri*. They are "written" simply by turning on a recorder and carrying out a series of actions in order. Turn off the recorder, name the algorithm, and you can use it whenever you like in the future.

13.13.2 Pattern-Block and Geometry Templates

Children in *Kindergarten* through *Third Grade Everyday Mathematics* use a Pattern-Block Template for explorations of plane figures. Beginning in fourth grade, students use a Geometry Template, which might better be called a Geometry-and-Measurement Template. There is a greater variety and number of shapes in the Geometry Template than the Pattern-Block Template to help students in their more detailed explorations of categories of triangles and quadrangles. The measuring devices include inch and centimeter scales, a Percent Circle useful for making circle graphs, and both a full-circle and a half-circle protractor.

13.13.3 Pattern Blocks and Geometric Solids

In *Kindergarten* through *Third Grade Everyday Mathematics,* children use building blocks and pattern blocks to motivate the study of 1- and 2-dimensional geometry. Beginning in fourth grade, these activities serve as background for a methodical approach to making 2-dimensional maps of structures and 3-dimensional models of prisms and pyramids from 2-dimensional patterns. Pattern blocks are also used for fraction work in Grades 2 through 5.

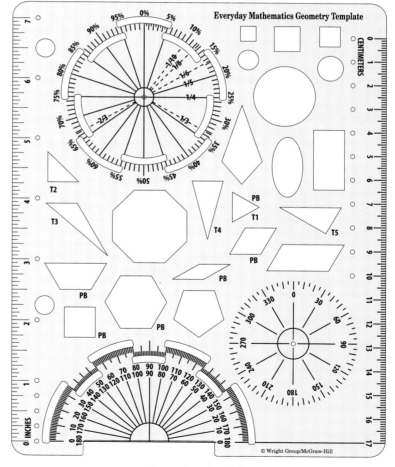

Geometry Template

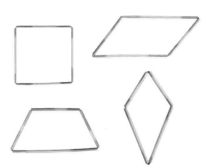

2-D straw constructions

13.13.4 Straws and Twist-Ties

From first through fourth grades, students construct 2- and 3-dimensional objects with straws and twist-ties. In fifth grade, they use straws and twist-ties to learn about congruent triangles and volumes of solids. Because these activities result in representations of geometric shapes, we include a few words here about the true nature of the shapes compared to the actual straw and twist-tie models of them.

Two-dimensional shapes such as polygons and circles are defined as boundaries of flat regions without the interiors. For example, a polygon is made up of line segments; the region inside a polygon is not part of the polygon. Straws and twist-ties make good models of polygons because the straws actually represent the sides of the figures and don't suggest including the interiors. In contrast, straw and twist-tie models for 3-D figures such as prisms and pyramids accurately show the edges, but not the interiors of the faces. So while straws and twist-ties can suggest 3-D shapes, a model such as an empty cereal box is truer to an actual rectangular prism.

13.13.5 Transparent Mirrors

Students in *Fourth Grade Everyday Mathematics* experiment with reflections using transparent mirrors to move and draw reflection images. You are familiar with a regular mirror and the symmetric image you see in it. A transparent mirror also reflects an image, but it has the advantage that you can see through it and trace the mirror image. The drawing in the margin illustrates the reflection of a squiggle as you might see it in a transparent mirror.

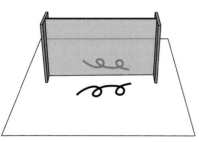

A transparent mirror

As with any new tool, students need time, practice, and patience to develop skills using a transparent mirror. For accurate placement of images, students should:

- Lean down and look directly through the transparent mirror.
- Use the ends of the mirror to keep it perpendicular to the paper; that is, they should not hold the mirror off the desk or table.
- Use the inner part of the recessed edge along the bottom of the mirror to place the mirror on points or lines, or to draw mirror lines.
- Hold the transparent mirror firmly in position with one hand while doing any tracing behind it or drawing lines along its recessed edge.

Students use transparent mirrors to study lines of symmetry in figures and to draw reflection images of their own artistic designs. The mirrors are especially useful for drawing reflections in tessellations.

14 Measurement

Contents

chapter 14

Measurement is one of the most widespread uses of mathematics in daily life. Even very young children show considerable interest in measurement. Questions such as *How tall is my block building? How long can we make this block train? How much water until the sink overflows?* and *How long until lunchtime?* are spontaneously pursued by preschool and primary-grade students. Older students continue to be curious about how much, how long, how far, and the like. Many become fascinated with measures and ways of determining them, whether it is the height of a tall building or the amount of water in a swimming pool. *Everyday Mathematics* recognizes and capitalizes on students' natural curiosity about measurement and measures. Throughout the grades, students engage in interesting and purposeful tasks as they learn how to measure and how to interpret other people's measures. Measurement tasks become more complicated as students gain experience.

Measurement is the source of many of the numbers that we use in everyday life. Measures, along with their units, tell "how much" of

For more information, see Section 14.11.1: Measurement and Estimation.

something there is. Arithmetic operations performed with measures lead to results that make sense in real-life contexts. For example, a 6-pound cabbage weighs twice as much as a 3-pound cabbage, and someone who spends 30 minutes on homework spends twice as much time as someone who spends 15 minutes on homework. Quantifying and comparing are common quests of childhood as well as adulthood, and both are important when exploring measurement. Furthermore, because all measures are approximate, knowing how to measure means knowing how to deal with error.

This chapter begins with a discussion of measurement systems and units, including personal measures, the metric system, and U.S. customary measures. Then it turns to specific uses of measurement in one, two, and three dimensions (length, area, and volume), followed by discussions of weight and mass, angle measures, elapsed time, and money. Measures in geography are a focus throughout *Fourth* through *Sixth Grade Everyday Mathematics*.

▶ 14.1 Personal Measures

Units for measures of length appeared relatively early in human history and were based on things familiar to people, namely, their bodies. Just as many early number systems were based on *ten,* probably because humans have ten fingers, many early linear measures were based on the lengths of certain body parts. This is the origin of such measures as *foot, digit, span,* and *hand,* each of which was, or still is, a commonly used unit for measuring length.

The problem with a measurement system based on body parts is that bodies differ. Who is to say whose *cubit,* a measure based on the distance between the elbow and fingertips, is the cubit to measure by? Without agreement, how do buyers know that they are getting their money's worth when someone sells them 56 cubits of cloth? In ancient Egypt, this problem led to the creation of a *royal master cubit* made of black granite. The royal master cubit was the *standard* against which every cubit stick in the land was periodically matched for building projects. For example, the length of any side of the Great Pyramid of Cheops at Giza differs only 0.05% from the mean length of all four sides. This precision is evidence of the consistency of the thousands of cubit sticks used to build the monument. Eventually, individual nations established their measures by agreeing on standards against which all measurement implements were compared.

Another problem arose when members of two or more groups that had been isolated because of distance, geography, or politics came into contact with one another. In the medieval trade fairs of Europe, for example, merchants from many nations gathered to sell their wool cloth. Most agreed to measure cloth in *ells,* but the length of an ell differed among the various nations' merchants. Therefore, an *iron standard ell* of 2 feet, 6 inches was made and left with the Keeper of the Fair. Each participating merchant was required to use this ell in all business dealings at the fair.

In England, cheating and abuse of measures became so common that a few years after the Magna Carta was signed in 1215, the *Assize of Weights and Measures* was drawn up. For almost 600 years, the Assize defined and standardized a broad list of units. One of these units, *The Iron Yard of Our Lord the King*, was divided into 3 feet of 12 inches each. Eventually, all kinds of measures became standardized in some way, and many national systems of measures came into being. Nearly all of these systems were replaced in Europe by the metric system during the 19th century. Britain and its former colonies in America kept to their old ways until well into the 20th century. The United States still uses the old system.

Several of the original common measures are still good for approximating lengths today. Some measures based on dimensions of an adult human body are listed below. For students, of course, these personal measurements are likely to be smaller than the standards.

- *Cubit* A very old unit of measure, based on the distance between the elbow and the extended fingertips. The Egyptians used the cubit as early as 3000 B.C. to build pyramids. The cubit has been standardized at various times at values between 18 and 22 inches.

- *Hand span* The distance from the end of the thumb to the end of the little finger in an outstretched hand, used to measure things smaller than a cubit. The span has been standardized at 9 inches.

- *Yard* The distance from the center of the chest to the tips of the fingers of an arm held out to the side of the body, often used to measure cloth. A yard has been standardized at 3 feet (36 inches).

- *Fathom* The distance from fingertip to fingertip of the outstretched arms; said to be derived from an Anglo-Saxon word meaning "embrace." Fathoms are often used to measure the depth of water. Perhaps this is because the "leadsman" on a boat or ship in the days before electronic depth finders would drop a lead weight on the end of a rope until it hit bottom and then count the number of fingertip-to-fingertip measures as he gathered in his line. A fathom has been standardized at 6 feet (2 yards).

- *Digit* The width of a finger. One 24th of the royal master cubit in ancient Egypt.

- *Hand* The width of a hand laid flat. Horses are said to be so many "hands" high. The hand has been standardized at 4 inches.

Units of length too long to be measured conveniently with body parts tended to vary widely from country to country before the adoption of the metric system. For example, for distances for which the United States used a *mile* (5,280 feet), the Russians used a *verst* (about 3,500 feet or about 1 kilometer).

Beginning in Kindergarten, children measure various items or parts of their classrooms with parts of themselves and discuss which body parts are more appropriate for which objects. This is a predecessor to choosing measurement tools and units that fit a given measuring task. These activities are expanded in first grade as children learn techniques for measuring with their body-part units, such as putting

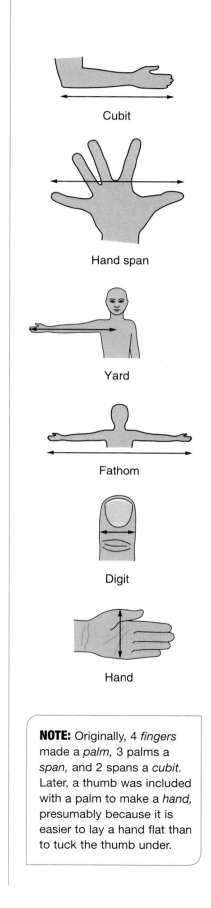

Cubit

Hand span

Yard

Fathom

Digit

Hand

NOTE: Originally, 4 *fingers* made a *palm,* 3 palms a *span,* and 2 spans a *cubit.* Later, a thumb was included with a palm to make a *hand,* presumably because it is easier to lay a hand flat than to tuck the thumb under.

the measuring device end to end to measure larger objects. They are also asked to make a habit of labeling their measures with appropriate "units." This habit is important not only for the act of measuring itself but as an important part of learning to solve number stories.

From second grade on, children continue to use personal reference measures, but the focus shifts to finding body parts that approximate customary or metric units. These parts can then be used to estimate measures without using a ruler, tape measure, or other standardized measuring device. For example, the width of a finger may be about 1 centimeter or a child's foot may be about 8 inches long. Body-part estimation activities continue in Grades 4 through 6; as students grow they need to adjust their personal reference measures.

▶ 14.2 Measurement Systems

This section discusses the two standardized measurement systems most commonly used today, the *U.S. customary system* and the *metric system*. By "customary" measures, we mean the ones commonly used in the United States. If you have students from other countries in your class, the metric system may be customary to them, so be sure the meaning of "customary" is clear in discussions.

There are also several commonly used measures that are neither metric nor U.S. customary: measures of angles, elapsed time, and monetary values, to name a few. *Everyday Mathematics* activities that engage students in understanding these measures are discussed later in this chapter.

14.2.1 U.S. Customary System

The *U.S. customary system* of measures is adapted from the English system, which was developed around the 13th century. Although most people in the United States are relatively comfortable with the U.S. customary system, it has definite drawbacks compared to the metric system. For one thing, because they evolved gradually out of specific, often local, needs, customary units of length, weight, and capacity are largely independent of one another. Another drawback is that the relationships among units are somewhat cumbersome. For example, a foot is $\frac{1}{3}$ of a yard, but an inch (the next-smaller standard unit) is $\frac{1}{12}$ of a foot. A quart is $\frac{1}{4}$ of a gallon, but a pint (the next-smaller standard unit) is $\frac{1}{2}$ of a quart.

14.2.2 Metric System

Scientifically minded people in France deliberately developed the metric system at the end of the 18th century. The basic unit of length in this system is the *meter*. Originally, the meter was defined as 1 ten-millionth of the distance from the North Pole to the equator along the global meridian through Paris. These days, the meter is defined as the distance light will travel in a vacuum in $\frac{1}{299,792,458}$ second.

In the metric system, many units are defined relative to the meter. Next-smaller or next-larger units are ratio comparisons by a power of 10 and so they are easily converted from one to another. For example,

NOTE: The relationships among inches, feet, yards, and miles are based on a *duodecimal* (base-12) number system. An advantage to this is that so many different whole numbers divide 12, including 2, 3, 4, and 6. In this way, the U.S. customary system is much like the ancient Egyptian system.

a *decimeter* is 1 tenth (0.1) of a meter, and a *centimeter* is 1 tenth (0.1) of a decimeter.

Metric units of length, area, volume, capacity, and weight are interrelated. For example, a liter is a measure of volume or capacity equal to 1 cubic decimeter, and a cubic decimeter is equal to the volume of 1 kilogram of distilled water at 4°C.

14.2.3 Converting between Measures

Because the United States uses both metric and customary measures, being able to convert between these systems can sometimes be important. For example, Minnesota, a neighbor of metric-using Canada, has posted road signs proclaiming that 55 miles per hour is 88 kilometers per hour. It is also important to be able to convert from one unit to another within a system. Knowing how many inches are in a foot, feet in a yard, yards in a mile, and so on provides the power to convert measures from one unit to another, which can be handy in many situations.

In the early grades of *Everyday Mathematics,* children learn what U.S. customary and metric measures are, how to estimate them generally, and how to approximate them using measuring tools. Children in *Kindergarten* through *Third Grade Everyday Mathematics* do not convert units from one system to the other, but only within a given system. Students convert between measurement systems in Grades 5 and 6.

Measures can be converted by multiplying by unit fractions. A *unit fraction* is a fraction with 1 in the numerator. The unit fractions used in making conversions between measurements have numerators and denominators that name equal quantities but have different units. Such unit fractions are equivalent to 1. For example, the numerator and denominator in the unit fraction $\frac{1\ ft}{12\ in.}$ name the same quantity in different units, so $\frac{1\ ft}{12\ in.} = 1$.

$\frac{1\ ft}{12\ in.}$	$\frac{1\ mi}{5{,}280\ ft}$	$\frac{1\ yd}{36\ in.}$
$\frac{1\ in.}{2.54\ cm}$	$\frac{1\ m}{100\ cm}$	$\frac{1\ km}{1{,}000\ m}$

Some unit fractions for converting between measures

Multiplying any number by 1 yields a product that equals the original number. So, multiplying a measurement by a sequence of unit fractions that each equal 1 yields a product that equals the original measurement. Similarly, multiplying a measurement by reciprocals of unit fractions equal to 1 also yields a product equal to the original measurement.

Example: Convert 36,000,000 inches to miles.

You can multiply by unit fractions involving inches, feet, and miles:

$$36{,}000{,}000 \text{ in.} * \frac{1\ ft}{12\ in.} * \frac{1\ mi}{5{,}280\ ft}$$

As indicated by the slash marks below, the inches and feet divide out leaving only the mile unit. Dividing 36,000,000 by 63,360 on a calculator yields approximately 570 miles.

$$36{,}000{,}000 \cancel{\text{ in.}} * \frac{1\ \cancel{ft}}{12\ \cancel{in.}} * \frac{1\ mi}{5{,}280\ \cancel{ft}} = \frac{36{,}000{,}000\ mi}{63{,}360} \approx 570 \text{ mi}$$

Because both metric and U.S. customary measures are used in the United States and because almost all of the rest of the world is metric, being able to convert between systems is useful, especially for travelers. Precise conversions are seldom necessary, although it helps to know that by definition 1 inch = 2.54 centimeters. Here are other helpful conversion tips:

- A centimeter is about $\frac{3}{8}$ inch.
- A meter is about 10% longer than a yard.
- A kilometer is about 0.6 mile; a mile is about 1.6 kilometers.
- A liter is a little more than a quart.
- A kilogram is about 10% more than 2 pounds.

More precise conversions between systems can be made in the same way as within a system.

> **Example:** Convert 1 kilometer, or 1,000 meters, to miles.
>
> Choose unit fractions and reciprocals so that meters, centimeters, inches, and feet divide out.
>
> $$1{,}000 \text{ m} * \frac{100 \text{ cm}}{1 \text{ m}} * \frac{1 \text{ in.}}{2.54 \text{ cm}} * \frac{1 \text{ ft}}{12 \text{ in.}} * \frac{1 \text{ mi}}{5{,}280 \text{ ft}} \approx 0.62 \text{ mi}$$

In this unit-fraction approach to conversions, unit names in quotients and products are treated as though they are numbers. This method works for all types of measures, not just linear ones as in the examples. It is part of what is called *units analysis* or *dimensional analysis* and is an important technique in scientific calculations. A long-time concern of science educators has been the neglect of units analysis in mathematics instruction. *Everyday Mathematics* is committed to teaching students about the meaning and use of measurement units.

▶ 14.3 Length

Distances along 1-dimensional objects, or along paths, are measured with *linear* measures. Like all measures, a linear measure consists of a value and a *unit*. For example, *The edge of my desk is about 3.5 long* makes no sense. However, *The edge of my desk is about 3.5 feet long* provides both the approximate length and a unit of measure.

Two common linear measures are *length,* the distance between two points on a line or arc, and *perimeter,* the distance around an object. The perimeter of a circle is called the *circumference* of the circle.

In all grades, students estimate length with and without tools. In Grades 2 through 6, they are expected to be able to measure to the nearest inch, $\frac{1}{2}$ inch, $\frac{1}{4}$ inch, $\frac{1}{8}$ inch, and $\frac{1}{16}$ inch, respectively. In second grade they are also expected to be able to measure to the nearest centimeter; in third grade to the nearest $\frac{1}{2}$ centimeter; and in fifth grade to the nearest millimeter.

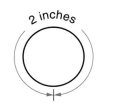

2 inches

2 inches

For information on tools to measure length, see Section 14.11.3: Rulers and Tape Measures.

14.3.1 Formulas for Linear Measures

There is no great need for formulas for most linear measures because they can be found easily enough with a direct measurement or by a direct measurement on a blueprint, map, or other model followed by a scale change. However, there are four formulas involving linear measures in *Everyday Mathematics*.

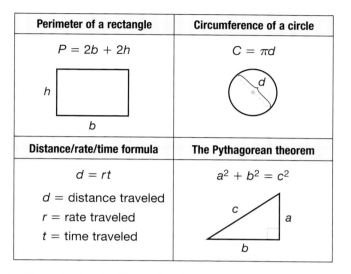

Perimeter of a rectangle	Circumference of a circle
$P = 2b + 2h$	$C = \pi d$
Distance/rate/time formula	**The Pythagorean theorem**
$d = rt$ d = distance traveled r = rate traveled t = time traveled	$a^2 + b^2 = c^2$

Students in *Fourth Grade Everyday Mathematics* develop a formula for the perimeter of a rectangle, and in fifth grade they develop one for the circumference of a circle. The latter is approached by measuring diameters and circumferences of various circles and looking at their ratios to approximate π, an activity third graders perform with tin cans to get an approximation of "about 3" for π. Students are also given a formula relating distance traveled, rate of travel (speed), and time of travel; and they look at a graph of points showing a constant rate. In these activities, the focus is on the use of variables and equations as models, rather than on the value or necessity of the formula itself.

The Pythagorean theorem is included in this section because the variables all represent 1-dimensional lengths of the sides of a right triangle, even though the values are squared. The theorem is useful in calculating the length of one of the sides of a right triangle when the other two side lengths are known. For example, to calculate the length of a hypotenuse c, a useful variation of the equation is the following:

$$c = \sqrt{a^2 + b^2}$$

In part, *Everyday Mathematics* introduces the Pythagorean theorem to help sixth graders understand the inverse relationship between squaring and taking square roots.

Just as 1-dimensional objects can be thought of as building blocks for 2- and 3-dimensional objects, so can length be considered a building block for 2- and 3-dimensional measures. These are called area and volume, respectively, and are discussed in the following sections.

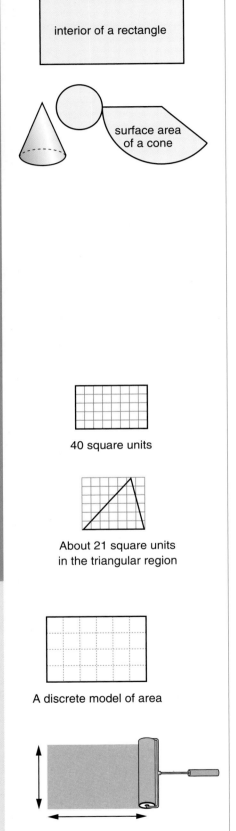

interior of a rectangle

surface area of a cone

40 square units

About 21 square units in the triangular region

A discrete model of area

A continuous model of area

▶ **14.4 Area**

While length and perimeter are measures of a finite distance along a path, *area* is a measure of a finite amount of a 2-dimensional surface. This surface may lie in a single plane, such as the interior of a rectangle, or it may exist in 3-dimensional space, such as the curved surface of a cylinder or cone. The latter type of area is called *surface area*.

Like other numerical measures, a measure of area always includes both a value and a unit. Units of area are typically square units based on linear units, for example, square inches, square centimeters, square yards, and square meters. Some traditional units of area are not square units. For example, it is said that long ago an acre of land was the amount of land a farmer could plow in one day.

14.4.1 Discrete and Continuous Models of Area

This section discusses two different models for thinking about area. Each model has its strengths and weaknesses in helping students understand a concept that many people find difficult.

Discrete Model of Area

In most schoolbooks, the definition of area is based on the idea of *tiling,* or covering a surface with identical unit squares without gaps or overlaps and then counting those squares. This is a *discrete model of area* because it involves separate, countable parts. If the surface is bounded by a rectangle, you can arrange the tiles in an array and multiply the number of tiles per row by the number of rows. The formula $A = l * w$ is then easily linked to array multiplication: area A is the number of square-unit tiles in one row (the length l of one side of the rectangle in some linear unit) times the number of rows (the width w of the rectangle in the same unit).

For other surfaces, defined by regular or irregular boundaries, the tiling with square units can be thought of as, or actually done by, laying a grid of appropriate square units on the region and counting, estimating, or otherwise calculating how many squares or partial squares it takes to cover the region.

Continuous Model of Area

Tiling activities develop a discrete model of area, as described above. In later grades, students touch on a *continuous model of area*. Imagine rolling a paint roller 1 foot wide on the floor of a rectangular room. For every foot the roller travels, a square foot of the floor is painted.

Now imagine that the room is 20 feet wide and that you use a roller the width of the room (a 20-foot-wide roller). Then, for every foot the roller travels, 20 square feet of floor will be painted. When the roller reaches the other side of the room, the entire floor will be painted.

If you think of the floor as the interior of a rectangle, then the area of the rectangle is obtained not by counting squares (a discrete model) but by *sweeping* the width of the rectangle across the interior of the rectangle, parallel to its base (a continuous model). The area is simply the product of the length of the base and the width of the rectangle. This can be shown by rubbing the long part of a piece of chalk on the chalkboard to mark a rectangular region; the farther it is swept along, the larger the rectangle and the greater the area.

Students have experience with area throughout *Everyday Mathematics*. Younger children focus on manipulating discrete conceptions of area through tiling activities. Beginning in third grade, children are asked to estimate area measures, and sometimes they check them by actually measuring. Beginning in Grade 4, students use formulas to model area symbolically. In Grades 4 and 5, students estimate areas of land and research areas of states, countries, and continents in the World Tour and American Tour, respectively.

14.4.2 Area Formulas

The first formulas seen by students of *Everyday Mathematics* are for area measures. Rather than being given formulas, fourth graders are asked to develop their own by doing experiments. The following are five useful area formulas.

Area of a triangle	Area of a rectangle	Area of a parallelogram
$A = \frac{1}{2}bh$	$A = bh$	$A = bh$

Area of a trapezoid	Area of a circle
$A = \frac{1}{2}(b_1 + b_2)h$	$A = \pi r^2$

The formula for the area of a rectangle is fairly easy for students to discover. Area formulas for a parallelogram and a triangle are found with a little more guidance, using paper-folding techniques and grid paper. The area of a circle can be estimated quite closely; eventually, π is defined, and fifth graders are given the formula.

NOTE: In general, the *surface area* of a 3-dimensional object is found by adding the areas of all its faces. So a formula for the surface area is a sum of the formulas for each face. For example, a formula for the surface area S of a cube with edge length e is $S = 6 * e^2$, or the total area of the six square faces of the cube. Surface area formulas for prisms, cylinders, and spheres are in the Tables of Formulas on page 371.

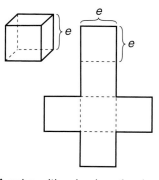

A cube with edge length e has surface area $S = 6 * e^2$.

Sixth graders find the area of a trapezoid by dividing it into a rectangle and one or two triangles and then adding the areas of the pieces. A shortcut to this method is to use the formula in the table on the previous page. In the formula, b_1 is the length of one of the parallel bases of the trapezoid, b_2 is the length of the other base, and h is the height, or altitude, as shown in the margin.

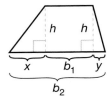

For more on the Distributive Property, see Section 17.2.3: Simplifying Expressions.

If the trapezoid is partitioned into two triangles and a rectangle as shown in the margin, then the area A of the trapezoid is equal to the sum of the areas of the triangles and rectangle, as follows:

$$A = \frac{1}{2}xh + \frac{1}{2}yh + b_1 h$$

This is equivalent to:

$$A = \frac{1}{2}xh + \frac{1}{2}yh + \frac{2}{2}b_1 h$$

By the Distributive Property of Multiplication over Addition:

$$A = \frac{1}{2}h(x + y + 2b_1)$$

This is equivalent to:

$$A = \frac{1}{2}h(x + y + b_1 + b_1)$$

But $x + y + b_1$ is the length of the bottom base b_2 in the drawing. So the formula can be written:

$$A = \frac{1}{2}h(b_1 + b_2)$$

The formula shows that the area of a trapezoid is equal to the average of the two bases, $\frac{1}{2}(b_1 + b_2)$, times the height, h. Because multiplication is commutative, you could write the formula to reflect this perspective:

$$A = \frac{1}{2}(b_1 + b_2)h$$

Developing the trapezoid area formula as shown above reviews many ideas in *Sixth Grade Everyday Mathematics* and is a good end-of-year challenge for students who are ready.

▶ 14.5 Volume (Capacity)

Volume, or *capacity,* is the measure of a finite amount of 3-dimensional space. As with measures in one and two dimensions, all measures of volume require a unit, and all are approximate. Volume units are often cubic units based on linear measures, such as cubic inches, cubic centimeters, cubic yards, and cubic meters. Other units for volume, such as milliliters, teaspoons, pints, quarts, and liters, are used to measure liquids or fine-grained materials such as sand and sugar.

NOTE: Dry ingredients such as sugar are sometimes measured by weight.

As with all measures, it is possible to convert from one unit to another. For example, a *fluid ounce* is 1.804 cubic inches. A *liter* is 1,000 cubic centimeters. You can see why the U.S. customary system is not as popular as the metric system when it comes to conversions.

14.5.1 Discrete and Continuous Models of Volume

Discrete and continuous models of volume are analogous to the corresponding models of area.

Discrete Model of Volume

In a *discrete model of volume*, imagine building 3-dimensional shapes with identical cubes or filling shapes completely with such cubes and then counting the cubes. If the shape is a rectangular prism, you can build one layer of cubes, count the cubes in that layer, and then multiply that number by the number of layers needed to fill the prism. Because the number of cubes in one layer corresponds to the area of the base, often represented by the formula $A = l * w$, this process of counting cubes can be linked to two standard formulas for the volume V of rectangular prisms: $V = B * h$ (the product of the area B of the rectangular base and the height h perpendicular to that base) and $V = l * w * h$ (the product of the length l and width w of the rectangular base and the height h perpendicular to that base).

Continuous Model of Volume

The formula $V = B * h$ for volume of a rectangular prism captures a *continuous model of volume* similar to the "sweeping out" of area. For example, imagine the base of a box as a rectangular region. Then imagine sweeping this rectangular region through the height of the box, and so filling the space. Or imagine gradually filling the box with water. The surface of the water is rectangular, like the base of the box, so the higher the water level, the more space the water occupies and the greater is its volume.

This model for a rectangular prism leads to a general formula for the volume of prisms and cylinders: the area of the base multiplied by the perpendicular height. Unlike $V = l * w * h,$ the formula $V = B * h$ works for any shape base.

Both models of volume are used throughout *Everyday Mathematics,* with a discrete approach dominating first and second grade as young children fill objects with cubes. In Grades 3 and 4, they experiment with a continuous approach by filling objects with water or sand. In Grades 5 and 6, students focus on the use of variables in formulas to model volume symbolically.

14.5.2 Volume Formulas

Volume formulas are developed with informal activities begun in *Third Grade Everyday Mathematics.* Fourth graders review box-packing experiments and generalize them into a formula for the volume of a rectangular prism. Fifth graders expand this formula to one for any prism or cylinder, and they develop formulas for the volume of any pyramid or cone.

NOTE: The formula $V = l * w * h$ is commonly used in elementary textbooks and on standardized tests. $V = B * h$ is used in many mathematics courses and technical applications.

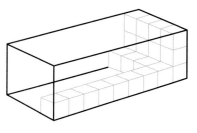

Filling a box with cubes is a discrete model of volume.

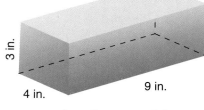

3 in.
4 in.
9 in.

A continuous model of volume

It should be emphasized that the *Everyday Mathematics* formula of choice is the more informal "area of base times height" formula rather than the specific ones shown below. If students remember the informal formula, then they can construct any of the others by knowing the area formulas for polygons and circles. The following are seven useful volume formulas.

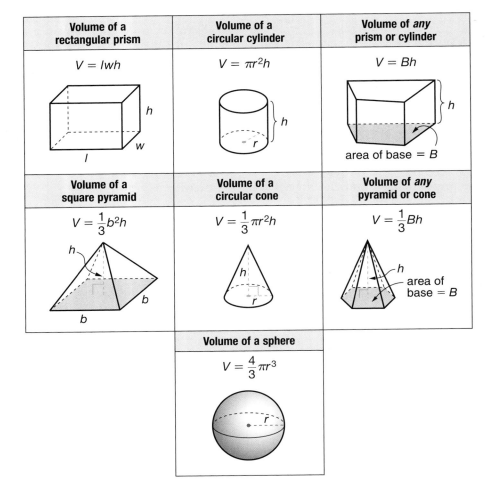

Volume of a rectangular prism	Volume of a circular cylinder	Volume of *any* prism or cylinder
$V = lwh$	$V = \pi r^2 h$	$V = Bh$
Volume of a square pyramid	Volume of a circular cone	Volume of *any* pyramid or cone
$V = \frac{1}{3} b^2 h$	$V = \frac{1}{3} \pi r^2 h$	$V = \frac{1}{3} Bh$

Volume of a sphere

$V = \frac{4}{3} \pi r^3$

14.5.3 Linking Area and Volume

The idea of dimension is at the heart of area and volume, and understanding dimension requires plenty of experience with 1-, 2-, and 3-dimensional figures, both individually and in relation to one another. This is one reason why measuring actual objects for their 1-dimensional attributes, such as length or perimeter, 2-dimensional attributes, such as area and surface area, and 3-dimensional attributes, such as volume, is such an integral component of *Everyday Mathematics* beginning in Kindergarten.

By fourth grade, students should be comfortable identifying attributes of 1-, 2-, and 3-dimensional figures and their measures. They will also have had many informal experiences relating objects in different dimensions. For example, each edge of a 3-dimensional cube is a 1-dimensional line segment; the four edges of each face form a 2-dimensional square. In *Fourth* through *Sixth Grade Everyday*

Mathematics, students explore relationships between the dimensions through the continuous models of area and volume described in previous sections of this chapter. Moving a point along a path models a change from 0 to 1 dimension. Moving a line segment to generate a plane figure with area models a change from 1 to 2 dimensions. Moving a plane figure to generate a 3-dimensional object with volume models a change from 2 to 3 dimensions.

14.6 Weight and Mass

Mass is a measure of the amount of matter in an object. *Weight* is the force of gravity on an object. If you weighed yourself on different planets on a trip around the solar system your weight would vary drastically depending on the size of the planet. You would weigh more on large planets because their gravitational pull is stronger. You would weigh less on small planets because they don't exert as much pull. Your mass, however, would be the same regardless of the planet you were on because the amount of matter in your body is not affected by gravity.

In *Everyday Mathematics,* students focus on measuring weight, not mass. It can be measured with a variety of scales. For example, a *balance scale* compares an object's weight to a standard set of weights, or it can simply compare relative weights of any two objects to see which is heavier without measuring. A *spring scale* measures the pull of gravity as evidenced by an object's push or pull on a spring.

The units of measure most common to your classroom will depend on the units defined by your scales. Some scales measure with U.S. customary units such as ounces and pounds, while others measure with metric units such as grams and kilograms.

14.7 Angle Measure

Angular measures quantify turns or rotations. In Kindergarten through third grade, children measure angles as fractions of a circle; for example, a right angle is a quarter-turn and a straight angle is a half turn.

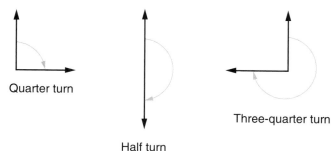

Quarter turn

Half turn

Three-quarter turn

Students in *Fourth Grade Everyday Mathematics* start using protractors to measure angles in degrees. A degree is $\frac{1}{360}$ of a full rotation and is the angle measure used in most practical situations. In Grades 5 and 6, angle measurement is often a part of contexts for problem-solving activities. In later mathematics courses, students will learn about other angle measures, especially the *radian* (2π radians $= 360°$).

Models across dimensions

NOTE: The movement of points, segments, or plane figures does not necessarily have to be at right angles as shown above. That is, higher dimensions are not perpendicular to lower ones, as the drawings may make them appear. However, there is pedagogical value to having students picture the changes as perpendicular, so there is no reason to belabor this point with students.

For more information, see Section 14.11.4: Scales and Balances.

NOTE: Your weight even varies slightly at different altitudes above sea level on Earth, yet your mass remains the same.

For more information, see Section 13.4.1: Angles and Rotations.

chapter 14

For more information, see Section 15.2: Time.

▶ 14.8 Elapsed Time

Numbers are used both to mark time and to measure it. We mark time by establishing reference frames, such as a calendar year and the number of days in a month. Events are then described by locations on one or more of these frames, such as *She was born August 15, 1989, at 2:00* A.M. These numbers are not measures because they cannot be added or subtracted with any meaning. For example, 2:00 P.M. plus 3:00 P.M. is not 5:00 P.M., nor is April 12 plus April 15 equal to April 27. The reference labels *P.M.* and *April* are not units of measure.

Once reference frames have been established, however, there are reference units that can be used as measures. For example, *The play lasted 68 minutes. He finished the race in 3.9 seconds. The past 4 years have been warm.* The use of time units to measure the duration of an event or the time between events is called *elapsed time.*

Our units of time have the longest-known history of any measuring units. The 24-hour day comes from the ancient Egyptians, who divided the period from sunrise to sunset into 12 equal parts and the period from sunset to sunrise into 12 equal parts as well. Because the times of sunrise and sunset vary, the lengths of these two kinds of "hours" changed daily. The 7-day week is credited to the Babylonians, who observed seven moving celestial bodies: the sun, the moon, and five planets. Also, the Babylonians used a numeration system based on 60, probably because 60 is divisible by many whole numbers. This led to the 60-second minute and the 60-minute hour.

Students use time measures frequently throughout *Everyday Mathematics,* most often in the context of number stories. As students learn new arithmetic skills, elapsed-time applications of these skills are developed. For example, in first and second grades, children use addition and subtraction to figure out elapsed times: *What time was it 2 hours ago? What time will it be in 3 hours?* In Grades 4 through 6, time measurements are important parts of rate problems. For example, students figure out gallons per minute of water flow, an animal's speed in feet per second, or calculations per millisecond by a computer. Students also answer ratio-comparison questions about time, such as *What fraction of a year is 9 months?*

▶ 14.9 Money

Money may be viewed as a reference frame because it is an arbitrary scale used to establish the value of goods and services. Like the variations in the linear measure *foot* before standardization, however, different people place different values on the same goods or services. To make matters even more complicated, the differences are not just physical but emotional, spiritual, and intellectual in nature. Even an individual's perceived value of something changes with time and experience.

However, in everyday life, money is more a *measure of relative value* than a reference frame. We measure the value of one thing versus another or of one thing now versus that thing yesterday or last year. Statements such as *This TV costs $50 more now than it did three* *months ago* and *Bananas are up 17% this season* are examples of how we use arithmetic to compare monetary values. This is a sign that money behaves like a measure, so it is categorized as such in *Everyday Mathematics*.

Young children are exposed to money, prices, buying, and selling on a daily basis, but few have experience with money details. That is, children observe money transactions, are given an exact amount to spend, or hand over coins and accept change without checking. Although there are exceptions, many first-grade children are unable to distinguish among coins; for example, nickels and quarters are often confused. Also, relatively few beginning first graders know the exchanges among coins or their links to the basic dollar unit.

Experience with money is important because of its inherent usefulness and, like most measures, because of the context it provides for number stories. Additionally, our base-ten monetary system is an excellent vehicle for the study of place value, fractions, and decimal notation. *Everyday Mathematics* provides students with early experiences to develop their knowledge about the details of money. Then the familiar context of money makes it easier for students to become acquainted with fractions and decimals at earlier ages than they would in a traditional mathematics curriculum.

In *Kindergarten* through *Third Grade Everyday Mathematics*, money is a focus of instruction. By fourth grade, it is assumed that most students have a good understanding of money and can use it in number stories without explicit coverage or review.

14.9.1 Money Facts

Talking about coins and bills also provides a unique opportunity to bridge various curriculum subjects. Money lore contains interesting facts about the history of our country, about the science of metals, and about symbols in our heritage. Use these facts liberally in your teaching about coins and bills in the *Everyday Mathematics* money lessons and at other times during the year. Selected definitions follow.

- *Alloy* A mixture of two or more chemical elements, at least one of which is a metal.
- *Denomination* The official value of a coin.
- *E Pluribus Unum* The original motto of the United States; translated from Latin as "From many, one." This motto is required by an 1873 law to appear on any coin that contains an eagle. In fact, it appears on all U.S. coins.
- *In God We Trust* A motto that was permitted, but not required, on coins by the 1873 law; a 1955 law required that the motto be placed on all coins and bills. In 1956, President Dwight D. Eisenhower signed a law making "In God We Trust" the official motto of the United States.
- *Intrinsic value* The actual worth of the metal in a coin.
- *Obverse* The face, or "front," of a coin; "HEADS."
- *Reverse* The back, or "rear," of a coin; "TAILS."

NOTE: In the wizard world of Harry Potter, there are 29 copper *knuts* in a silver *sickle* and 17 sickles in a gold *galleon.* This is certainly a context in which a calculator can help with conversions.

NOTE: To make it easier to distinguish it from a quarter, which is about the same size, the Sacagawea dollar coin is *not* reeded.

- *Rim* The edge of a coin, which is quite functional because it allows coins to be stacked and protects the design from damage. Most U.S. coins worth more than 5 cents have always had rims that are ornate, lettered, or *reeded,* that is, with parallel grooves that are perpendicular to the face of the coin, as in our dime and quarter. This is intended to discourage the scraping of the coin edges to steal some of its metal; it also makes it easier to identify coins by touch, which is necessary for people with visual impairments and useful for pulling a specific amount of change out of your pocket without looking.

New designs for coins and bills are adopted periodically, putting currency in the United States in a constant, albeit slow, state of flux. Recently, the U.S. Treasury Department produced a series of quarters commemorating each state in the United States and has minted a new American-bison nickel. A rewarding cross-curricular activity is to explore individual coins and their designs while touching upon history, metallurgy, and architecture. For example, some interesting facts about nickels are given below.

Nickels

Until 1866, 5-cent pieces were called "half-dimes." The word *nickel* comes from the metal in the coin. Currently, nickels are made of an alloy of 75% copper and 25% nickel.

Obverse The Jefferson bust was designed by Felix O. Schlag, whose initials, FS, appear between the rim and the bottom of the bust on nickels produced after 1965.

Obverse

Information about Thomas Jefferson	
Born	April 13, 1743; Shadwell (now Albemarle County), Virginia
Died	July 4, 1826; at Monticello, his estate in Albemarle County, Virginia. Jefferson died on the 50th anniversary of the signing of the Declaration of Independence. The second President of the United States, John Adams, died on the same day.
Occupations	Lawyer; delegate to the Continental Congress; author of the Declaration of Independence; Governor of Virginia; ambassador to France; Vice President; President; founder of the University of Virginia; farmer; architect
Important Dates	1797 elected Vice President under President John Adams 1801 inaugurated as third President 1803 Louisiana Purchase 1804 reelected President

Reverse Monticello appears on the reverse, along with its name. President Franklin D. Roosevelt suggested this coinage design in 1938.

Reverse

Information about Monticello	
Location	Albemarle County, Virginia
Architect	Thomas Jefferson
Built	First version, 1769–1793 Second version, 1793–1809

14.9.2 Money History

The history of money in our country is also quite interesting. The first coin used extensively in the American colonies was the *Spanish milled dollar,* a silver coin referred to as a *piece of eight* because it was worth 8 *reales,* pronounced "ray-al-ays." The coin was also called a *peso.* Even today, our $ symbol is the same as that for the Mexican peso. The milled dollar was often cut into eight pieces to allow for smaller denominations. Each of the eight pieces was called a *real* or a *bit.* Thus, for many years, a dollar was referred to as eight bits, a half-dollar as four bits, and a quarter as two bits.

When the United States began to produce its own coins, it used the Spanish milled dollar as its model. The first U.S. dollars, which weighed exactly as much as the Spanish coins, were made of an alloy composed of 15 parts silver to one part gold. In 1792, Congress passed the first coinage act for the new country and authorized the production of coins in various denominations: an eagle ($10), a half-eagle ($5), coins with the modern values, and a half-cent. With the exception of the cent and the half-cent, these early coins did not show their denominations. An Act of Congress corrected this oversight in 1837. Until 1909, the heads, or busts, of all people represented on U.S. coins were abstractions, such as Liberty, or generic figures, such as a Native American. In 1909, Abraham Lincoln appeared on the first coin picturing a real person.

The American eagle, which appears by law on all coins with a value of more than 10 cents, is the likeness of an actual eagle, "Peter the Mint Bird," the mascot of the Philadelphia Mint in the 1840s and 1850s. After his death, Peter was stuffed and is, to this day, preserved in a glass case in the Philadelphia Mint.

NOTE: Cheers like "Two bits, four bits, six bits, a dollar! . . . All for Springfield, stand up and holler!" continue to carry the early terms for coins into the present. "Shave and a haircut, two bits" may be dying out, but the rhythm behind the saying lives on.

Resources on Money

Information about U.S. coins and bills and the history of money can be found in the following books and Web site:

Barabas, K. (1997). *Let's Find Out About Money.* New York: Scholastic.

Doty, R. (2008). *America's Money, America's Story.* Atlanta, GA: Whitman Publishing.

U.S. Treasury Web site: www.ustreas.gov/topics/currency/

Yeoman, R. S. (Yearly). *Guide Book of United States Coins.* New York: Golden Books Adult.

14.10 Measures in Geography

The use of measures in geography is a special focus throughout *Everyday Mathematics.* Geographic measurements are obtained directly by applying measuring methods to Earth itself or are obtained indirectly by applying measuring methods to maps, aerial photos, satellite images, and so on.

14.10.1 Linear Measures in Geography

Linear, or 1-dimensional, measures have been culturally and politically important since humans began keeping records of territory. Linear measures can be vertical, that is, above or below sea level, or along the surface of Earth. The *datum plane* is the mean, or average, sea level based on many, many measurements. Nowadays, reflecting laser beams from satellites off the earth's surface allow these measures to be continually refined. The following are important linear geographical measures.

Elevation of a city The U.S. Geological Survey (USGS) sets a concrete benchmark with this measurement, the *city datum,* somewhere in the downtown area of major cities. Surveyors use *stair-step leveling,* as shown in the margin, to determine the vertical distance of the benchmark from the datum plane. An instrument with a horizontal line of sight is set at point *A* of known elevation. It is aligned with a graduated pole at point *B* of unknown elevation. The reading on the pole is used to find the elevation of *B.* The process can continue by moving the instrument to another point *C,* taking a reading from the pole at *B,* and using it to find the elevation of point *C.* The elevation of point *C* can be used to find the elevation of point *D,* and so on.

Height of a mountain pass This is the elevation of the pass at its highest point. Surveyors use stair-step leveling from nearby benchmarks, often from both sides of the pass. Rugged terrain and adverse atmospheric conditions may affect the accuracy of the measurement.

Depth of an ocean Sonar signals are sent to the ocean floor and reflected back to determine water depth. The total time for the signal to make the trip is recorded and corrections made for water temperature and other factors. The final result, often accurate to the nearest 10 feet, requires precise measurement of the position above or below the datum plane of the apparatus used to send the signal.

Depth of a lake or inland sea The same techniques and difficulties apply as those described for measurement of the lowest point from the surface of an ocean. A major difference is that each inland body of water is assigned its own datum plane based on an average water level.

Length of a river This measurement is usually made on a map developed from satellite photography and perhaps other sources. The measurement is made guiding a hand-held instrument about the size of a ballpoint pen slowly and steadily along the full length of the river as represented on the map. This instrument has a very small wheel rather than a ball at its tip. A meter counts the number of rotations, which, along with the map scale, are used to compute a preliminary estimate of the length of the river. The estimate is then adjusted to take into account the slope of the river from its source to its mouth. Accuracy may be expected within 0.1% of the actual length. Reported variations in lengths may be due to disagreement on which of several headwater streams is the river proper and whether or not the river changed course since the map was made.

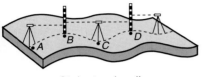

Stair-step leveling

NOTE: While the measure of a city benchmark is based on careful engineering, the choice of the benchmark's location is not standard. Some cities use a landmark or revered building. Others average the elevations of several downtown points and put the benchmark in a place at that mean elevation. The USGS's role is to maintain the records and verify the measures.

NOTE: Unlike depths of lakes or inland seas, which are based on averages, depths of oceans tend to be the extreme values. For example, the deepest point in the world, located in the Pacific Ocean, is a point in Challenger Deep in the Mariana Trench. This depth is 10,924 meters, according to the *2005 CIA World Fact Book.* The depth of the Pacific as a whole is certainly much less, just as the average height above sea level of Earth is certainly less than the height of Mt. Everest.

14.10.2 Area in Geography

Area measurements are based on accurate maps. Important applications include the following:

Area of a country Although most countries have irregular shapes, their areas can be estimated using transparent graph paper or by projecting a grid on an accurate map. The whole squares that fit within a country's boundaries are counted. Smaller squares or triangles are used to refine the measurement, and the map scale is used to calculate the area. Reported areas vary from reference book to reference book and should be accepted with caution.

Areas of countries are also inaccurate for the following reasons:

- There may not be agreement on a country's boundaries or claims to territorial waters.

- Measuring the area of a country as if its entire surface were a horizontal plane understates the land surface in mountainous territory.

Area of an ocean, sea, or lake This measurement relies on agreement on an average water level of the body of water. That level determines a shoreline that bounds the area to be calculated. As with the area of a country, the area of a body of water is found by covering a carefully produced map with squares. Because the world's oceans are separated from each other by arbitrary boundaries rather than shorelines, ocean areas should be accepted with caution, even those rounded to the nearest 100 square miles.

Area of a continent The square-counting process is also used for estimating areas of continents, with the same cautions. Assuming that the country is flat results in understated areas in mountainous territory, and there may be uncertainty in identifying shorelines. Some estimates include the continental shelf, which extends out under water from the shoreline, and others do not. Most continental area estimates use shoreline limits but others include offshore land. For example, one source's area estimate for North America includes Greenland and the islands of the Caribbean and rounds the approximation to the nearest 100,000 square miles.

Area of a desert Although the measurement of desert area uses the same square-counting process, estimating desert area is also challenging because the edges of deserts are unstable due to climatic change or development by humans.

Note that there are different definitions of a desert. *Desert* generally means land where there is no agriculture without irrigation because rainfall or other natural sources of water are insufficient. To some people, desert means land where there is no grazing, so that *tundra*, very cold places where the water is always frozen, are considered deserts. Regardless of the definition, area estimates are made in the same way.

In the *Everyday Mathematics* World and American Tours, students discuss in their own language the appropriateness (*validity*) and the

NOTE: Most of the geographic measures in *Everyday Mathematics* come from the *World Almanac and Book of Facts*.

chapter 14

quality *(reliability)* of geographical area measures. For example, *Which is more appropriate for measuring the area of Texas, square centimeters or square miles? Is any reliable estimate of the water level of the Black Sea possible because the level rises and falls?* As with all measurements, geographical ones are estimates and should be taken as such.

14.10.3 Fractals: Geography between Dimensions

Studying many different 1-dimensional measures of height, depth, and length in the context of geography may help students see the *similarities* among linear measurements such as feet and miles or meters and kilometers rather than the obvious *differences* in size. It also provides a strong, informal experience that may help some interested students investigate fractal geometry in later grades. *Fractal geometry* is a relatively new branch of mathematics—it got its name in the 1970s. A part of fractal geometry was developed when investigators tried to measure the length of the coastline of England to a greater degree of accuracy than before. IBM scientist Benoit Mandelbrot determined that the dimension of a mathematical model of a coastline is somewhere between 1 and 2 dimensions. This *fractional dimensional property* led to the name *fractal*.

A crumpled sheet of aluminum foil models a fractal dimension. Fresh off the roll, the sheet of foil is more or less 2-dimensional. Crumpled into a ball, it is 3-dimensional but retains many indentations and irregularities with 2-dimensional characteristics. So it models a dimension somewhere between 2 and 3 dimensions.

Fractal geometry is now a major focus of mathematicians, who use sophisticated computers to study the roughness, brokenness, or irregularity of objects or events as well as to make fascinating graphical designs. You have probably seen fractals on computer screens and in science-fiction movies. Fractal designs demonstrate order and pattern in apparently highly irregular designs.

Basically, a fractal is a figure created by endlessly repeating a defining algorithm. For example, the figures at left show the beginning of a Koch Snowflake, named for its inventor, Swedish mathematician Niels Fabian Helge von Koch (1870–1924). Each side of an equilateral triangle is divided into equal thirds, and two sides of an equilateral triangle are constructed on the middle third. The outward-pointing sides of the new triangles are divided into thirds, and new equilateral triangle sides are constructed on the middle thirds. Each figure in the process is called an *iteration* of the snowflake. Theoretically, a "complete" Koch snowflake has an infinite number of iterations.

The computer graphics image at left, titled "Birth of Lightning," is derived from the *Mandelbrot set,* one of the most famous fractal images. The definition of a Mandelbrot set involves *complex numbers* and *iterated functions* and is therefore beyond the scope of this book. But you can get an idea of how the set is defined by imagining a Frames-and-Arrows diagram with the arrow rule "Square and add *c*,"

Three iterations of a Koch snowflake

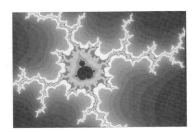

chapter 14

where c is a complex number. A point is in the Mandelbrot set if the sequence of complex numbers in the Frames-and-Arrows diagram that start with that point do not get infinitely large.

Complex numbers have two parts, one real and one imaginary. So each number can be graphed as a point in a coordinate plane with a real axis and an imaginary axis. Each point in the Mandelbrot set is plotted and is assigned a color depending on how many times the rule was applied before it settled down in its position in the plane. The illustration at right is a close-up of a part of the "Birth of Lightning," hinting at how infinitely complex the Mandelbrot set is.

At the risk of oversimplifying the process, after a lot of "chaotic" iterations, points in the Mandelbrot set calm down and stay put. Based on the study of other functions that behave chaotically, a branch of mathematics called *chaos theory* is used to model real-world phenomena such as fluctuations in stock-market prices or population dynamics.

For more information, see Section 9.6: Real Numbers.

Resources on Fractals

Google Images: "Fractal". (2005). *See 121,000 image results for fractal.* Retrieved from images.google.com/images?q=fractal&hl=en&lr=&sa =N&tab=ii&oi=imagest

Shodor: A National Resource for Computational Science Education. (1994–2010). *The Fractal Microscope.* Retrieved from www.shodor.org/ Master/fractal/software/mandy/index.html

▶ 14.11 Measurement Tools and Techniques

No matter which system or unit is being used, measuring tools provide ways to attach numbers to many common and uncommon things in everyone's life. There are measuring tools to measure in any unit or system; some tools even provide help with conversions. The history of science is intertwined with the development of improved measuring instruments. New scientific discoveries often hinge on new and more precise measuring tools, and verification or rejection of theories often depends on increasingly precise measurements. Much of modern industry and technology depends on using very precise measures that are standardized throughout the world. Students learn that the measuring tools that we all use are based on mutually agreed-upon standards and that our own measurements are mere approximations, as the following section explains.

14.11.1 Measurement and Estimation

All measurements are approximate. Even measures that seem exact are actually estimates that are "close enough" for practical considerations. We can never line up the precise edge of an object with a precise point on a measuring tool. For example, this page is not exactly 11 inches long. If you look at its edge under a microscope you will see that it is not even straight. So, is the actual measure the

For more information on precision, see Section 16.2: Approximation and Rounding.

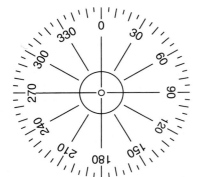

A full-circle protractor

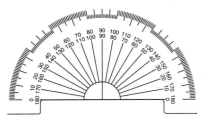

A half-circle protractor

Protractors as they appear
on the Geometry Template

straight-line path from one corner to the other, or is it the path following all the dips and curves of the paper's edge? No matter how careful the measurer, no physical measurement can be exact.

The measuring tool also affects how good a measurement can be. A ruler marked only with inches can be used only to give measures to the nearest inch. And no matter how small the subdivisions on a ruler, there are always unmarked spaces between the marked lines. In general, the *precision* of a measuring tool is the smallest interval on its scale.

So when students learn to measure, whether it be with inexact body measures in Kindergarten or to the nearest half-inch, quarter-inch, or centimeter in later grades, they also are learning to approximate and deal with error.

14.11.2 Protractors and the Percent Circle

Unlike most of us, who had only a half-circle protractor to measure angles when we learned geometry, *Everyday Mathematics* students have three tools: *half-circle protractors, full-circle protractors,* and *percent circles.*

Protractors

In *Third Grade Everyday Mathematics,* children explore rotations and angles using straws and measure angles informally, identifying, for example, a right angle as a quarter-turn. Fourth graders review angles with straws, and then use both kinds of protractors to find more precise measures of angles. First they make 360° angle measurers from journal drawings and straws. Next they use full-circle protractors on transparencies made from a Math Master. To use a full-circle protractor, students must measure angles in a clockwise direction.

Later, students graduate to half-circle protractors, which are slightly more complicated to use because, unlike full-circle protractors that measure angles in a clockwise direction, half-circle protractors have scales for measuring in either a clockwise or counterclockwise direction.

Take whatever time is necessary to help students interpret various ways of marking angles. Figure 1 below shows a right angle marked in four different ways. The arcs in angles 1a and 1b have arrows and represent a $\frac{1}{4}$-clockwise turn and $\frac{1}{4}$-counterclockwise turn, respectively. Using a full-circle protractor, students must measure both of these in a clockwise direction, but you may want older students to qualify the direction of their measures. Using a half-circle protractor, students could be asked to measure in the direction of the arrow to see if they use the tool properly.

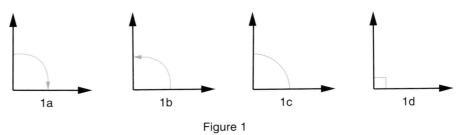

Figure 1

Angle 1c is marked with an arc with no arrows, as is often the case when angles are marked in a polygon. Angle 1d is drawn with the symbol for a right angle. The important idea for beginning angle measurers is that all four angles in Figure 1 measure 90°.

In many cases, an angle may be drawn but no arc is drawn to indicate a direction of rotation as in Figure 2, angle 2a. Without an arc, this angle could represent either of angles 2b or 2c. If no arc is shown in an angle, the usual convention is that the smaller of the two angles is to be used. Angle 2c is called a *reflex angle* because its measure is between 180° and 360°.

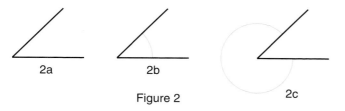

2a   2b   2c

Figure 2

It is likely that students will find it harder to draw angles of a given measure than to measure existing angles. To give students practice in measuring and drawing angles, ask them to draw any angle and then measure it or have someone give a number between 0° and 180° and ask them to draw an angle with that degree measure. In fifth grade, students play the game *Angle Tangle* to practice estimating and measuring angle size.

The Percent Circle

The authors of *Everyday Mathematics* developed the Percent Circle to make measuring and constructing circle graphs easier. The *Percent Circle* is a full-circle protractor on the Geometry Template with the circumference marked in percents rather than degrees. This allows fifth graders to interpret and construct circle graphs before they tackle the complicated calculations needed to construct circle graphs with a protractor, which they learn in sixth grade.

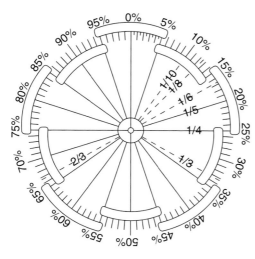

The Percent Circle

NOTE: Part of the reason *Everyday Mathematics* students learn to use half-circle protractors is to think about the direction angles are measured and not learn a hard-and-fast rule that clockwise is "right" and counterclockwise is "wrong." In high school, when students measure angles on a coordinate plane, the convention is to start at the positive *x*-axis and measure counterclockwise for positive angles and clockwise for negative angles.

For more information, see Section 14.7: Angle Measure.

NOTE: All the protractors used in *Everyday Mathematics* are *planar protractors*, but they are not the only kinds. For example, navigators and astronomers use *spherical protractors* to measure spherical angles on and above Earth.

NOTE: Full-circle protractors are described in the previous section.

To construct a circle graph with a protractor, students first express each piece of data as a fractional part of the whole, calculating the degree measure of each slice of the circle graph by finding the appropriate fraction of 360°. Then they draw the computed angle in the circle with a protractor.

14.11.3 Rulers and Tape Measures

Along with weighing scales and balances, *rulers* and *tape measures* are among the first tools used for practical everyday measurements, both in human history and in the lives of students. In the early grades, students learn to give ballpark estimates of heights and lengths; then, over the years, they get progressively more sophisticated in their use of measuring instruments to find approximate lengths. In later grades, *carpenters' rules* are important tools for applying the "half" fractions—$\frac{1}{2}, \frac{1}{4}, \frac{1}{8}$, and so on, each fraction being half the previous one. Metersticks and centimeter rulers are instructive when teaching about decimals.

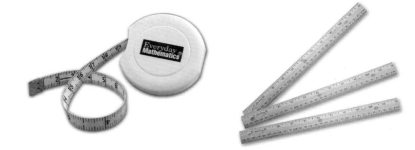

If your students are using retractable tape measures, teach and enforce the "2-inch, 5-centimeter no-zap rule": Do not "zap" the tape measure until no more than 2 inches or 5 centimeters show. This will extend the life of these tools, as well as make your own life quieter and easier.

14.11.4 Scales and Balances

A scale is another historically old measuring tool. *Scales* are used to measure how heavy things are according to a standard weight. There are many different kinds of scales. Some of the scales that *Everyday Mathematics* students will become most familiar with are highlighted here.

For more information, see Section 14.6: Weight and Mass.

A *balance scale* is the first known device for weighing. It was used in Egypt about 3500 B.C. and made use of a simple lever. In ancient Egypt, gold dust was used as currency and needed to be weighed very precisely in order to determine its value.

A balance scale

NOTE: The balance scales most widely used in *Everyday Mathematics* are pan balance scales, or *pan balances* for short.

Balances with the *fulcrum,* the support on which a lever moves, at the center of a horizontal bar are called *equal-arm balances.* The material being weighed is placed in a pan at one end, and known weights are placed in a pan at the other end until a pointer at the fulcrum indicates that the pans are balanced. The ancient Romans developed balances with unequal arms, known as *steelyards*. The object to be weighed is placed on the shorter arm, and a weight is moved along the longer arm until it balances the load.

Beam scales use a counterweight that is moved along the beam until the load is balanced. Calibrations on the beam give the weight. Many health-care providers use this type of scale to weigh patients. Similarly, platform scales use a system of levers, so that a heavy object can be balanced by a relatively small counterweight on the beam. Truck and railroad scales are often of this type.

Spring scales, such as bathroom scales, use linkages to stretch or compress one or more springs. One spring causes the weight indicator to move and automatically give the weight. With simple spring scales, a pan or hook at the bottom of the spring holds the object to be weighed. This type is often seen hanging from ceilings in the produce sections of supermarkets.

Electronic scales were first commercially used in the 1950s and are now seen everywhere, notably in grocery stores and markets. They use a device called a "strain-gauge load cell," which measures the stress an object puts on a mechanical element. The measurement is converted into an electrical signal and transferred to an electronic weight indicator, which gives the weight reading. Some high-precision scales determine weight by measuring the magnetic force needed to counter the downward pull of gravity and support the load on the scales.

Different scales are designed to measure different amounts of weight. There are scales with a variety of capacities and a variety of increments. High-precision scales can measure the weight of a piece of hair or a dose of medicine in increments as small as 0.001 gram or 0.000001 pound. Some platform scales can accommodate trucks weighing as much as 100 tons or railroad cars weighing 825 tons.

Scales have a variety of uses. In the kitchen, they are used to weigh food for cooking and for monitoring diets. Bathroom, nursery, and doctor's scales help monitor personal health. All kinds of scales are used by businesses that sell produce, meat, fish, and bakery items. The post office and other delivery services determine shipping prices based on package weight. Scales are used to weigh trucks to determine the amount of tax that drivers must pay for using the roads. Scales are also used to count pieces, such as the number of nails in a box or pennies in a bag. Scales may give the weight on a dial or digital display in U.S. customary units, metric units, or both.

A beam scale

A spring scale

An electronic scale

15 Reference Frames

Reference frames are something of an oddity in mathematics. Unlike measurements or counts, numbers in reference frames locate things only within definite systems or contexts. Examples include dates, times, Celsius and Fahrenheit temperatures, and coordinates on maps. The numbers in reference frames are set to meet the needs of their creators. For example, the year 2000 in our calendar system is not the same as the year 2000 in the traditional Chinese calendar system, and the Celsius temperature scale is quite different from the Fahrenheit scale.

Most reference frames have a *zero point*, or *origin*. Positive and negative numbers may describe locations on one side of zero or the other. Zero in a reference frame means something different from zero as a count or a measure. A measure or count of zero means that there is none of whatever is being measured or counted. In contrast, the zero point in a reference frame is simply a starting point; it does not necessarily correspond with nothingness or a lowest bound for positive numbers. As a result, numbers in reference frames are not necessarily governed by the same mathematical rules as other numbers.

Doing arithmetic with numbers in reference frames often makes no sense. For example, adding the year 1950 to the year 2010 gives no meaningful result, 30°C is not 3 times as warm as 10°C, and 3:00 P.M. plus 2:00 P.M. does not equal 5:00 P.M. On the other hand, the numbers in reference frames can be used to find the distance from one point to

chapter 15

another in the same reference frame. For example, 1950 was 60 years earlier than 2010, 30°C is 20 degrees warmer than 10°C, and 5:00 P.M. is 2 hours later than 3:00 P.M.

Frank and Ernest

In *Everyday Mathematics,* students learn about a variety of contemporary and historical reference frames. This chapter discusses reference frames for temperature and time, along with coordinate systems and maps, which are often based on coordinate grids.

▶ 15.1 Temperature

Temperature is the amount of heat something has relative to a reference frame usually called a temperature scale.

15.1.1 Temperature Scales

The two *temperature scales* with which most people are familiar are the Fahrenheit and Celsius scales. Each scale has a zero point based on when water freezes (but not the same kind of water) and each has a unit interval called a *degree* (but Fahrenheit degrees are smaller than Celsius degrees).

The Fahrenheit Scale

German physicist D. G. Fahrenheit developed the *Fahrenheit scale* in the early 1700s, although it may have been based on a similar scale invented by Danish astronomer Ole Christensen Romer. The zero point of this scale (0°F) was originally the freezing point of a saturated salt and water solution (*brine*) at sea level. The point at which pure water freezes at sea level was set at 32°F for reasons that are not clear. After Fahrenheit's death, the scale was recalibrated to the temperatures that pure water freezes (32°F) and boils (212°F), and brine was left out of it. The normal temperature for the human body is 98.6°F. The Fahrenheit scale is used primarily in the United States.

The Celsius Scale

Swedish astronomer Anders Celsius developed the *Celsius scale* in 1742. The zero point for this scale (0°C) is the freezing point of pure water at sea level. The boiling point of pure water at sea level was set at 100°C in order to divide the span of temperatures into a convenient 100 parts. For this reason the Celsius scale is also called the *centigrade scale*. The normal temperature for the human body is 37°C. The Celsius scale is standard for most people living outside of the United States and for most scientists everywhere.

NOTE: Both the Fahrenheit and Celsius scales are examples of a reference frame that first defines where two points are on the scale and then arbitrarily divides the distance between the points into unit intervals, in this case, called *degrees.*

NOTE: A Fahrenheit degree is $\frac{1}{180}$ of the difference between the boiling and freezing temperatures of pure water, and a Celsius degree is $\frac{1}{100}$ of that difference. Once again, U.S. customary units are much more difficult to calculate with than metric units.

NOTE: The *Kelvin scale,* suggested in 1848 by British physicist Lord Kelvin, is used in science and engineering. Its zero point is a temperature at which the atoms and molecules in any substance have minimum energy. Thus there are no negative temperatures on the Kelvin scale. Pure water at sea level freezes at 273.15 K and boils at 373.15 K. The zero point of this scale (0 Kelvins or 0 K) is called *absolute zero.* The Kelvin unit interval is the same as the Celsius degree.

A thermometer with a circular scale

NOTE: The Celsius and Fahrenheit scales are equal at −40°.

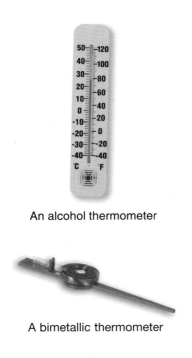

An alcohol thermometer

A bimetallic thermometer

15.1.2 Thermometers

Thermometers have been evolving since the late 16th century. Galileo built the first known thermometer, an inaccurate device called a *thermoscope,* in about 1592. In 1709, D. G. Fahrenheit made an accurate thermometer using alcohol. In 1714, he built a mercury thermometer like those still in use today. In 1954, U.S. Army Colonel George T. Perkins invented an electronic thermometer.

The designs of thermometers depend on the temperature scale(s) they intend to display and the range of temperatures of interest. Common thermometers include those used to measure cooking temperatures, (candy; deep-frying; oven), machine temperatures (automobile engine; climate control), body temperatures, and air temperatures. Some thermometers have circular scales, others are straight, and still others have digital readouts. The zero point and scale intervals are often not evident on the third type, making them less desirable as learning tools than the circular and straight-line designs.

The form of the display is perhaps less interesting than how thermometers are constructed. Three common types of thermometers are described below. Each of them can be calibrated to quantify temperature in degrees Celsius or degrees Fahrenheit.

Mercury or Colored-Alcohol Thermometers

When their temperature rises, most liquids increase in volume. So if a liquid is contained in a little bulb attached to a thin, straight tube with a sealed end, the liquid rises in the tube as the temperature increases. Both *alcohol* and *mercury* are commonly used in thermometers. Mercury freezes at a little above −40°F or −40°C. Alcohol thermometers are used to display temperatures lower than that. These liquid-in-glass-type thermometers are the least expensive and are quite popular. They are the kind often used in homes to determine if someone has a fever or to measure how warm or cold it is inside or outside.

Bimetallic Thermometers

When their temperature rises, most solids expand, but different solids expand by different amounts. For example, brass expands about twice as much as iron when heated. If a *bimetallic* bar is made by fastening a strip of brass next to a strip of iron, the bar will bend as the temperature rises. The bend will be toward the iron side, which expands less. If one end of the bar is fixed in place, the other end can act as a pointer on a scale. Most home thermostats contain bimetallic thermometers.

Thermocouple Thermometers

A *thermocouple* contains a loop made by joining end to end two wires of different materials, such as copper and iron. If the temperatures at the two joints are different, a voltage proportional to that difference is created. One joint is placed where the temperature is to be taken, while the other is kept at a constant lower temperature. The voltage is read by a measuring device and translated into a temperature reading.

In *Kindergarten Everyday Mathematics,* children keep daily temperature charts that are color-coded by temperature range for easier reading. Most air-temperature thermometers use mercury or colored alcohol and are based on straight-line, vertical, or circular number-line scales. In first grade, the Fahrenheit temperature scale is emphasized. In second and third grades, both Fahrenheit and Celsius scales should be available.

In all grades of *Everyday Mathematics,* temperature is the context for number stories, data exploration, and graphical displays. Students use formulas beginning in fourth grade. In sixth grade, they use these formulas for converting from degrees Fahrenheit F to degrees Celsius C and vice versa:

$$C = \frac{5}{9}(F - 32) \qquad \text{and} \qquad F = \frac{9}{5}C + 32$$

For example, to find the Celsius equivalent of 72°F, replace F with 72 in the first formula to get

$$C = \frac{5}{9}(F - 32)$$
$$= \frac{5}{9}(72 - 32)$$
$$= \frac{5}{9}(40)$$
$$\approx 22 \qquad \text{So, 72°F is about 22°C.}$$

Be careful about doing arithmetic with temperatures. Temperature changes can be calculated within one scale but not across different scales. For example, if it was 58°F this morning and the temperature rose 30°F to the high for the day, then the high was 58°F + 30°F = 88°F. Differences in Fahrenheit and Celsius temperatures are not meaningful; for example, 30°F minus 20°C does not equal 10° of anything.

The limitations of doing arithmetic with reference-frame numbers can be a difficult concept. Although some students will grasp it intuitively, others will need to work with many examples over time before they understand when reference frame numbers cannot be manipulated like other numbers and when they can be meaningfully added and subtracted.

15.2 Time

As with many reference frames, locating an event or a point in time requires a zero, or starting, point and a unit interval. Both of these depend on the context in which time is being examined. This section begins with discussions of clocks, to keep track of short-term time passage, and calendars and timelines, to keep track of broad expanses of time, from days to millennia.

As with units in other reference frames, it does not always make sense to compute with numbers pertaining to time. For example, June 8 plus June 13 is not June 21; and 8:30 P.M. minus 1:20 P.M. is not 7:10 P.M. Within one reference frame, however, you can calculate elapsed time as a difference, or distance, between two times.

NOTE: In 2001, the National Institutes of Health (NIH) recommended that the public switch to nonmercury-based thermometers because mercury is classified as a hazardous toxin. This classification means not only that mercury is poisonous to humans, but that it is not even legal for them to clean it up if their thermometer breaks and it spills. However, mercury thermometers are much more accurate than other forms, so in science applications the NIH recommends using Teflon-coated ones.

NOTE: Pressure and volume affect the temperatures at which physical events occur. For a fixed volume, if pressure decreases, temperature decreases. For example, the higher the elevation, where there is less air pressure, the lower the temperature you need to boil water. Increasing pressure on a fixed volume increases the temperature. This is how pressure cookers work; they cook at higher pressures and, therefore, higher temperatures.

In *Kindergarten* through *Third Grade Everyday Mathematics,* children engage in many everyday activities with clocks and calendars that help them develop a *time sense* and become familiar with the language of time. Older students are expected to be comfortable with clocks and calendar reference frames; they use them as a context for number stories, investigations, and other problem-solving situations.

15.2.1 Clocks

Clock time is a reference frame with second, minute, and hour intervals that, although logical to most adults, can seem quite arbitrary and confusing to students. Learning to tell time accurately on an analog clock is one of the objectives of *Kindergarten* through *Second Grade Everyday Mathematics.* For older students, elapsed time is a common context for number stories.

Clocks have been important in the development of many human enterprises, such as navigation, business, and science. Three important types of clocks are analog, digital, and atomic. In *Kindergarten* through *Third Grade Everyday Mathematics,* children practice telling time using both digital and analog clocks.

Analog Clocks

Analog clocks, which used to be called simply "clocks" before the invention of digital clocks, are clocks with hands. In general, *analog* refers to any system that measures a *continuously* changing quantity, such as time, with continuously varying markers of some kind. The first analog clocks may have been trees with markers showing where their shadows fell at different times during the day. These were precursors to sundials, which work on the same principle. For thousands of years, water clocks have been a standard for telling time. They work even when the sun is down or behind a cloud. In a water clock, the water flows from one vessel to another, the flow being the analog for the time. The first successful mechanical clocks were constructed late in the Middle Ages, a development that thoroughly transformed the world.

Nowadays, most people who say "analog clock" mean the type with hands on a round face. The first of these, with only an hour hand on it, is credited to the German inventor Henry de Vick in the 1300s. More advanced features came along in the 1700s, including minute and second hands and a pendulum. Electric analog clocks use an alternating current that vibrates 60 times per second to keep the clock on time.

Digital Clocks

Digital clocks are not analog because time is displayed in *discrete* units, not in a continuous manner. Every digital clock has a smallest unit of time that it displays without changing until an interval of that unit has gone by. Commonly, the smallest unit is a minute. For example, a display of 10:10 on a digital clock does not change until a minute has passed.

An analog clock

A digital clock

On some digital clocks, the colon in the time display blinks on and off once per second to indicate that time is still passing or perhaps just to let you know the clock is still working. Yet even the seconds are discrete. A "hand" does not sweep from one second to the next. Instead, the time displayed on a digital clock jumps discretely from one minute or second to the next. Most digital clocks work on alternating current.

Atomic Clocks

Atomic clocks keep time according to the vibrations of atoms or molecules. The vibrations are so reliable that an atomic clock may lose or gain only a few seconds in 100,000 years. There are both analog and digital versions of atomic clocks.

15.2.2 Calendars

There are many different calendric systems, each one its own reference frame for marking the passage of time. The word *calendar* has roots in the Latin word *kalendae,* meaning "first of the month." *Kalendae,* in turn, is rooted in the word *calare,* which means "to call out solemnly." This etymology points to the importance that people have always placed on keeping track of months and marking their beginning and passing.

In the earliest times, the lunar month of 29.5 days was an important measure because of its close association with seasonal planting and harvesting schedules. Unfortunately, no whole number of lunar months coincides with a solar year of 365 days, 5 hours, 48 minutes, and 46 seconds (about 365 and 1 fourth days). Twelve lunar months are 354 days; 13 lunar months are 383.5 days. The fact that these important, naturally occurring cycles can't easily be reconciled has led to the peculiar natures of the calendar systems used throughout history. According to *The World Book Encyclopedia,* some noteworthy calendars include the following:

- *Babylonian Calendar* This ancient Middle-Eastern calendar was based on a now unknown zero point and a lunar month interval. The calendar had alternating 29- and 30-day months, with an extra month added three times every 8 years to make up for error.

- *Egyptian Calendar* This ancient calendar had a zero point at the annual flooding of the Nile when the Dog Star, Sirius, first appeared. The year was broken into twelve 30-day months, with 5 days added at the end of the year. Because the extra 1 fourth of a day per year wasn't accounted for, the calendar slowly became inaccurate over the years. It has been calculated that the earliest recorded date on this calendar corresponds to 4236 B.C. on our current Gregorian calendar.

- *Roman Calendar* According to legend, Romulus, the founder of Rome, introduced the earliest Roman calendar in the eighth century B.C. It came from the Greeks and was made up of 10 months and a 304-day year. The zero point was March 1 by our current calendar. It is not clear how the other 61-odd days were accounted for.

The names of eight of our current months came from the names for the ten Roman months: *Martius, Aprilis, Maius, Junius, Quintilis, Sextilis, September, October, November,* and *December.* Quintilis through December came from the numbers 5 through 10. The name *Martius* came from Mars, a Roman god; *Junius* from Juno, a Roman goddess; and *Maius* from Maia, a Greek goddess. It is thought that *Aprilis* may derive from the Latin word *aperire,* "to open," referring to the unfolding of buds and blossoms during this month. Another possibility is that it may derive from Aphrodite, the Greek goddess of love and beauty.

Every two years, a 22- or 23-day month was added to account for error with the solar year. Later, two more months, *Januarius* and *Februarius,* were added to the end of the year. *Januarius* was likely named after Janus, the Roman god of gates and doorways, and *Februarius* took its name from Februa, a Roman festival of purification held on the 15th day of this month.

- *Julian Calendar* In 46 B.C., Julius Caesar acted on suggestions from his astronomer Sosigenes to upgrade the Roman calendar. A system close to our own was implemented, including what we now know as a leap day in February every fourth year. To accommodate the fact that the Roman calendar was three months out of line with the seasons, Caesar made 46 B.C. 445 days long. Later, *Quintilis* was renamed July for Julius Caesar and *Sextilis* was named August to honor Emperor Augustus Caesar.

  The Christian version of the Julian calendar was invented in A.D. 532 by an abbot named Dionysius Exiguus, or Dennis the Short. In his plan, the Christian era began January 1st of the year after Christ was born. He called the beginning year the Year of Our Lord, or Anno Domini (A.D.) 1. The Christian version of the calendar was not taken up immediately by church authorities but became widely used in Western Europe beginning in the 11th century. The abbreviation B.C. for "Before Christ" was introduced later. However, Dennis got the year of Christ's birth wrong. It now seems likely that Christ was born in 4 B.C., if not earlier. The abbreviations C.E. (Common Era) and B.C.E. (Before the Common Era) are sometimes used instead of A.D. and B.C.

- *Gregorian Calendar* By 1582, the Julian calendar was off by about 10 days because of the slight difference between $365\frac{1}{4}$ days and 365 days, 5 hours, 48 minutes, and 46 seconds. So Pope Gregory XIII dropped 10 days from October. He then decreed that February should continue to get an extra day every four years, as in the Julian calendar, except in century years that were not divisible by 400. This calendar is so accurate that, more than 400 years later, the time is only about 26 seconds off. Most of the Western World uses the Gregorian calendar.

- *Hebrew Calendar* The zero point for the Hebrew calendar is Creation, which has been calculated at 3,760 years and 3 months before the Christian era began. To find a year on the Hebrew calendar, add 3,760 or 3,761 to the year in the Gregorian calendar.

NOTE: 46 B.C. is known as the "year of confusion" because of calendar reform.

NOTE: There is no year 0 in the Julian, or Gregorian, calendar, but just a "zero moment" at which Christ was born, which was labeled as year "1". So this is a reference frame without a real zero point; that is, from 1 B.C. to A.D. 1 is only 1 year, not 2.

The Hebrew year is based on the phases of the moon and usually has 12 months, each 29 or 30 days long. Seven times every 19 years, an extra 29-day month is added.

- *Islamic Calendar* The zero point for the Islamic calendar is Muhammad's flight from Mecca to Medina in A.D. 622 on the Gregorian calendar. This calendar is also lunar, with 12 months alternating between 29 and 30 days long. The months do not keep to the same seasons relative to the sun each year, and so the Islamic New Year moves backward through the seasons. Nineteen of every 30 years have 354 days each, and the other 11 years each have an extra day.

There are groups that advocate standardizing all calendars around the world. Three such calendars have been proposed: The Thirteen-Month calendar, with 13 months each 4 weeks long; the World calendar; and the Perpetual calendar. The latter two propose variations on a 12-month, 30- or 31-day-per-month design. And, according to *Star Trek* creator Gene Roddenberry, the calendar will be metric by the 24th century.

15.2.3 Timelines

Timelines, which are number lines labeled with time units, are also reference frames. As with all reference frames, a timeline's zero point and unit interval vary according to its intended use. For example, a timeline designed to track the development of Earth may have "The Big Bang" as its zero point and use a large interval (millions or perhaps billions of years) to allow for a display over billions of years. A family history timeline might use generational intervals and mark its zero point with the most distant known relative.

For more information on number lines, see Section 15.3.1: 1-Dimensional Coordinate Systems.

A timeline of someone's life might use the person's birth date as its zero point and a 1-year unit interval corresponding to the person's age. For example, a timeline of a young child's landmarks might include such events as rolling over at about $\frac{1}{2}$ year, learning to walk at age 1, having a sibling when she was 3, and going to Kindergarten shortly after her fifth birthday. A timeline such as this could also include numbers that refer to the Gregorian dates for the above events, for example, birth (1999), walking (2000), sibling (2002), and Kindergarten (2004), but it would not need to include these dates if birth were established as the zero point and age intervals were the specified unit. Keep in mind that in each instance above, times before the chosen zero point exist. This is true with most reference frames.

You may have timelines associated with social studies or science units, or your colleagues teaching different grades may have them. If they are available and appropriate, it would be instructive to review them with your students from a reference-frame point of view. Ask *What is the zero point? What is the unit interval? Why did they choose this zero point and these intervals for this timeline?* Students can make their own timelines to demonstrate or reinforce knowledge in other content areas, especially social studies. Because timelines are visual, they are very useful tools for many students as they learn about history.

▶ 15.3 Coordinate Systems

Coordinate systems are reference frames in which one or more numbers, called *coordinates,* are used to locate points. The simplest coordinate system is a number line, a 1-dimensional reference frame on which one number corresponds to one point. Coordinate planes and coordinate space are 2- and 3-dimensional reference frames in which to locate points.

15.3.1 1-Dimensional Coordinate Systems

Grid is short for *gridiron,* an old English word for a framework of metal bars or wires used to grill meat or fish. Generally, a grid is any set of equally spaced parallel lines, squares, or rectangles used to help establish locations of objects.

In *Everyday Mathematics,* students use many types of grids, including number grids, coordinate grids, grids for estimating area, and grids for interpreting maps. The tick marks on a number line form perhaps the most primitive grid structure. Lattices and arrays are organizations of objects into gridlike formations, a common example of which is a calendar.

Number Grids

A *number grid* consists of rows of boxes, usually ten in each row, containing consecutive integers (positive and negative whole numbers). In *First Grade Everyday Mathematics,* children are introduced to number grids early in the year.

−9	−8	−7	−6	−5	−4	−3	−2	−1	0
1	2	3	4	5	6	7	8	9	10
11	12	13	14	15	16	17	18	19	20
21	22	23	24	25	26	27	28	29	30
31	32	33	34	35	36	37	38	39	40
41	42	43	44	45	46	47	48	49	50
51	52	53	54	55	56	57	58	59	60
61	62	63	64	65	66	67	68	69	70
71	72	73	74	75	76	77	78	79	80
81	82	83	84	85	86	87	88	89	90
91	92	93	94	95	96	97	98	99	100
101	102	103	104	105	106	107	108	109	110

A number grid

NOTE: Some readers of past editions of the *Teacher's Reference Manual* feel strongly that this section on number grids, scrolls, and lines belongs in this chapter on reference frames. Others feel just as strongly that the discussion belongs in Chapter 9: Numeration and Order. Believing that teachers should find help wherever they look, it is now included in both chapters.

For more information, see Section 15.3.2: 2- and 3-Dimensional Coordinate Systems.

Number grids have many wonderful features that can help students with pattern recognition and place value. However, their original use in *Everyday Mathematics* was simply to solve the problem of number lines being unmanageably long. Number lines can be cumbersome even when stretched along a classroom wall, and it is nearly impossible to print them in students' books without breaking them into chunks. Number grids may be considered number lines that fit nicely on a page or a classroom poster.

A number grid lends itself to many activities that reinforce place-value concepts. For example, by exploring the patterns in rows and columns, students discover that any number on the number grid is:

- *1 more* than the number to its left;
- *1 less* than the number to its right;
- *10 more* than the number above it;
- *10 less* than the number below it.

Number grids are useful for addition and subtraction. For example, to find the difference $84 - 37$, start at 37, count the tens from 37 to 77 *(4 tens),* and then count the number of ones from 77 to 84 *(7 ones).* So $84 - 37$ is 4 tens plus 7 ones, or 47. This difference corresponds to the *distance* between the points 37 and 84 on a number line.

From the time they are introduced, students see that number grids can be extended to negative numbers. This is especially useful when ordering negative numbers or finding differences.

−19	−18	−17	−16	−15	−14	−13	−12	−11	−10
−9	−8	−7	−6	−5	−4	−3	−2	−1	0
1	2	3	4	5	6	7	8	9	10
11	12	13	14	15	16	17	18	19	20

A grid extended to −19

Number Scrolls

Number scrolls are extended number grids. You can make them by adding single sheets of 100 numbers to existing sheets, either forward (positively) or backward (negatively). Among other things, scrolls give students the chance to experience the ongoing repetitive patterns of our base-ten number system beyond 100—*101, 102, 103, . . .*—so that they do not continue, as students often do, with *200, 300, 400, ...* Teachers have found that many students get excited when they discover these patterns and realize that they are capable of writing bigger and bigger numbers.

Number Lines

A *number line* is a line on which points are indicated by *tick marks* that are usually at regularly spaced intervals from a starting point called the *origin,* the *zero point,* or simply "0." Numbers are associated with the tick marks, and the interval from 0 to 1 on the line is called the *unit interval.*

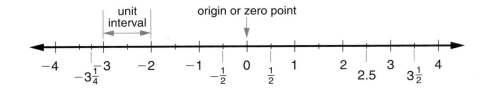

Like any line, a number line extends without end in both directions. Any drawing of a number line is a model of just part of the line. Where you place the zero point is arbitrary, and how you space the numbers depends on the situation you wish to illustrate. You might, for example, mark every other unit-interval point and label by 2s as in Figure 1 below; or you may mark every half-interval point and label by halves as in Figure 2. In *Everyday Mathematics,* students are often asked to solve incomplete-number-line problems that help them understand these concepts.

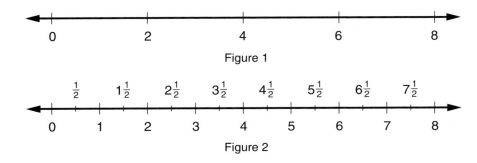

Figure 1

Figure 2

Any scale can be assigned to a number line. For example, a unit interval on a number line could represent one mile on a map. It is also possible to have nonlinear scales on number lines. For example, slide rules and radio dials are based on logarithmic scales, which are beyond the scope of *Everyday Mathematics.*

All number lines have a zero point, although sometimes it is not shown. Or, as in the following line, it is shown along with a break to indicate that a piece of the line has been omitted. This device is often used in technical drawings to focus on important details and still show the reader that part of the object is missing. A variety of broken-line symbols all mean the same thing.

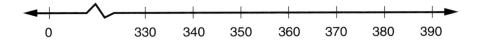

Beginning in Kindergarten, children use number lines in context in counting and measuring activities. Both horizontal and vertical number lines appear. Number lines in coordinate graphing systems are introduced in third grade and are expanded upon and treated more formally in Grades 4 through 6. Number lines also continue to serve as one or more of the axes in data displays such as coordinate graphs, bar graphs, and line plots. In sixth grade, students use a real-number line to order rational and irrational numbers.

15.3.2 2- and 3-Dimensional Coordinate Systems

A *coordinate grid,* or *coordinate system,* is a reference frame defined by two or more number lines called *axes.* Axes are usually, but not always, perpendicular to each other and intersect at a common point called the *origin* where the zero points of the axes coincide. In a 2-dimensional coordinate grid in a plane, one axis is usually horizontal, the other vertical, and the axes usually have the same scale. A grid with perpendicular axes is called a *rectangular coordinate grid.* A 3-dimensional coordinate grid in space begins with a coordinate grid in a plane to which a third axis is added, perpendicular to the other two through the origin.

In *analytic geometry,* or *coordinate geometry,* points on geometric objects are located using coordinates. On a number line, the coordinate is a single number. In a 2-dimensional *coordinate plane,* points are located using *ordered pairs* of numbers. In *Everyday Mathematics,* they are called *rectangular coordinate planes* because the axes are always perpendicular. By convention, the first number in a pair locates the position of a point relative to a horizontal axis. This axis is often called the *x-axis,* and the number is called the *x-coordinate.* The second number locates a position relative to a vertical axis. This axis is often called the *y-axis,* and the number is called the *y-coordinate.* The point (3,2) is plotted and labeled in the drawing in the margin.

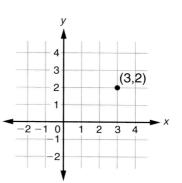

Point (3,2) plotted on a coordinate plane

Coordinate planes have many practical uses. For example, the streets in many cities and towns are laid out in a grid pattern and are sometimes numbered accordingly. Many maps are based on coordinate planes, as is discussed in the next section.

Coordinate planes have been used for centuries. The ancient Egyptians and Romans used them to survey fields. Coordinate planes received a big boost in the early 17th century when the French philosopher and mathematician René Descartes (1596–1650) made significant advances in coordinate geometry. Today, rectangular coordinates are often called *Cartesian coordinates* in honor of his work.

Since Descartes, coordinate geometry has been a powerful tool for advances in many areas of mathematics. In *Everyday Mathematics,* the serious study of coordinate geometry begins in fourth grade. Before that, work with coordinate geometry is restricted mostly to number lines and graphing data.

In a 3-dimensional coordinate system, or *coordinate space,* points are identified by *ordered triples* of numbers. Imagine a coordinate plane with x- and y-axes on a table in front of you. Now imagine a vertical z-axis perpendicular to the coordinate plane and passing through its origin toward the floor and ceiling. A point in space can be located by measuring along the x-axis, then the y-axis, and then the z-axis, in that order. For example, the point (2,3,4) is plotted in the drawing in the margin. Three-dimensional coordinate spaces are beyond the scope of *Everyday Mathematics.*

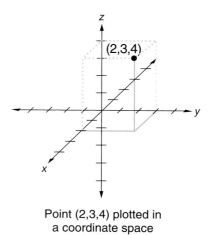

Point (2,3,4) plotted in a coordinate space

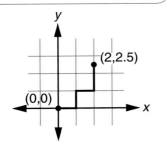

Practical, or "taxicab," distance in a coordinate plane

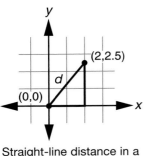

Straight-line distance in a coordinate plane

For more information on the Pythagorean theorem, see Section 13.4.2: Polygons (*n*-gons).

For more information, see Section 17.1.3: Functions.

Distance on a Coordinate Grid

On a number line, the *distance* from one point to another on the line is equal to the difference of the coordinate of the second point and the coordinate of the first point. For example, the distance from a point at 3 to a point at 8 on a number line is $8 - 3 = 5$ units. The distance in the opposite direction, from the point at 8 to the point at 3 is $3 - 8 = -5$ units. These are examples of *directed distance*. If you walked from one point to the other, a positive distance means you walked right and a negative distance means you walked left. If you don't care about the direction, you use the positive distance. In this case, the distance between the point at 3 and the point at 8 is the same as the distance between the point at 8 and the point at 3, that is, 5 units.

In a coordinate plane, there are two common ways to look at distance. In a city, the *practical distance* between two houses is measured along streets. So the shortest practical distance from the origin, (0,0), to a house at (2,2.5) is 4.5 blocks. The drawing in the margin shows one of several possible paths with length 4.5. Practical distance is sometimes called *taxicab distance* because it measures distance along a route a taxicab might take.

The *straight-line distance* between (0,0) and the house at (2,2.5), or distance "as the crow flies," does not follow streets. Calculating straight-line distance in a coordinate plane uses the Pythagorean theorem, which is introduced in *Sixth Grade Everyday Mathematics*. In the drawing in the margin, the length of the straight-line distance between the origin and the house is *d*. This path is the hypotenuse of a right triangle, with a horizontal leg 2 blocks long and a vertical leg 2.5 blocks long (the *x*- and *y*-coordinates of (2,2.5), respectively). By the Pythagorean theorem,

$$d = \sqrt{2^2 + 2.5^2} = \sqrt{10.25} \approx 3.2 \text{ blocks.}$$

In secondary school, students will generalize the procedure above to develop a *distance formula* for the distance between any two points in the coordinate plane.

Coordinate Graphs

Plotting points on coordinate grids is also called *coordinate graphing*, and a collection of plotted points is a *coordinate graph*. Coordinate graphing is a major topic in middle school and high school mathematics courses, particularly pre-algebra and algebra. In these grades, graphs and tables of values are used to illustrate the behavior of *functions* given in equation form. Unfortunately, most first-time algebra students have had little previous experience with coordinate graphing and probably no experience at all with the relationships between stories, number models (equations and inequalities), tables of values, and graphs. *Everyday Mathematics* students will benefit from their relatively early exposure to these topics.

▶ 15.4 Maps

A common use of reference frames in *Everyday Mathematics* is with maps, where coordinate grids help locate geographic points within a given region. In Kindergarten through Grade 6, mapping activities range from using maps to track steps from classroom to classroom in the school to estimating distances between cities and towns to interpreting temperature contour maps. Maps also serve as rich supplies of ideas students can use to invent number stories.

15.4.1 Map Coordinates

Often, the reference frame for a map is a 2-dimensional, rectangular coordinate grid. One axis is usually horizontal, the other vertical, and they usually have the same scale. Often, the full grid is not drawn on the map. Rather, points along each axis are labeled at the outer edges of the map. You can envision drawing horizontal and vertical lines across the page and through or between these points to complete the coordinate grid upon which the map is built.

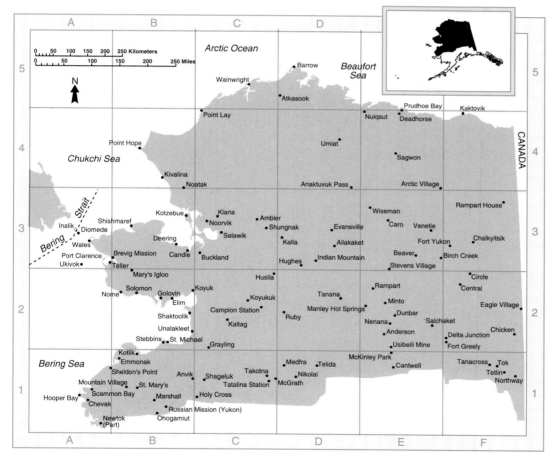

A map with a coordinate grid

Unlike mathematical coordinate grids, an ordered pair on a map grid refers to more than just a single point. Rather, it refers to a rectangular region centered at the point located by the ordered pair. For example, in the map of Alaska above, Indian Mountain is in the region centered at (D,3), or "D3." But several other towns are located "at" D3, such as Allakaket and Hughes. An index of towns on the map would locate all three of these towns, and others, as being "at" D3. Note that the gridlines on the map are not centered on the coordinates in the margins, but rather halfway between coordinates. This approach highlights the rectangular regions that the coordinates such as D3 define.

Different maps label their coordinates differently, some with all numbers, some with letters and numbers (but not always in the same order as on the Alaska map), and some with other markings. However, in each case, ordered pairs identify points or regions within the coordinate grid.

Many cities and towns use a 2-dimensional coordinate grid to determine the address of each building in town. For example, 200 Third Avenue NE may locate a house two blocks north and three blocks east of the intersection (the zero point) of two central roads in that town. The map scale is a block. Assuming that north is "up" on the vertical axis and east is to the right of the zero point, the position of the house is given by the ordered pair (3,2).

15.4.2 Map and Model Scales

A *map scale* is an application of a *size-change factor,* usually in which one of the figures is from real life and the other is a model. For example, a model train is a scaled-down version of a real train; a map is a scaled-down model of a real landscape. More precisely, a *scale* is a ratio comparison. It is a number used to quantify the relative sizes of two things being compared.

For example, a scale of 1:36,000,000 (inches) on a map means 1 map inch represents 36,000,000 real inches; that is, a distance on the map is $\frac{1}{36,000,000}$ of the real distance. Note that a scale, as any ratio, has no unit. This example could be rewritten with the word *inch* replaced by *centimeter* or any other linear measure. However, a unit must be chosen before any specific map can be drawn and the map itself is drawn using that unit.

Scales are often given graphically on a map, where the overall length of a line segment represents a map unit and real units are marked along the segment. You can simply mark a string (or the edge of a piece of paper) to show the length of the segment and then lay the string repeatedly on the map to determine distances in real units. Using string even allows you to follow winding roads with greater accuracy than is possible with a ruler.

Other scale drawings follow conventions similar to those used in maps. For example, in architectural drawings, $\frac{1}{4}$ inch often represents 1 foot, so the scale is 1:48. A drawing of an insect might have the notation "2 times actual size," meaning that every linear measure in the drawing is twice the actual measure of a part of the insect.

Map scales are introduced in *Third Grade Everyday Mathematics,* when students use them to estimate mileage between cities on a U.S. map. Fourth-grade students make scale drawings of their classroom. In fifth grade, students continue to practice reading maps in the American Tour, and in sixth grade they work with scale in several contexts.

For more information on scale, see Section 13.7.2: Size-Change Transformations, and Section 10.3.2: Multiplication and Division Use Classes.

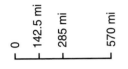

scale 1:36,000,000

One inch represents 570 miles.

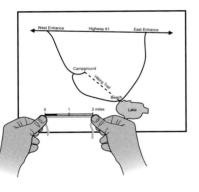

Using string to read map distances

Woodpecker (8 in.) at $\frac{1}{4}$ scale

15.4.3 Contour Maps

Most people in the United States have seen temperature contours on daily weather maps in newspapers and on television. Many people have used contour maps that show elevations of mountains, hills, and valleys. Such 2-dimensional maps are much easier to produce and more convenient to put into a backpack or take to a construction job than a 3-dimensional model. With experience, a user can get almost as much information from a contour map as from a 3-dimensional model.

Average Yearly Precipitation in the U.S.

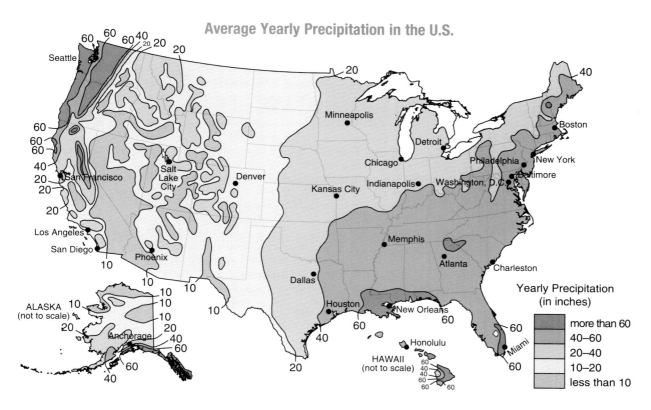

In *Fifth Grade Everyday Mathematics,* students investigate contour maps as part of the American Tour. The precipitation map above is like one in the Grade 5 *Student Reference Book.* The curves that separate the different shades of gray are called *contour lines.* The numbers that are printed on or at the end of contour lines indicate inches of precipitation. Each contour line links points on the map with the same average annual precipitation, and so they might also be called "equal-measure" or "equal-value" lines.

Topographical maps are contour maps of Earth showing elevations above and below sea level. Based on work of surveying parties led by John Wesley Powell, Ferdinand V. Hayden, and George Wheeler, the first detailed topographical maps of the western United States were completed around 1875. The United States Geological Survey (USGS) was organized in 1879 and has been making detailed maps to the present day. A USGS topographical map of part of northwest Indiana is shown on the next page.

Most topographical maps are now made by computers, which trace contours on satellite and other aerial photographs.

NOTE: Contour lines that show equal atmospheric pressure are called *isobars,* short for "equal barometric pressure."

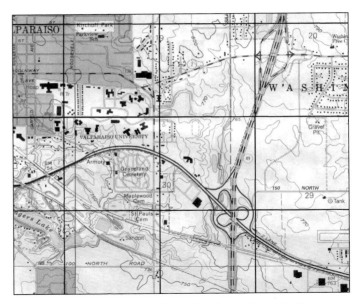

A topographical map of a region in northwest Indiana

15.4.4 The Global Grid System

Important components of the *global grid system* include the *North* and *South Poles, equator, prime meridian,* circles of *latitude,* and semicircles of *longitude.* Students are introduced to the global grid system in *Fourth Grade Everyday Mathematics.* In a project, they make a cut-away model of a globe, including important grid markings. By applying their knowledge of geometry to construct the global grid, students develop a better understanding of the origins and functions of this reference frame.

Students begin by locating the North and South Poles on their spheres and drawing the equatorial circle. Then they mark the prime meridian semicircle connecting the North and South Poles and subdivide their model globes with longitude semicircles, first marking 90° quadrants and next subdividing these into 30° intervals. Students draw latitude circles parallel to the equator. They also locate and describe places on the globe.

There are several important ideas to emphasize in the context of the global grid system. Generally, it does not make sense to perform arithmetic operations on latitude and longitude readings. For example, the sum of the coordinates for Rome (12° E, 42° N) and Bombay (73° E, 18° N) is meaningless. As parts of a reference frame, however, global coordinates can be used to calculate the distance, in degrees, from one point to another on a parallel or a meridian.

It is also important for students to understand that latitude circles are in parallel planes and that longitude semicircles are not parallel but share theoretical endpoints at the poles. Students should also know why latitude and longitude readings must have two parts: a number of degrees and a direction with reference to the equator or prime meridian. By reconstructing the global grid system on their own models, students gain insight into the spherical geometry that ties this information together.

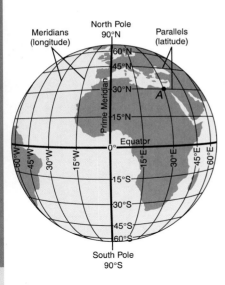

Point *A* is located at
latitude 30°N, longitude 30°E.

16 Estimation, Mental Arithmetic, and Number Sense

Contents

If you list everyday situations that involve arithmetic and identify the kind of answer and method of calculation that is likely in each situation, you may end up with something like the table below:

Situation	Kind of Answer	Likely Method
doubling a recipe	exact	mental arithmetic
making change	exact	mental arithmetic
deciding if you have enough money for a purchase	estimated	mental arithmetic
planning a daily schedule	estimated	mental arithmetic
balancing a checkbook	exact	calculator
computing gas mileage	estimated	mental arithmetic
comparing prices	estimated	mental arithmetic
calculating a discount percent	estimated	mental arithmetic
figuring income tax	exact	calculator
tipping	estimated	mental arithmetic

Of course, in certain situations you may seek a different kind of answer or use a method different from that listed above; but, in any case, your list is likely to reveal how common and valuable estimates and mental arithmetic are in everyday life. The practical importance of paper-and-pencil computation for daily living, which was never very great, is even further diminished in today's highly technological society. Sensible use of calculators and proficiency at mental arithmetic are more important than ever.

This diagram displays six ways to find answers to arithmetic problems. The traditional school mathematics curriculum focuses almost exclusively on just one of these—obtaining exact answers with paper-and-pencil algorithms. The authors of *Everyday Mathematics* believe that students deserve to be proficient in all six.

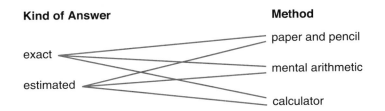

Paper-and-pencil and calculator algorithms for finding exact answers are discussed in Chapter 11. This chapter examines the other varieties of computation shown in the diagram above. The first part discusses why estimates may be necessary or desirable and how estimates may be obtained. The second part describes the *Everyday Mathematics* approach to mental arithmetic for exact and estimated answers. The last part is about basic facts, which must be mastered if facility at mental arithmetic and paper-and-pencil algorithms is to be achieved.

▶ 16.1 Estimation

Estimation is a major thread in *Everyday Mathematics* because of its importance in mathematics and everyday life. We estimate counts, measures, and results of calculations. In practical matters, ballpark estimates are often as important as exact answers.

Despite its utility, many students and some adults feel that estimation is like cheating or lying. In reality, estimation is not a shoddy alternative to doing things right. Estimation requires good intuition about numbers, good understanding of problem situations, and a flexible repertoire of techniques. Good estimation skills take years to develop but are worth striving for. Focusing on estimation can help students develop mental flexibility, good number sense, and confidence that mathematics makes sense.

The next section of this chapter outlines the principal reasons for estimating. Later sections address "extreme" numbers, estimates in calculations, rounding, number sense, and mathematical connections.

16.1.1 Why Estimate?

Sometimes we use estimates because we have no choice; other times, because they are easier to understand than exact quantities; and still other times to help us solve problems or to check answers given by machines.

Estimates May Be Necessary

Estimates are necessary in many situations because exact values are unobtainable for a variety of reasons:

- *A number may simply be unknown.* Predictions about the future, guesses about the past, measurements of economic conditions, and even educated guesses about what groceries will cost are all examples of estimates necessitated by lack of precise knowledge.

- *A quantity may be different each time it is measured.* Temperatures, populations, air pressures, and keyboarding speeds are examples of this type of estimate, as are situations involving random processes such as the number of HEADS to come up in 100 tosses of a coin.

- *Physical measurements are never exact.* Even measures that seem exact are approximate, although they may be close enough to exact for all practical purposes. For example, no sheet of paper is exactly 11 inches long; if you look at the edge under a microscope, it will appear quite rough and uneven.

- *Getting an exact value may be too expensive.* In many situations, the numbers are so large that exact counts cannot be easily obtained. More often than not, large counts are estimated by taking samples and using statistics. To estimate how many people saw a particular TV program, pollsters interview just a sample of the viewing public, not the entire viewing public.

- *Decimal or fractional results may not make sense.* For example, if the price of items is 3 for $1, you do not pay $33\frac{1}{3}$¢ for each item because there are no longer coins for fractions of pennies. Instead, you pay 34¢ for the first item and 33¢ for each of the other two items.

- *Some situations require a built-in margin of error, so quantities are overestimated.* For example, you overestimate the costs of items you are buying to make sure you have enough money to pay the cashier. Safety factors in new buildings are overestimated to more than meet minimal requirements.

- *Numbers may not be in a form suitable for computation.* For example, to compute with irrational numbers like $\sqrt{2}$ or π, you need to replace them with rational approximations.

In the situations above, there is no choice about whether to estimate. People who believe that estimates are inferior to exact answers are thus ignoring many situations in which it is necessary to estimate.

Estimates Are Easy to Understand

Estimates help us communicate by making numbers easier to understand.

- *Estimates may be clearer than exact values.* A school budget of $148,309,563 for a school population of 62,772 students might be reported as "about $150 million for 63,000 students." A house on a lot with a surveyed width of 40.13 feet is likely to be described as being on a 40-foot lot. In such cases, estimates are easier to understand than more precise numbers are.

  Sometimes estimates themselves are approximated to make them easier to understand. For example, an almanac estimates the area of Canada to be 3,849,674 square miles. Approximating this estimate to 3.8 million or 4 million square miles makes the measure easier to understand and communicate.

For more information on precision, see Section 16.2: Approximation and Rounding.

Students in *Everyday Mathematics* encounter many examples of estimates made for clarity. Many are found in data-analysis activities throughout the program.

- *Estimates provide consistency.* Estimates for consistency are often prompted by a desire to show data uniformly in tables, charts, and graphs. For example, government unemployment reports often give a percent rounded to the nearest tenth. So, if 8.5 million of 99 million potential workers are unemployed, the government reports 8.6% unemployed rather than 8.59% or any closer approximation to 8.5858 . . .%. Here an estimate is necessary because the original data are inexact, but the particular choice to report in tenths is done both to be consistent from month to month and to reflect the 2-digit precision of the original data.

  Sometimes the desire for consistency comes from tradition. For example, the batting average of a baseball player is found by dividing the number of hits by the number of times at bat. The answer is rounded to the nearest thousandth and is usually referred to as a percent in tables, even though it is shown as a 3-place decimal. A batting average is usually cited as if the decimal point were not there. For example, in 1941 Ted Williams made a hit in over 40 percent of his times at bat when he hit *406,* usually pronounced "four-oh-six."

Everyday Mathematics does not emphasize the need for students to make their estimates consistent. All around them, however, students see numbers that are written with just this goal in mind, so point out such instances when they arise.

Estimates Can Help in Problem Solving

Estimation can be useful in solving problems both before and after an answer is obtained. During the early phases of the problem-solving process, estimating may help you better understand the problem. Estimating helps clarify what is known and what is unknown and helps guide your search for a solution. Even if an estimate made early in the problem-solving process turns out to be very inaccurate, simply having made one may help you get insight into a particularly difficult problem.

Once an answer is obtained, an estimate can be used to check its reasonableness. Looking back over the problem-solving process is valuable, and estimating to verify the accuracy of a result is a good activity to encourage such reflection. Estimating to check answers also emphasizes that results obtained in different ways should agree and, more generally, that mathematics makes sense.

In *Everyday Mathematics,* students are often asked to make estimates to check their answers obtained from either paper-and-pencil or calculator methods. Sometimes they are asked to estimate before calculating in order to let the calculated answer verify their estimating skills. More often, they estimate after calculation in order to check the reasonableness of the answer.

Students should be encouraged to estimate answers in problem situations in which exact answers are unnecessary or not justified. Because many people are uncomfortable with estimates, it is important to discuss the differences between exact and estimated answers and to identify situations in which an estimate is good enough or even makes more sense than an exact answer. For example, *I have 75¢. I want to buy an eraser for 29¢ and a notebook for 39¢. Do I have enough money?* Sharing strategies can help students develop their estimation skills. Students should become aware that there is no single "correct" estimate; the purpose of estimation is to find a reasonable answer, not the exact answer.

This kind of interaction is worth your setting aside two or more 10–15 minute periods each week in addition to the basic lessons, at least at the beginning of the school year. Continue until students feel comfortable sharing their strategies and are able to talk about them fluently and listen to one another attentively.

16.1.2 Extreme Numbers

Students are interested in very large and very small numbers, which *Everyday Mathematics* calls *extreme numbers.* They appear in exact and estimated counts such as the populations of countries, stars in galaxies, hairs on a head, cells in the brain, and the national debt. Extreme numbers also appear in measurements, such as the distances between galaxies, years since the dinosaurs, the area of a continent, and the speed of light.

Extreme numbers are difficult for many people to understand, so relating them to familiar counts or measures can help. For example, it takes about 60 city blocks to cover one square mile. That means it would take about 6 million city blocks to cover the 104,000 square miles recorded as the area of Colorado (104,000 square miles assumes that Colorado is flat). Comparisons of a smaller, familiar measure to a larger, somewhat unfathomable one, and vice versa, are useful applications of ratio comparison and similarity.

It can be difficult to compare large numbers to each other. Many people can visualize a comparison of 1 to 1,000 by comparing a 1-cm cube to a 10-cm by 10-cm by 10-cm block. Comparing 1,000,000 to 1,000,000,000, however, may not be quite as easy, even if the 1-cm cube is considered to represent 1,000,000. In Grades 4 through 6, students look at ratio comparisons of extreme numbers. For example, they study 1 billion as 1,000 *times* 1 million, not as 1,000 *more than* 1 million, as many people think it is. Expressions such as *10 times as much* and *10 times as many* (or *fewer*) indicate ratio comparisons. Increasing or decreasing something by a factor of 10 makes a big difference. Students experience an application of magnitude when examining the structure of the decimal number system. Students are also introduced to the concept of *order of magnitude,* in which a ratio of two numbers is expressed as a power of 10.

Word Name	10^n
One million	10^6
One billion	10^9
One trillion	10^{12}
One quadrillion	10^{15}
One quintillion	10^{18}
One sextillion	10^{21}
One septillion	10^{24}
One octillion	10^{27}
One nonillion	10^{30}
One decillion	10^{33}
One undecillion	10^{36}
One duodecillion	10^{39}
One tredecillion	10^{42}
One quattuordecillion	10^{45}
One quindecillion	10^{48}
One sexdecillion	10^{51}
One septendecillion	10^{54}
One octodecillion	10^{57}
One novemdecillion	10^{60}
One vigintillion	10^{63}
One googol	10^{100}
One googolplex	10^{googol}

NOTE: Add the suffix *-th* to any of the word names to name the corresponding very small number less than 1. For example, 10^{-18} is "one quintillionth."

NOTE: Some scientists call a 10-times increase in value a *magnitude* increase. A *magnitude estimate* is an estimate of whether a count, measure, or result of an operation is in the tens, hundreds, thousands, ten-thousands, and so on.

Brief Times	Seconds
One millisecond	10^{-3}
One microsecond	10^{-6}
One nanosecond	10^{-9}
One picosecond	10^{-12}
One femtosecond	10^{-15}
One attosecond	10^{-18}

Some extremely small numbers

Working with extreme numbers illustrates the need for estimating and approximating. Extreme numbers may need to be estimated if the things with which they are associated cannot be accurately counted, if they are measurements, or if the number is a large product or a small quotient.

In third grade, children are exposed to numbers in the millions when they encounter population figures. In fourth grade, students extend the place-value system beyond millions and explore the relative sizes of thousands, millions, and billions. They are also introduced to exponential notation. In fifth grade, students are asked to think about big numbers by using guess-and-test strategies. For example, they estimate how long it would take them to tap their fingers one million, one billion, or one trillion times. In sixth grade, students use large numbers in a project on the mathematical modeling of the solar system.

In many situations, the numbers are so large that exact counts or accurate measurements cannot be obtained. *The number of books in a large library at the end of a day is exact, but how would it be determined? How many grains of sand are on a beach? What is the population of the United States?* Although the Census Bureau attempts to count every person in the United States every 10 years, census takers may miss people, count incorrectly, or make other errors.

Taking samples and using statistics often give good estimates of large counts. In *Everyday Mathematics,* students explore many different ways of estimating large counts and measurements using surveys, polls, and experiments. Through class discussions, they are also encouraged to cultivate a healthy skepticism for claims that are based on such estimates.

16.1.3 Estimates in Calculations

Ballpark estimates make calculations easier when exact answers are not needed. For example, when you plan a trip, estimates of the costs of driving and flying are easier to compare than are exact values. Your thinking might be as follows: *The trip will be about 800 miles, my automobile gets about 25 miles per gallon, and gasoline costs about $3.10 per gallon; but there will be two days' extra driving and the motel will cost $120 and meals on the road about $60. On the other hand, the cheapest way to fly costs about $350, and I'll need to rent a car at the destination for 5 days at $80 per day . . ..*

Even with calculators and computers taking much of the work out of computation, estimating may make things a lot easier with no important loss in the quality of the answers. In fact, answers derived using estimates may be more reasonable and more realistic than exact answers, as in planning a car trip.

For situations in which exact answers are required and a calculator is used to find them, estimation can help check the results. Most of us have heard the story about the cashier at the fast-food restaurant who entered the price for an item incorrectly but couldn't tell that the total was incorrect. This story is often used to support the argument that people depend too much on machines and, therefore, that calculators should be banned from the classroom and students should master the traditional paper-and-pencil algorithms.

This argument misses the point entirely. Few people would want the cashier to stop using a machine and do the work on paper. What the cashier needs are estimation skills to check whether the machine total is reasonable. If it isn't, then it should be recalculated. In the cashier's defense, many traditional mathematics curricula don't teach estimation skills in conjunction with arithmetic operations. In fact, such skills are sometimes reviled as being merely trial and error. *Everyday Mathematics,* on the other hand, sees these skills as an integral component of a comprehensive and balanced approach to computation. Students are encouraged to compute either exactly or approximately, working mentally, with paper and pencil, or with a calculator, depending on what is most appropriate for each situation.

In Grades 4 through 6, students estimate to forecast sums and differences, extending the practice to larger and smaller numbers than the ones they encountered in earlier grades. They also estimate products, quotients, and powers, beginning with simple activities, such as making magnitude estimates that predict whether a product is in the thousands, ten-thousands, or hundred-thousands. Students use calculators extensively to find exact products and quotients of multidigit numbers. A general awareness of the magnitude of the results is especially important in checking calculator computations.

Probability activities provide *Everyday Mathematics* students with informal and natural contexts for estimating with division, for example, when they estimate the likelihood of future events. Students make such predictions in two different ways. First, they make educated guesses about events such as how a coin might land and test their guesses with experiments. Second, they use data-collection techniques and concepts from statistics and probability when predicting answers to less intuitive questions, such as *What might a population or wage be in the future?* In *Fifth Grade Everyday Mathematics,* such estimation problems are periodic challenges.

16.2 Approximation and Rounding

Estimation is a reasoned guess at an unknown or unknowable value. *Rounding* is a technique to approximate *known* numbers. Three common rounding algorithms and their uses are described on the next page. Each one requires you to first pick a *target place value* for the rounded number.

- *Round up* This algorithm is used to *overapproximate* a value.

  Example: A school bus holds 28 children. How many school buses should be scheduled to take 300 children on a field trip?

  Solution: The target is a *whole number* of buses.

  300/28 → 10 R20

  The quotient 10 R20 means that 10 buses would leave 20 children behind, so 11 buses must be ordered.

- *Round down* This algorithm is used to *underapproximate* a value.

  Example: An elevator manufacturer tests the maximum weight an elevator can hold and finds that the cable breaks at an average of 2,023.5 pounds. What should the posted weight limit be?

  Solution: The target is usually *hundreds of pounds,* although this varies.

  Round down to be safe. Perhaps the limit should be posted as 1,500 pounds.

- *Round to the nearest* This algorithm is intended to be as fair as possible. The traditional version says to round up if the digit to the right of the target place is 5 or greater and to round down if the digit is less than 5.

  Example: What is 17.688 centimeters rounded to the nearest tenth of a centimeter?

  Solution: The target is *tenths.*

  The digit to the right of the 6 in the tenths place is an 8. 8 > 5, so round up to 17.7 centimeters.

NOTE: A more formal round-to-the-nearest algorithm is given on page 263.

NOTE: The Texas Instruments TI-15 rounds to the nearest, and the Casio *fx*-55 rounds down. For more information, see Section 3.1.1: Calculators.

When writing approximations, the symbol $\approx$ means *is approximately equal to.* So in the last example, the solution could be written $17.688 \approx 17.7$.

All calculators round decimals to fit the display screen. Some 4-function calculators use the round-to-the-nearest algorithm, but most round down. Most scientific calculators round to the nearest value of the place at the far right of the display. Almost all calculators hold more digits accurately in memory than they display. Understanding the principles and effects of rounding is important when using a calculator.

Most scientific calculators have a *fix* feature that lets you set (fix) the number of decimal places your calculator displays. For example, you can set it to round to the nearest hundredth when doing calculations involving money and always see values rounded to the nearest penny. For most calculators, including the Casio *fx-55*, a key sequence to round to the nearest hundredth is [FIX] 2. On a TI-15, a sequence is [FIX] [0.01]. On both calculators, [FIX] [·] disables the fix.

How do calculators round to the nearest value? Perhaps they run an algorithm similar to the following one from *Fourth Grade Everyday Mathematics*.

Algorithm: Rounding to the Nearest				
Here is an algorithm to *round a number to the nearest value in a given decimal place:*	**Example 1:** Round 4,538 to the nearest hundred.	**Example 2:** Round 26,781 to the nearest thousand.	**Example 3:** Round 5,295 to the nearest ten.	**Example 4:** Round 3.573 to the nearest tenth.
Step 1: Find the target digit in the place you are rounding to.	4,**5**38	2**6**,781	5,2**9**5	3.**5**73
Step 2: Rewrite the number, replacing all digits to the right of the target with zero. This is the lower approximation.	4,500	26,000	5,290	3.500
Step 3: Add 1 to the digit in the place you are rounding to. If the sum is 10, write 0 and add 1 to the digit to its left. This is the higher approximation.	4,600	27,000	5,300	3.600
Step 4: Is the original number closer to the lower approximation or to the higher approximation?	lower approximation	higher approximation	halfway	higher approximation
Step 5: Round to the closer of the two numbers. If it is halfway between the higher and the lower number, round to the higher number.	4,500	27,000	5,300	3.600 = 3.6

Often, numbers are rounded to make them easier to work with. Usually, you round either up or down to a number that is close to a known number but easier to work with, where "close" and "easier" are determined by the context of a problem. In the following example, rounding makes estimation easier.

Example: You want to buy 4 cans of tennis balls that cost $4.57 a can. Estimate the least number of dollar bills you need in order to pay for your purchase.

Solution 1: Rounding up to $5 per can, a reasonable estimate for the cost of 4 cans is 4 * $5 = $20. However, because you rounded up, you will definitely not need more than $20. So 20 $1 bills will be enough.

Solution 2: Rounding down to $4.50 per can, a closer estimate to the cost of 4 cans is $18, because 4 * $4.50 = $18. However, 4 * $4.57 is a bit more than $18, so you will need at least 19 $1 bills.

chapter 16

Both solutions are good applications of rounding. Which solution is right? Although the second solution of $19 is closer to the exact cost of $18.28 than the first solution of $20, it is not necessarily a better estimate. In class, you might discuss both solutions and compare them to each other. Students may realize that to estimate a result to a nearest dollar, they don't necessarily round to the nearest dollar first.

A Note on Significant Digits and Precision

The important, yet difficult, topic of *significant digits* is treated informally in *Everyday Mathematics* but is not taught explicitly. The basic idea is that computation cannot yield a result that is more precise than the least precise count or measure in the computation, as indicated by the *significant,* or meaningful, digits in the counts or measures. For example:

- If one length is measured to the nearest centimeter (say 15 cm), a second to the nearest half-centimeter (say 4.5 cm), and a third to the nearest millimeter (say 2.8 cm), their sum is best reported to the nearest centimeter (22 cm).

- If a rectangular wall is 3.6 meters by 4.8 meters, multiplication gives the area as 17.28 square meters. However, each dimension has only two significant digits, so the area to two significant digits is 17 square meters.

- If the population of a city is estimated to the nearest thousand and the population of a second city to the nearest ten-thousand, the difference in population of the cities should be estimated to the nearest ten-thousand.

The smallest interval on the scale of any measuring tool establishes the *precision* of the tool. The precision establishes the number of significant digits allowable in measurements using the tool. For example, a standard foot-long ruler typically has a smallest interval of $\frac{1}{16}$ inch. So the most precise measure using such a ruler is the nearest $\frac{1}{16}$ inch, and all calculations with measures from that ruler should be rounded to the nearest $\frac{1}{16}$ inch. If there is a metric scale on the other side of the ruler with a smallest interval of a millimeter, then the precision on that scale is 1 millimeter.

A ruler with $\frac{1}{16}$-inch precision on the right side and 1-millimeter precision on the left

▶ ## 16.3 Mental Arithmetic

Although people frequently associate mental arithmetic with estimation, it is also useful for finding exact answers. In many situations, an exact answer is required but a calculator is not available and *mental arithmetic* is a convenient alternative. Even most paper-and-pencil algorithms for finding exact answers involve mental arithmetic. Paper-and-pencil division, for example, is likely to require mental addition, multiplication, and subtraction.

In *Everyday Mathematics,* students practice mental arithmetic to learn useful techniques; to develop flexible thinking; and to gain *fact power,* or the automatic recall of basic addition/subtraction and multiplication/division facts. These skills contribute to students' *number sense,* which includes a flexible understanding both of numbers and of operations on those numbers. *Everyday Mathematics* also emphasizes number sense because calculators and computers have actually increased the importance of estimation and mental arithmetic in daily life. Complicated paper-and-pencil computation has become relatively less important in everyday life and in the curriculum, while mental arithmetic and skillful use of calculators have become relatively more important.

An important part of being a flexible problem solver is to add continually to a personal tool kit of mental-arithmetic skills. Some of these mental-arithmetic skills should become automatic so they can be used reflexively, almost without thinking.

Mental-arithmetic skills are developed throughout the *Everyday Mathematics* curriculum as an integral part of the program. Each lesson in first through sixth grades begins with a brief set of oral or slate exercises called Mental Math and Reflexes. In Grades 4 through 6 *5-Minute Math* provides many activities for practicing mental-arithmetic and problem-solving skills. In *Everyday Mathematics,* problems to be solved without calculators are identified with a no-calculator icon. Whenever students use calculators, they need to verify that the calculator answer makes sense.

Strategy sharing is vitally important throughout *Everyday Mathematics.* Perhaps the most important part of learning mental-arithmetic skills is to have students share their solution strategies after they solve a problem. Sharing strategies requires students to verbalize their thinking, thus making them conscious of a process that is often intuitive. Students also get insights into alternative approaches from their classmates and develop creative and flexible thinking processes. Importantly, students learn that common sense applies to mathematics and that they can solve difficult problems by themselves.

16.3.1 Mental-Calculation Strategies

There are many strategies and techniques for mental arithmetic. Some are formally introduced in *Everyday Mathematics,* and students develop others on their own. Students are exposed to many techniques, learn how they work, master a few, and build some into reflexes. A few examples of strategies follow. All may be justified mathematically, but we describe them here briefly in terms that you may hear in the classroom.

- *Round* Techniques include rounding, as appropriate, to the nearest ten, hundred, thousand, and so on, and computing with rounded numbers. For example, 647 + 284 is approximately 600 + 300 = 900, or perhaps 650 + 280 = 930.

- *Adjust the numbers* A sum is unchanged if one addend is increased by a given amount and the other addend is decreased by the same amount. For example, in 86 + 37, think *86 + 4 = 90 and 37 − 4 = 33, so 90 + 33 = 123*. This is called the *opposite-change rule for addition.*

For more information, see Section 16.3.2: Basic Facts and Fact Power and Section 16.4: Number Sense and Mathematical Connections.

A no-calculator icon

For more information, see Section 18.4.2: Sharing Students' Strategies and Solutions.

chapter 16

A similar rule is the *same-change rule for subtraction*: a difference is unchanged if the same amount is added to or subtracted from both the minuend and the subtrahend. For example, in 54 − 37, think *37 + 3 = 40 and 54 + 3 = 57, so 57 − 40 = 17.*

- *Look for easy combinations* For example, in 17 + 25 + 3 + 15, add 17 and 3 (*20*) and 25 and 15 (*40*). So 17 + 25 + 3 + 15 = 20 + 40 = 60.

- *Estimate, then adjust* An approximate answer is obtained first and then adjusted to make it more accurate. For example, 647 + 284 is approximately 640 + 280 (*920*); then add 7 + 4 (*11*) to that sum (*920 + 11 = 931*).

- *For multiplication of whole numbers* (*only*), *attach zeros* To multiply by a multiple of 10, 100, 1,000, and so on, multiply the nonzero part of the factors and append as many zeros to the result as there are zeros in the factors. For example, in 12 ∗ 300, think *12 ∗ 3 = 36 with 2 zeros is 3,600.*

- *For division of whole numbers* (*only*), *cross out zeros* To divide multiples of 10, 100, 1,000, and so on, cross out the same number of ending zeros in the divisor as in the dividend. For example, in 4,500/50 cross out 1 zero in each number and get 4,50̸0/5̸0 = 450/5 = 90.

- *Estimate magnitude* As a useful check for answers found another way, ask *Is a reasonable answer in the tens? hundreds? thousands?*

- *Quick division by a 1-digit number* Rewrite the dividend as a sum of extended facts of the divisor. For example, to calculate 364/7 mentally:

Rewrite 364 using extended 7s facts:	$364 = 350 + 14$
Divide each part by 7:	$364/7 = (350/7) + (14/7)$
	$= 50 + 2$
Add:	$= 52$

Note that quick division is an application of the Distributive Property. The strategy also works for problems that do not divide exactly. For example, to calculate 727/4:

Rewrite 727 using extended 4s facts:	$727 = 400 + 320 + 7$
Divide each part by 4:	$727/4 = (400/4) + (320/4) + (7/4)$
	$= 100 + 80 + 1\frac{3}{4}$
Add:	$= 181\frac{3}{4}$

For more information, see Section 9.8.1: Prime and Composite Numbers: Divisibility.

Miscellaneous Strategies

- To multiply a whole number by 10, append one zero to the number; to multiply by 100, append two zeros.

- To multiply a decimal by 10, move the decimal point one place to the right; to multiply a decimal by 100, move the decimal point two places to the right. Append zeros as necessary.

- To divide a decimal by 10, move the decimal point one place to the left; to divide a decimal by 100, move the decimal point two places to the left. Append zeros as necessary.

- To rename a decimal as a percent, move the decimal point two places to the right and append a percent sign; reverse the process to rename a percent as a decimal. Append zeros as necessary.

- To multiply a whole number by 5, multiply by 10 and find half of the result.

- To determine whether a number is divisible by 3, find the sum of its digits. If the sum is divisible by 3, then the number is divisible by 3. For example: 117 is divisible by 3, because the sum of the digits, 9, is divisible by 3; 117 is also divisible by 9 because the sum of the digits is divisible by 9.

- To multiply a 2-digit number by 11, add the two digits and write the sum between the two digits. For example: To multiply 11 * 34, add the two digits in 34 and place the sum between the 3 and 4. So 3 + 4 = 7 and 11 * 34 = 374.

  To multiply 11 * 69, add the two digits in 69. Because 6 + 9 = 15, add a 1 to the first digit and place the 5 between 7 and 9. So 11 * 69 = 759.

16.3.2 Basic Facts and Fact Power

Automatically knowing basic number facts is as important to learning mathematics as knowing words by sight is to reading. This has not gone unnoticed among educational researchers. Benjamin Bloom (1986) has written at length on the importance of *automaticity* as part of any complex talent and *Everyday Mathematics* co-creator Max Bell has long emphasized the importance of number-fact reflexes. Students are often told that habits, good and bad, come from doing something over and over until they do it without thinking. Developing basic number-fact reflexes can be likened to developing good habits.

In *Everyday Mathematics,* good fact habits are called *fact power.* In Grades 1 through 3, children keep *fact power tables* of the facts they know. The grades in which *Everyday Mathematics* activities help children gain fact power for each of the four basic arithmetic operations are shown in the table on the next page. For each operation, easier facts are introduced, explored using a variety of strategies, and practiced before harder facts are introduced, usually in the next grade.

Grade-Level Development of Students' Fact Power							
	K	1	2	3	4	5	6
Addition							
Easy	E/S	S	R	M	M	M	M
Hard	E	E/S	R	M	M	M	M
Subtraction							
Easy	E/S	S	S/R	R	M	M	M
Hard	E	E/S	S	R	M	M	M
Multiplication							
Easy			E/S	S/R	M	M	M
Hard			E/S	S/R	M	M	M
Division							
Easy			E/S	S	R	M	M
Hard			E/S	S	R	M	M

E Exploration **S** Strategies **R** Recall **M** Maintenance

Several stages can be distinguished in the development of fact power, as indicated by the letters in the table above:

- **E**xploration. Students use concrete and pictorial representations to model basic fact problems. Conceptual understanding of the operation is a primary goal. Practice for speed is not appropriate.
- **S**trategies. Students develop and use a variety of strategies for solving basic fact problems. Over time, students develop more efficient strategies and begin to gain automaticity with basic facts. Some practice for speed may be appropriate.
- **R**ecall. Students attain automatic recall of basic facts. Practice to build speed is appropriate.
- **M**aintenance. Students maintain automaticity with basic facts. Fact work focuses on fact extensions and general mental arithmetic.

The early stages of this process should not be rushed. As students explore basic fact problems, they develop their understanding of the operation and come to understand that mathematics is sense-making rather than just memorizing. As students develop, share, and compare strategies for solving basic fact problems, they build skills that will be useful for mental arithmetic with larger numbers, learn that there are often many ways to solve a problem, and practice important communication skills. If practice for speed and timed tests are introduced too early, these valuable understandings can be undermined.

Key Reflexes

Students in *Everyday Mathematics* are expected to develop other mathematical reflexes that extend their fact power beyond just the basic arithmetic facts, reflexes that will serve them in school mathematics and in everyday life. By the end of sixth grade, students are expected to be able to automatically:

- Recall basic arithmetic facts;
- Round, estimate, and do simple mental arithmetic;

NOTE: *Everyday Mathematics* includes practice and assessment activities that can be used with students who may not achieve automatic recall as quickly as others.

- Compute with powers of 10;
- Give many equivalent names for fractions;
- Mentally calculate 1%, 5%, and 10% of a number;
- Identify equivalencies among important fractions, decimals, and percents, especially halves, fourths, eighths, thirds, fifths, and tenths;
- Manipulate symbols in algebraic expressions and equations.

16.3.3 Fact Practice

Practicing the facts traditionally involves pages and pages of drills. This can be tedious and lead students to dislike mathematics. Teachers of *Everyday Mathematics* have reported great success using these alternative approaches.

50-Facts Multiplication Drills

Early in fourth grade, students take a timed multiplication-facts test. They graph their scores on the 50-facts test after 1 minute and after 3 minutes. You can use this test as a screening tool to identify students who need additional support. Students who need extra practice can take additional tests about once per unit.

Labels

Because numbers in real life nearly always occur in some context, *Everyday Mathematics* recommends that you and the students select *labels for the day* to use with fact practice. The kinds and numbers of labels you need depend on the operations being used. In addition and subtraction, only one label is needed. For example, on one day choose the label *pencils* and read the problem $7 + 9 = ?$ as 7 pencils + 9 pencils = ? pencils.

In multiplication and division, two or three related labels are needed. For example, one day you might use *cartons, pounds per carton,* and *pounds* so that the problem $5 * 8 = \_\_$ becomes 5 cartons * 8 pounds per carton = __ pounds. Sometimes it makes sense for the two factors in multiplication to have the same label. For example, when finding an area, 5 feet * 8 feet = 40 square feet.

Post the labels and refer to them occasionally as students practice the facts. The labels of the day reinforce the idea that numbers refer to something real and useful. Keep the labels simple. They can be true-to-life or fanciful, serious or silly. They can be units of measure such as centimeters, minutes, and pounds or countable objects such as cats, hats, and ribbons. Although the main purpose for using labels is to keep numbers from becoming too abstract, labels are also important in other curriculum areas, especially reading, the sciences, and language arts.

Fact Families and Fact Triangles

A *fact family* is a collection of four related facts linking two inverse operations. For example, the following four equations symbolize the fact family relating 3, 4, and 12 by multiplication and division.

$$3 * 4 = 12 \qquad 4 * 3 = 12$$
$$12/3 = 4 \qquad 12/4 = 3$$

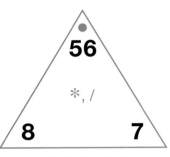

A multiplication/division
Fact Triangle

You may recognize that the two multiplication facts in this family taken together are an instance of the Commutative Property of Multiplication. Although *Everyday Mathematics* does not require students to learn mathematical names for properties, it is handy to have a name for occasional use. The *turn-around rule for multiplication* is the name used in *Everyday Mathematics* for the Commutative Property of Multiplication. From a practical point of view, the turn-around rule means that any time you learn a new multiplication fact, you get a second one for free! Note that there is no turn-around rule for either subtraction or division. For example, $7 - 4 \neq 4 - 7$ and $12/4 \neq 4/12$.

Everyday Mathematics calls properties of arithmetic *shortcuts,* and the four facts in a fact family are all related by shortcuts. A major reason for teaching fact families is to give students different options when solving problems that are new or difficult. By recalling a shortcut, a student can reword or rewrite the problem in a more meaningful way. For example, when faced with $56/8 = ?$, a fourth grader may think *Hmm, lemme think. What times 8 is 56? Ah, that's easy, it's 7.*

Fact Triangles are the *Everyday Mathematics* version of flash cards. Fact Triangles are more effective than traditional flash cards because they emphasize fact families. An addition/subtraction Fact Triangle has two addends and a sum; a multiplication/division Fact Triangle has two factors and a product. A Fact Triangle for the $8 * 7 = 56$ fact family is shown in the margin.

Fact Triangles are best employed in a cooperative-learning situation. One player covers a corner with a finger and the other player gives a fact that has the hidden number as an answer. For example, one player might cover up the 8 in a {8, 7, 56} multiplication/division Fact Triangle. The other player might say, "$56/7 = 8$." Fact Triangles can also be sorted into known/unknown facts or by a strategy such as doubles, near doubles, times 3, and divided by 5, to make for efficient practice. Because Fact Triangle activities are easy to do at home, they can be used as Study Links.

In *First Grade Everyday Mathematics,* children establish and emphasize addition/subtraction fact families through $9 + 9$. In second grade, the addition/subtraction fact families are further developed and multiplication/division Fact Triangles are introduced. In all grades, new facts are usually introduced through concrete manipulations, drawings, games, and connections to previously known facts.

Fact Extensions

Fact extensions are powerful mental-arithmetic strategies for all operations with larger numbers. For example:

- If students know $3 + 4 = 7$, they also know $30 + 40 = 70$, $70 - 30 = 40$, and $300 + 400 = 700$.
- If students know $6 * 5 = 30$, they also know $60 * 5 = 300$, $600 * 5 = 3,000$, and $3,000/600 = 5$.

Fact extensions are introduced in first grade and continue throughout the program. In fifth grade, fact families are extended further as students learn equivalent values for decimals, fractions, and percents.

16.3.4 Games for Fact Practice

Frequent practice is necessary in order for students to build and maintain strong mental-arithmetic skills and reflexes. Although drill has its place, much of the practice in *Everyday Mathematics* is in game format. Games are not merely attractive add-ons but essential parts of the complete *Everyday Mathematics* program.

In "Playing games and real mathematics," Ainley (1988) writes,

> The most effective mathematical games are those in which the structure and rules of the game are based on mathematical ideas, and where winning the game is directly related to understanding this mathematics. (p. 241)

All grades of *Everyday Mathematics* include games that have been developed to help students learn specific arithmetic and other skills at an appropriate developmental level. Some, in fact, are so targeted to the development of certain skills that once a child becomes proficient, the game is no longer necessary.

Drill and games should not be viewed as competitors for class time, nor should games be thought of as time-killers or rewards. In fact, games satisfy many, if not most, standard drill objectives with many built-in options. Drill tends to become tedious and, therefore, gradually loses its effectiveness. Games relieve the tedium because students enjoy them. Indeed, students often wish to continue to play games during their free time, lunch, and even recess.

Arithmetic practice through games is also recommended to help you deal with individual differences in students' motivations and abilities. Seckinger, Mitchel, and Lemire (1989) found that games improve students' attitudes about mathematics as well as improve achievement among low-achievers. Alternatively, Johnson (2000) advocates using mathematical games with gifted students, who tend to invent new rules or increase difficulty of games on their own. Researchers such as Wolpert (1996) also support games or other play to encourage automaticity of arithmetic skills by learning-disabled students.

Drill exercises aim primarily at building fact and operation skills. Practice through games shares these objectives, but at the same time, games often reinforce calculator skills, logical thinking, geometric intuition, and intuition about probability and chance because many games involve randomly generated numbers.

Using games to practice number skills also greatly reduces the need for worksheets. Because the numbers in most games are generated randomly, the games can be played over and over without repeating the same problems. Many of the *Everyday Mathematics* games come with variations that allow players to progress from easy to more challenging versions. Games, therefore, offer an almost unlimited source of practice material.

NOTE: Cognitive and educational psychologists have long supported children's playing games in school. For a concise summary, see *Theories of Childhood: An Introduction to Dewey, Montessori, Erickson, Piaget and Vygotsky* by C. G. Mooney. A full reference can be found on page 273.

NOTE: The federal and some state education departments advocate children playing mathematics games in school and at home. The U.S. Department of Education (2004) places high value on games in *Helping Your Child Learn Mathematics.* A full reference can be found on page 273. The New York State Department of Education has recommended games along with concrete objects, number lines, and other approaches for more than 25 years. For more information on New York's position, see this Web site: www.emsc.nysed.gov/ciai/mst/math/home.html

chapter 16

▶ 16.4 Number Sense and Mathematical Connections

It is perhaps the single greatest goal of *Everyday Mathematics* that students completing the program acquire number sense. People with *number sense:*

- Have good mental-arithmetic skills as well as reliable algorithms and procedures for finding results they can't produce mentally;
- Are flexible in thinking about numbers and arithmetic and will look for shortcuts to make their efforts as efficient as possible;
- Can use their number and arithmetic skills to solve problems in everyday situations;
- Are familiar with a variety of ways to communicate their strategies and results;
- Can recognize unreasonable results when they see them in their own work, in everyday situations, or in the media.

Number sense develops only with wide mathematical experience, including instruction and practice in specific techniques. But good number sense also depends on attitudes and beliefs, especially the belief that mathematics makes sense. People with good number sense expect their mathematical knowledge to connect with the rest of what they know, including their common sense and whatever they know about the situation at hand. Number sense thus depends on making connections between various kinds of mathematical knowledge and between mathematics and other subjects.

Everyday Mathematics helps students develop number sense in the contexts of data analysis, geometry, and elementary explorations of functions and sequences. In *Everyday Mathematics,* students make connections across mathematical topics and come to view mathematics as a coherent, consistent discipline rather than a hodgepodge of disconnected procedures and skills.

Number sense also involves making connections between mathematics and other subjects in the curriculum. Many activities in *Everyday Mathematics* are designed to show how number sense applies to science, social studies, and geography. Throughout *Everyday Mathematics* there are connections between mathematics and history, including both the history of mathematics and how mathematics has shaped human endeavors.

Everyday Mathematics also connects mathematics to the community through efforts to share the authors' commitment to number sense with students' families and other caregivers. Family Letters explain how *Everyday Mathematics* introduces students not only to the traditional mathematics people expect but also to a richer mathematics curriculum that older family members may not have experienced. Study Links enable parents or guardians to see the kinds of mathematics their students do in school and pass along some interesting ideas for family involvement as well.

References and Resources on Estimation, Mental Arithmetic, and Number Sense

Ainley, J. (1988). "Playing games and real mathematics." In Pimm, D. (Ed.) *Mathematics, Teachers and Students.* London: Hodder and Stoughton.

Bell, M., and Usiskin, Z. (1983). *Applying Arithmetic.* Chicago: University of Chicago. Available in three parts from Educational Resources Information Center (ERIC): ED 264087, ED 264088, and ED 264089.

Bloom, B. (1986). "Automaticity: The Hands and Feet of Genius." *Educational Leadership (43)5,* pp. 70–77.

Kamii, C., and DeVries, R. (1980). *Group games in early education: Implications of Piaget's theory.* Washington, DC: National Association for the Education of Young Children.

Mooney, C. G. (2000). *Theories of Childhood: An Introduction to Dewey, Montessori, Erickson, Piaget, and Vygotsky.* St. Paul, MN: Redleaf.

Office of Intergovernmental and Interagency Affairs. (2004). *Helping Your Child Learn Mathematics.* Washington, DC: U.S. Department of Education.

Peters, S. (1998). "Playing games and learning mathematics: The results of two intervention studies." *International Journal of Early Years Education (6)1,* pp. 49–58.

Schoen, H. L., and Zweng, M. J. (1986). *Estimation and Mental Computation: 1986 Yearbook.* Reston, VA: National Council of Teachers of Mathematics.

Steen, L. (Ed.) (1997). *Why Numbers Count: Quantitative Literacy for Tomorrow's America.* New York: College Entrance Examination Board.

Wolpert, G. (1996). *The Educational Challenges Inclusion Study.* New York: National Down Syndrome Society.

chapter 16

17 Patterns, Sequences, Functions, and Algebra

Contents

Patterns can be found in sounds, in movements, in shapes, in numbers, in graphs, and in data. Indeed, patterns can be found almost anywhere. Patterns are especially important in mathematics. Some people even define mathematics as the science of patterns.

Most of mathematics deals with patterns that are predictable. This means that objects, colors, or numbers are arranged so that you can predict what comes next. You can "see" or continue such patterns; and in many cases, it is possible to find a rule that underlies a given pattern. The first part of this chapter deals with such patterns, including sequences and functions.

The second part of the chapter discusses uses of variables and how to read and write open number sentences. It closes with a description of methods of simplifying expressions and solving open sentences.

Patterns and algebra are closely related. Pattern activities involve many mathematical processes that are fundamental in algebra. Among these are looking for patterns; making, testing, and proving conjectures about patterns; and representing patterns in several ways. Looking for patterns helps students develop modeling skills, which are crucial to many applications of algebra. By making and justifying conjectures about patterns, students develop habits of generalization and verification that will serve them well in algebra and beyond. Finally, working with multiple representations for functions, such as function machines, tables, rules, graphs, words, and symbols, helps students to build the conceptual understandings that will eventually support the symbol-manipulation skills so necessary for success in algebra.

17.1 Patterns, Sequences, and Functions

Most of the patterns in *Everyday Mathematics* are either *visual patterns,* such as those found in colored manipulatives, geometric shapes, and data or coordinate graphs, or *number patterns,* such as those found in sequences and functions.

The program includes many activities involving visual patterns; and in many of them, students explore properties of geometric shapes. These visual patterns are discussed in other chapters of this manual. For example, pattern-based classifications of polygons are discussed in Chapter 13: Geometry, and visual patterns in graphs are discussed in Chapter 12: Data and Chance.

The next three sections discuss number patterns and arithmetic rules that may generate them. The main focus is on two important types of number patterns that students will continue to study in high school mathematics and beyond: *sequences* and *functions.* A goal of *Everyday Mathematics* is to provide students with a rich set of tools for examining these patterns concretely, symbolically, and visually, and so prepare them for more formal investigations later on.

17.1.1 Number Patterns

For centuries people have studied number patterns in a branch of mathematics called *number theory.* This section discusses perhaps the simplest of these patterns, *odd* and *even* numbers.

For more information, see Section 9.8: Number Theory.

Odd and even numbers are simple, but exploring them can lead students to generalizations that are of fundamental importance in number theory. For example, it is easy to observe that pairing odd numbers of things always leaves one left over. Building on this simple observation, some students discover relationships such as the following:

- The sum of any two even numbers is even (there are no leftover pieces).
- The sum of an even number and an odd number is odd (the leftover piece remains).
- The sum of any two odd numbers is even (the leftovers pair up).
- The statements are still true if a *positive difference* is substituted for *sum.* For example, the positive difference of any two even numbers is even.

Similar relationships exist for the products of odd and even numbers, although students are less likely to discover these relationships on their own. A product is even if at least one of the factors is even. If none of the factors is even, then the product is odd. For example, $3 * 7 * 5$ is odd because all the factors are odd. $27 * 3 * 4$ is even because one of the factors is even.

Division is a bit trickier, and applies only to quotients with no remainder. A quotient is even if the dividend is "more even" than the divisor; otherwise the quotient will be odd. For example, $12/6$ is even because 12 has two 2s ($12 = 2 * 2 * 3$) and 6 has only one 2 ($2 * 3 = 6$). But $24/8$ is odd because both 24 and 8 have three 2s ($24 = 2 * 2 * 2 * 3$ and $8 = 2 * 2 * 2$).

Odd numbers of people or things are often seen as a nuisance. An odd number of people cannot be assigned equally to two different teams. Similarly, two people cannot equally share an odd number of unbreakable objects, such as marbles. On the other hand, it is easier to find the middle value, or median, of an odd number of data values because an even number of values has no single middle value.

Making generalizations based on observations of patterns is fundamental to mathematics and science. When students discover and "prove" simple relationships about odd and even numbers, they are learning powerful ways of thinking that will serve them throughout their mathematical careers.

17.1.2 Sequences

A *number sequence* is a list of numbers. Many sequences are important enough to have names:

- Whole numbers: 0, 1, 2, 3, 4, 5, 6, . . .
- Odd numbers: 1, 3, 5, 7, 9, 11, . . .
- Even numbers: 2, 4, 6, 8, 10, 12, . . .
- Prime numbers: 2, 3, 5, 7, 11, 13, . . .
- Square numbers: 1, 4, 9, 16, 25, 36, . . .

Number sequences often have a *rule* that governs what the next number in the sequence is. The rule may involve one or more arithmetic operations. For example, the counting numbers can be generated by starting with 1 and then repeatedly applying the rule, "Add 1." The even numbers can be generated by starting with 2 and then applying the rule "Add 2."

Many number sequences can be linked to visual patterns. The square numbers, for example, can be modeled by a sequence of square arrays. The even numbers and triangular numbers can also be modeled by sequences of dot patterns. The interplay of number sequences and visual patterns is fertile ground for investigations in elementary school mathematics.

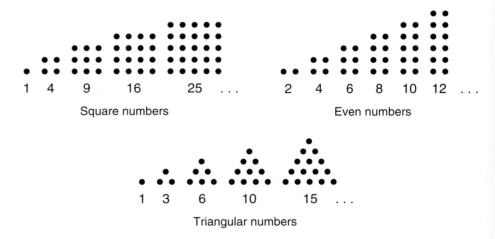

Square numbers

Even numbers

Triangular numbers

Patterns in many number sequences are accessible to students of any age. Starting in *First Grade Everyday Mathematics,* children use Frames-and-Arrows diagrams to invent or extend sequences or to find a rule or rules for a given sequence. Although fourth- through sixth-grade students do not use the diagrams, they are briefly described below to help you understand the past experience of your students.

Frames and Arrows

Frames-and-Arrows diagrams consist of a sequence of frames connected by arrows. Each frame contains a number; each arrow represents a rule that determines which number goes in the next frame. The numbers in a Frames-and-Arrows diagram form a sequence; the arrow rule(s) represent the mathematical structure that generates the sequence. Frames-and-Arrows diagrams are also called *chains.* A simple example of a Frames-and-Arrows diagram for the rule "Add 1" is shown below.

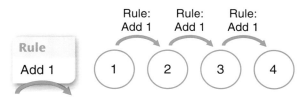

In Frames-and-Arrows problems, some information is given and some is missing; for example, a rule may be given and the frames are empty, or some frames are filled in but other frames and the rule are missing. Children figure out the missing pieces of the diagram.

Incomplete Number Lines

In the early grades, children begin filling in missing numbers on a number line. In later grades, these number-line activities are extended to sequences of fractions, decimals, and negative numbers. In the following examples, students start with the numbers in the boxes and fill in the numbers on the blanks.

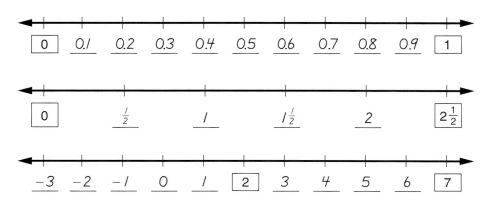

As this work with number lines continues, students may discover the amazing fact that between any two points or numbers, there is always another point or number.

> **NOTE:** A more sophisticated variation on Frames and Arrows is the "What's My Rule?" activity described in detail in Section 17.1.3: Functions.

For more information on number lines, see Section 15.3.1: 1-Dimensional Coordinate Systems.

17.1.3 Functions

Function is one of those everyday words that mathematicians use in a special way. This section begins with descriptions of how *Everyday Mathematics* approaches this powerful idea in ways that even Kindergartners can understand. The mathematical definition of function follows that idea, along with a discussion of the many ways functions can be represented or modeled.

Function Machines

A *function machine* is an imaginary device that receives inputs and generates outputs. For example, the function machine in the margin takes an *input* number and *outputs* its double.

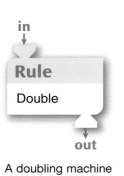

A doubling machine

Students can imagine putting a number into this machine, waiting a moment, and then getting its double out. If a 1 is put in, then a 2 comes out. If a 5 is put in, then a 10 comes out. Whatever number goes in, twice that number comes out.

The inputs and outputs from a function machine can be recorded in a *function table.* Each row in the table holds an *ordered pair* in which the first number is the input and the second number is the output. Here is a table for the doubling function machine.

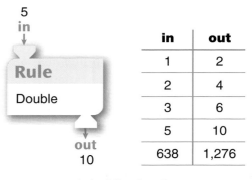

in	out
1	2
2	4
3	6
5	10
638	1,276

A doubling function

An important feature of a function machine is that it *always* gives the same output for a given input number. If two rows in an input-output table have the same number in the input column, then they must also have the same number in the output column.

Often, every input number has a different output number as in the doubling machine, but this is not required. For example, a function machine might always output the same number, no matter what is put in. Such functions are called *constant functions* and are perfectly legitimate, if a bit dull.

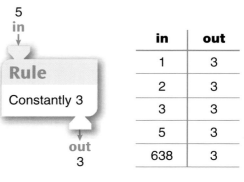

in	out
1	3
2	3
3	3
5	3
638	3

A constant function

A function machine captures the key features of most of the functions that are studied in pre-college mathematics, in which there are a set of inputs, a set of outputs, and a rule associating each input with exactly one output.

In *Kindergarten* through *Third Grade Everyday Mathematics,* function machines and function tables help children visualize how a rule associates each input value with an output value. A principal activity for developing this concept further is called "What's My Rule?"

"What's My Rule?"

Generally, in a "What's My Rule?" problem, two of the three parts of a function (input, output, and rule) are known. The goal is to find the unknown part. There are three basic types of problems:

- The rule and some input numbers are known. Give the corresponding output numbers.

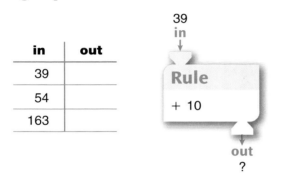

in	out
39	
54	
163	

- The rule and some output numbers are known. Give the corresponding input numbers.

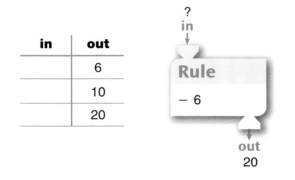

in	out
	6
	10
	20

- Some input and output numbers are known. Give a rule.

in	out
55	60
85	90
103	108

You can combine more than one type of problem in a single table. For example, you could give a partially completed table with an unknown rule. If you give enough input and output clues, students can fill in blanks as well as figure out a rule, as in the problem below.

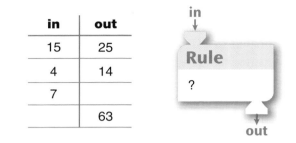

in	out
15	25
4	14
7	
	63

What Is a Function?

Like many ideas in mathematics, the concept of a function is simple, yet powerful. Also like many ideas in mathematics, the definition of function seems at first to be rather odd. According to a dictionary of mathematics, "A *function* is a set of ordered pairs (x, y) in which each value of x is paired with exactly one value of y." A few examples may help clarify what this means:

- Doubling: $\{(1,2), (2,4), (3,6), (4,8), \ldots\}$
- Squaring: $\{(1,1), (2,4), (3,9), (4,16), \ldots\}$
- Adding 1: $\{(1,2), (2,3), (3,4), (4,5), \ldots\}$

In each of these sets of ordered pairs, the first number is paired with exactly one second number. According to the definition, then, each of these sets is a function.

This definition applies to all the functions discussed so far in this chapter, but you will note that there is no mention of a rule. *The pairings in a function don't have to follow any rule.* The only requirement is that *each* first value has to be paired with *exactly one* second value. For example, you have a function if you pair each whole number less than 100 with any other whole number less than 100.

- A function with no rule: $\{(0,10), (1,82), (2,15), (3,74), \ldots, (98,17), (99,92)\}$

Such a function may not be very useful, but it is still a legitimate function. A more interesting example of a function with no rule is one that takes a date as the input and gives the closing price of IBM stock as the output. If you could find a rule for such a function, you could get rich quickly. Unfortunately, economists have proved that no such rule can exist. The only way to find the closing price of IBM stock on a future date is to wait and see what it is.

In *Everyday Mathematics,* students do not explore functions without rules. Most interesting functions are interesting because they have rules. So all the functions in the program are associated with rules that are either given or may be deduced. To keep the rules interesting to students, the authors based many of them in real-life situations.

Along with no mention of rules, the mathematical definition of a function does not mention numbers. In fact, *functions do not have to involve numbers at all*—just a set of paired inputs and outputs. A function might take polygons in and output a name based on number of sides (triangle, quadrangle, pentagon, and so on). Another function might take triangles in and output a name based on angles (acute, right, or obtuse). All that is required for a function is a set of ordered pairs (*input, output*)—in which every input has exactly one output.

Many real-world situations may remind you of functions. A bathroom scale is a function machine; when you stand on it, it outputs your weight. A gasoline pump has a built-in function machine, in which the input is an amount of gasoline pumped and the output is a total cost including tax. One way to think about science is as a search for functions that relate real-world variables.

Sequences can also be considered to be functions. Some sequences are *iterative* functions, in which an output comes from applying a rule to the previous output, that is, to the previous number, or *term,* in the sequence, rather than to an independent input value. For example, to get the next even number, just add 2 to the previous even number. Other sequences are not iterative because there is no rule that gives the next term from the previous terms. In a sequence of closing prices for IBM stock, knowing the previous term or terms is not enough to determine the next term.

Another way to think of sequences as functions is to number, or *index*, the terms. For example, indexing a sequence of even numbers beginning with 2 led to the table at the right. The indices can be thought of as input values, and the even numbers in the sequence as the output. Thinking of a sequence in this way can sometimes lead you to a rule that will give any term in the sequence without having to find all the previous terms. From the table, it appears that a rule to find the nth even number is to simply double n.

in	out
1	2
2	4
3	6
4	8
5	10

In *Everyday Mathematics,* sequences are not treated as functions. It's easier to think of sequences as lists of numbers, often with a rule for generating the next term, as in Frames-and-Arrows diagrams. However, activities with sequences are quite helpful for developing students' understanding of functions.

Representing Functions

In *Everyday Mathematics*, students approach functions *concretely, pictorially, verbally,* and *symbolically.* Students see *concrete* representations in activities such as sorting objects according to some measure or attribute, lining up by height, or ordering pattern blocks by shape. All of these concrete activities include patterns that lead to functions.

NOTE: A *relation* is a set of ordered pairs (*x,y*) in which each value of *x* is paired with a value of *y*, but not necessarily exactly one value of *y*. The ambiguity of not knowing which *y* to output is why relations are not a big topic in mathematics courses. However, in many high school and college algebra courses, relations are defined first, and then functions are defined as relations with exactly one *y* for each *x*.

NOTE: Functions are not restricted to a single input variable and a single output variable. For example, a function with two input variables and one output variable is a *set of ordered triples*—perhaps the number of gallons of gasoline and the price per gallon as the inputs and total cost as the output. *Everyday Mathematics* is restricted to functions with only two variables.

For more information about these four representations, see Section 18.2: Problem Representations.

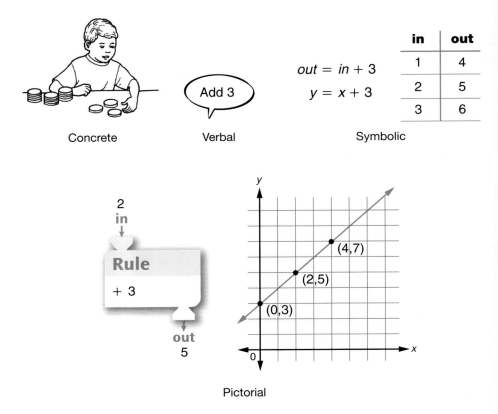

in	out
1	4
2	5
3	6

$$out = in + 3$$
$$y = x + 3$$

Concrete   Verbal   Symbolic

Pictorial

Four representations of functions

Verbal representations of functions include rules like "Double" or "Add 5." Verbal representations can often be made more concise by using *symbolic* representations like + 3 or *out* = *in* + 3 or $y = x + 3$, where x is input and y is output. The symbolic representation of functions as equations is explored extensively in fourth through sixth grades.

Frames-and-Arrows problems, incomplete number lines, and function machines are *pictorial* representations of functions and sequences. In Grade 3, children get their first exposure to graph models when they plot ordered pairs on a coordinate grid. Coordinate graphs are particularly important pictorial representations that are investigated extensively in *Fourth* through *Sixth Grade Everyday Mathematics*.

Everyday Mathematics provides three kinds of activities that reinforce links between these several representations of functions.

- Given a graph, students read the coordinates of points and make a table of values. The graph may consist of a set of discrete points, or it may be a graph of a continuous line or curve. For example, given the graph of polygon *FRED* on the next page, students make a table of values for the vertices like the one to the right of the graph. Or, given a graph of the function $y = 2x$, they make a table of values by picking several values for x and finding the corresponding values for y.

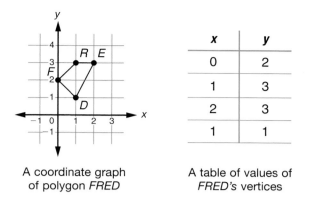

x	y
0	2
1	3
2	3
1	1

A coordinate graph of polygon *FRED*

A table of values of *FRED*'s vertices

- Given a table of values, students interpret it as a set of ordered pairs and graph the pairs as a set of discrete points. For example, given the table of polygon *FRED*'s vertices, they plot them and connect the dots in the order given in the name.

- Given an equation for a function, students make a table of values by choosing several values for the input variable (*x* in the following example) and calculating the corresponding values for the output variable (*y* in the example). Then they graph these values and connect the points with a smooth, continuous line.

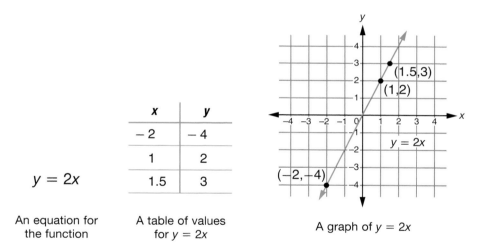

y = 2x

x	y
− 2	− 4
1	2
1.5	3

An equation for the function

A table of values for *y = 2x*

A graph of *y = 2x*

Of course, students develop these skills gradually over years. Simple "What's My Rule?" games begin in Kindergarten. Writing number sentences to model number stories begins in Grade 1. In third and fourth grades, students graph sets of ordered pairs on a coordinate plane, sometimes given in a table of values.

Starting in fifth grade, the connection between rules, tables, and graphs is explored through investigations of patterns in data. Students also use ordered pairs to define the vertices of polygons and to examine the effects on these polygons when the coordinates are operated on arithmetically. Also beginning in fifth grade, students examine "mystery graphs" in the coordinate plane to identify which graphs best represent given behaviors.

Descriptions of two activities that focus on multiple representations of a function are given on the next page.

chapter 17

In Grade 5, students use the distance formula $d = 8t$ to calculate the distance d an airplane travels in t minutes at a constant rate of 8 miles per minute. They fill out a table of values using the formula and then plot the points and connect the dots to make a continuous line graph. Then, they use the graph to answer questions about distances and times not included in their table, which they can check using the formula. For example, to find how long it will take to fly 12 miles, follow $d = 12$ right to the line and then read the corresponding value of t on the horizontal axis. The graph suggests that the plane will travel $d = 12$ miles in about $t = 1.5$ minutes. Check with the formula: *Does 12 = 8 * 1.5? Yes.*

Time (min) t	Distance (mi) $8 * t$
0	0
1	8
2	16
3	24
4	32
5	40
6	48

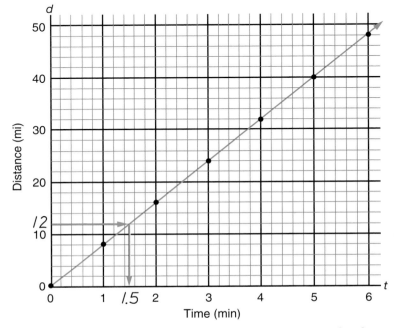

In a similar manner, sixth-grade students investigate the formula $d = 16t^2$, which gives the distance d, in feet, that an object will fall in t seconds under Earth's gravity (ignoring air resistance).

The authors expect that *Everyday Mathematics* students will enter middle and high school mathematics courses with a strong, informal understanding of graphs and their relationships to tables of values and equations. This prepares them for learning to write equations for functions given a table of values or graph in later algebra courses.

▶ **17.2 Algebra and Uses of Variables**

Most adults in the United States probably remember algebra as a junior or senior high school course devoted to learning how to manipulate equations containing variables. But algebra is actually far more than just symbol manipulation. Algebra can be thought of as generalized arithmetic, as a set of powerful problem-solving procedures, as a study of numeric relations, or as a study of the structure of mathematics. The authors of *Everyday Mathematics* believe these are all valid descriptions of algebra. Accordingly, although the formal study of algebraic syntax is not appropriate for most elementary school students, *Everyday Mathematics* includes many activities involving algebra.

NOTE: For more on the place of algebra in the elementary school curriculum, see *The Ideas of Algebra, K–12,* edited by Art Coxford and Al Shulte. A full reference can be found on page 297.

Algebra is a branch of mathematics that deals with variables and operations on variables. As soon as first graders encounter problems like $8 + \_\_ = 12$ they are thinking algebraically because the blank is a kind of variable. Later in *Everyday Mathematics,* students experience variables as *unknowns* ($5 + x = 8$), in *formulas* ($A = lw$), in statements of mathematical *properties* ($a + b = b + a$), and in *functions* ($y = x + 5$). All of these experiences with variables prepare students for eventual success in algebra.

Algebra has important links to the patterns, sequences, and functions strand, as well as to the problem-solving thread in *Everyday Mathematics.* The diagram below identifies the four representations that are featured in the program to model problems: concrete, verbal, pictorial, and symbolic. To represent problems symbolically, students need to understand the usefulness of algebraic notation and variables.

For more information, see Section 18.2: Problem Representations and Section 17.1.3: Functions.

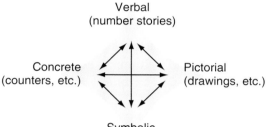

Verbal
(number stories)

Concrete
(counters, etc.)

Pictorial
(drawings, etc.)

Symbolic
(number models)

Four problem-solving representations

17.2.1 Uses of Variables

A *variable* is a letter or other symbol that stands for a number. In *Fourth* through *Sixth Grade Everyday Mathematics,* variables are used in several different ways.

Variables as Unknowns

As students write number sentences to fit problem situations, they often find that they need to represent numbers that are *unknown.* For example, the problem *There are 24 students in our class, but today only 18 are here. How many are not here?* might be modeled using any of these three equations using ? as the variable:

$$24 - \, ? = 18 \qquad 18 + \, ? = 24 \qquad 24 - 18 = \, ?$$

Alternatively, a *letter,* a *blank,* or a *box* can be used to indicate the unknown number:

$$24 - n = 18 \qquad 18 + \_\_ = 24 \qquad 24 - 18 = \boxed{}$$

All four of the symbols ?, n, __, and $\boxed{}$ are variables.

In *Kindergarten* through *Third Grade Everyday Mathematics,* variables are used primarily as unknowns in open sentences, so introducing the term *variable* is unnecessary. Also, in sentences such as $5 + n = 13$, the unknown is a single number that doesn't vary, and so explaining the root of the word variable (*vary*) is not helpful.

chapter 17

Besides being used to represent single unknown numbers, such as x in $x + 6 = 12$, variables can represent more than a single unknown number in certain situations. For example, *I'm thinking of a number less than 10* can be modeled as $x < 10$, which has the whole-number solutions $0, 1, \ldots, 9$, and many more solutions if fractions, decimals, or negative numbers are allowed.

There can also be more than one unknown in situations modeled by equations. For example, *What pairs of whole numbers have 8 as their sum?* can be modeled as $m + n = 8$. Solutions are the pairs 0 and 8, 1 and 7, 2 and 6, and so on. Students in Grades 4 through 6 use more than one unknown when they write and interpret open sentences for "What's My Rule?" problems or geometric formulas.

Variables in Formulas

A *formula* uses variables to state concisely a relationship that would otherwise require many words to describe. For example, *The area of a rectangle can be found by multiplying the length of the rectangle times the width* may be written as the formula $A = l * w$, or simply $A = lw$. Students use area and volume formulas for many geometric figures in *Fourth* through *Sixth Grade Everyday Mathematics.*

For more information, see Section 1.3.6: Unit Boxes.

It is important to keep track of the units associated with variables in formulas and to make sure that those units are consistent with the relationship expressed by the formula. For example, an area formula for a rectangle will not give a correct result if the length is measured in feet and the width in meters. In Grades 1 through 3, children use *unit boxes* to help them develop the habit of thinking about units. In Grades 4 and 5, students use a *whole box* to name the entire quantity, or 100%, being considered.

In formulas with three variables, such as $A = lw$, if the values of any two variables are known, the value of the third variable can be calculated. A similar rule applies to relationships expressed with a greater number of variables; if a formula has n variables, then knowing values for $n - 1$ of them lets you calculate the remaining value.

Formulas are introduced in Grade 4 and revisited frequently in Grade 5, where students use formulas to find areas of plane figures and volumes of right rectangular prisms. Students are also introduced to the connection between formulas, tables, and coordinate graphs when they explore the relationship $d = rt$ of distance d and time t at a constant rate r.

For more information, see Section 3.1.3: Spreadsheets.

In *Sixth Grade Everyday Mathematics,* students continue to use formulas given to them, but they also develop some of their own, such as a formula used to calculate the number of bricks needed to build a wall. They continue to explore connections between formulas, tables, and graphs using a formula for the distance traveled by a freely falling object. Students also use formulas in sixth grade while making spreadsheets.

Variables in Properties of Numbers and Operations

Variables are also used to express basic mathematical *properties*. For example, the *turn-around rule for addition* says that adding two numbers in either order results in the same sum. Expressed with variables, the turn-around rule is $a + b = b + a$, or, more formally, "For any two numbers a and b, $a + b = b + a$."

Mathematical properties describe patterns seen in instances with specific numbers and operations. For example, $2 + 3 = 3 + 2$ and $12 + 8 = 8 + 12$ are two instances of the turn-around property. With practice, describing a pattern with variables can make the pattern much simpler to understand than using words or relying on many instances. For example, which is a simpler way to present the Multiplicative Identity Property, using four examples and hoping the reader catches on, or stating the property written with a variable?

> Instances: $1 * 1 = 1$ Property: For any number n,
> $1 * 2 = 2$ $1 * n = n$.
> $1 * 5 = 5$
> $1 * 20 = 20$

Note that using variables in properties differs from using variables in formulas. In properties, the level of generality, that is, the level of abstraction, is much higher. There is no specific physical or mathematical situation underlying a property as there is underlying, for example, an area or volume formula. For this reason, students begin writing formulas in fourth grade and begin to describe patterns of numbers and operations with variables in fifth grade.

Variables in Functions

An important use of variables in higher mathematics is to write *functions*. Simply defined, a function is a rule that gives a certain output for a given input. For example, "Add 2" is a simple function relating a set of input numbers with a set of output numbers. Using variables, this function can be written $output = input + 2$ or $y = x + 2$, where x represents a number in the input set and y represents the corresponding number in the output set.

In *Kindergarten* through *Third Grade Everyday Mathematics,* children explore functions through function machines and by playing "What's My Rule?" In Grades 5 and 6, students make tables of values for functions such as $y = x + 2$. Then they graph the ordered pairs from the table and connect the points to get a picture of the relationship, in this case, a line.

Variables as Storage Locations

In computer programs, variables serve as names for *memory locations* where values are stored. Computer variables may consist of more than one letter; often they name the quantity being stored. For example, *price* might name the location of the current price of an item. INPUT *price* in some computer languages means to place a value into the storage location *price*. To find a price plus 8% sales tax, the computer could calculate $1.08 * price$.

NOTE: A less child-friendly name for the turn-around rule for addition is the Commutative Property of Addition.

For more information, see Section 17.1.3: Functions.

NOTE: More formally, the input variable x in a function is called the *independent variable* because its value does not depend on any other variables. The output variable y is called the *dependent variable* because its value depends on at least one other variable.

chapter 17

17.2.2 Reading and Writing Open Sentences

Just as English words are more meaningful when they are in sentences, mathematical symbols are more meaningful in number sentences. And just as proper punctuation and grammar make written English easy to read, rules and conventions for reading and writing number sentences ease mathematical communication.

Number sentences such as $10 = 7 + 3$, $12/n = 6$, and $14 > 3$ have a left-hand side, a relation symbol, and a right-hand side. Symbols for numbers, unknowns, and operations can appear on either side of the relation symbol. Each side of a number sentence is a *numerical expression.* In the sentences above, 10, $7 + 3$, $12/n$, 6, 14, and 3 are expressions. In practice, however, single numbers are usually just called "numbers" and expressions usually include one or more operations.

Equations are number sentences in which the relation symbol is =, meaning *equals* or *is equal to.*

Inequalities are number sentences in which the relation symbol is one of the following:

< (*is less than*)	≤ (*is less than or equal to*)
> (*is greater than*)	≥ (*is greater than or equal to*)
≠ (*is not equal to*)	≈ (*is approximately equal to*)

A number phrase with a variable but no relation symbol, such as $3 + y$, is called an *algebraic expression* or simply an *expression.* A single number, called a *constant,* or a product of a constant and one or more variables is a *term* of an expression. Terms are operated on in expressions, if they are not the whole expression itself. For example, in the expression $75 + 3x$, the terms are 75 and $3x$. In $y = 3x$, the expression $3x$ is also a term.

An *open sentence* is a number sentence that is neither true nor false because it contains a variable or unknown. Examples are $14 = t - 9$ and $81 + c < 100$. Any number can replace the variable. A number that makes an open sentence *true* is called a *solution* of the sentence. The process of determining a value, or values, for a variable that make a number sentence true is called *solving the sentence.*

In *Everyday Mathematics,* children in first grade encounter unknowns in situation diagrams. These diagrams display the numbers in number stories so that the quantitative relationships are easier to understand. For example, a parts-and-total diagram models the problem below. The empty cell in a diagram represents the unknown, or the variable.

> Twelve fourth graders, 8 third graders, and 5 first graders are on a bus. How many students in all are on the bus?

First-grade teachers are encouraged to write open sentences to model number stories using blanks or question marks for variables. For the example above, a teacher might write $12 + 8 + 5 = \_\_$ or $? = 12 + 8 + 5$. Beginning in second grade, children write their own open sentences using blanks and question marks. In fourth grade, students use letter variables.

Total		
?		
Part	**Part**	**Part**
12	8	5

Open sentences with inequalities, and the terms *expression* and *equation,* are introduced in fourth grade. In fifth and sixth grades, students begin to solve open number sentences using algebraic manipulations. Various forms of variables and names for open sentences are used so students become familiar with a variety of mathematical symbols and with algebraic language.

For more information, see Section 10.2.4: Teaching with Number Sentences and Number Models.

17.2.3 Simplifying Expressions

Students use expressions throughout *Everyday Mathematics* but have no need to call them by that name until Grade 5. Also, in their explorations of number models, students seldom need to focus on an expression by itself, because expressions are usually parts of number models that fit number stories drawn from real life.

In preparation for solving the more challenging equations of secondary school mathematics, sixth-grade students are introduced to *simplifying expressions.* First, here are some vocabulary terms:

- A *constant term,* or *constant,* is a term without a variable. For example, in $11x + 5 - 6x + 4$, the numbers 5 and 4 are constants.

- A *variable term* contains one or more variable factors. For example, x, $4x$, $3x^2$, and xy are variable terms.

- A number factor in a variable term is called the *coefficient* of the term. In x, $4x$, $3x^2$, and xy, 4 is a coefficient of $4x$ and 3 is a coefficient of x^2.

- *Like terms* have exactly the same variable factors. All constant terms are like terms with no variable factors. Of x, $4x$, $3x^2$, and xy, only x and $4x$ are like terms. $3x^2$ has another x factor, and xy has a y factor.

To simplify an expression, you *combine like terms.* In each example below, the expression on the left-hand side simplifies to the expression on the right-hand side. Arrows show combinations of like terms.

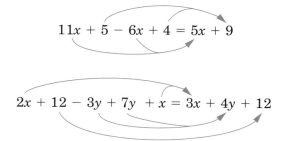

$$11x + 5 - 6x + 4 = 5x + 9$$

$$2x + 12 - 3y + 7y + x = 3x + 4y + 12$$

Sometimes like terms *cancel* each other, meaning they add to zero as in the following equation:

$$2 - x + 3x - 2x = 2$$

The sum of the three like terms $-x$, $3x$, and $-2x$ is $0x = 0$, which is not written on the right-hand side of the equation.

Combining like terms relies on the order of operations and properties of the rational-number system, especially the Distributive Property, which is discussed in the next section.

For more information, see Section 10.2.3: The Order of Operations.

chapter 17

The Distributive Property

Students in *Everyday Mathematics* see the Distributive Property beginning in Grade 4. There is one property for addition and another for subtraction.

> **The Distributive Property of Multiplication over Addition**
>
> For any three numbers *a*, *b*, and *c*,
>
> $$a(b + c) = ab + ac.$$

> **The Distributive Property of Multiplication over Subtraction**
>
> For any three numbers *a*, *b*, and *c*,
>
> $$a(b - c) = ab - ac.$$

Commonly, "the Distributive Property" refers to both of these properties.

Rewriting an expression using the Distributive Property from left to right as shown above is called *expanding* the expression, or *distributing a* over $(b + c)$ or $(b - c)$. The property also applies when there are more than two terms inside the parentheses. For example, $2(x + y + z) = 2x + 2y + 2z$.

The Distributive Property also applies when read from right to left.

$$ab + ac = a(b + c)$$
$$ab - ac = a(b - c)$$

This use of the property is called *factoring a* from the other two terms, that is, "undistributing" it. Because *a* is a factor of both terms, it is a factor of the whole expression.

Because of the turn-around rule for multiplication, the property can also be written as follows:

$$ab + ac = (b + c)a$$
$$ab - ac = (b - c)a$$

Simplifying expressions often makes use of the Distributive Property for both expanding and factoring, even though it may not be obvious. In the following examples, steps have been added to highlight how the property is used.

Example 1: Simplify $11x + 5 - 6x + 4$.

$$11x + 5 - 6x + 4 = 11x - 6x + 5 + 4$$
$$= (11 - 6)x + \quad 9$$
$$= \quad 5x \quad + \quad 9$$

Example 2: Simplify $2x + 12 - 3y + 7y + x$.

$$2x + 12 - 3y + 7y + x = 2x + x - 3y + 7y \quad + 12$$
$$= (2 + 1)x + (-3 + 7)y + 12$$
$$= \quad 3x \quad + \quad 4y \quad + 12$$

In a sense, children use the Distributive Property beginning in Kindergarten, when they add and subtract counts. For example,

6 bananas + 8 bananas = (6 + 8) bananas = 14 bananas

Beginning in Grade 3, *Everyday Mathematics* students use the Distributive Property to:

- Invent mental arithmetic procedures. For example, *To find 15 times 6, I can take 10 sixes and add 5 sixes.*
- Play the *Multiplication Wrestling* game, which applies the Distributive Property twice, as shown in the margin.
- Use the partial-products algorithm and lattice multiplication.
- Add and subtract fractions with common denominators.

The Distributive Property is connected beautifully to geometry by an area model illustrated in *Sixth Grade Everyday Mathematics.* The area of the big rectangle below is the product of the overall dimensions, or $5 * (3 + 7)$. Its area is also equal to the sum of the areas of the two smaller rectangles, or $(5 * 3) + (5 * 7)$; that is, $5 * (3 + 7) = (5 * 3) + (5 * 7)$.

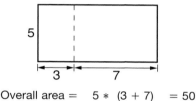

Overall area = $5 * (3 + 7)$ = 50
Overall area = $(5 * 3) + (5 * 7)$ = 50

---

1. *Multiplication Wrestling*

$27 * 32 = (20 + 7) * (30 + 2)$

$= (20 * 30) + (20 * 2) + (7 * 30) + (7 * 2)$

$= 600 + 40 + 210 + 14$

$= 864$

2. Partial-Products Multiplication

$$\begin{array}{r} 27 \\ *\,32 \\ \hline 600 \\ 210 \\ 40 \\ +\,14 \\ \hline 864 \end{array}$$

3. Adding Fractions

$\frac{1}{5} + \frac{3}{5} = \frac{1}{5}(1 + 3) = \frac{1 + 3}{5} = \frac{4}{5}$

Three applications of the
Distributive Property

17.2.4 Solving Open Sentences

Open sentences are number sentences with one or more variables. In *Everyday Mathematics,* students first encounter open sentences as they work with situation diagrams, which display the relationships among the quantities in simple number stories such as the following example.

Number Story: Twelve girls and 18 boys are in class today. How many students are in class?

Situation Diagram:

students	
?	
girls	boys
12	18

Number Model: $12 + 18 = \underline{}$

For more information, see Section 10.3: Use Classes and Situation Diagrams.

The empty part of a situation diagram represents an unknown number, or variable. In the example, the unknown is the total number of students. Beginning in first grade, teachers are encouraged to write an open sentence for a problem after it has been modeled in a situation diagram. Open sentences are introduced as another way to represent the quantitative relationships in the problem situation.

By third grade, the responsibility for writing simple sentences using the four basic operations and grouping symbols is in the children's hands. In fourth grade, students begin to graduate from writing informal open sentences with blanks, spaces, or question marks for unknowns to a more consistent use of letter variables.

For the first several years of the program, number models are used for two main reasons.

- Number models are useful for representing relationships among quantities in problem situations. Once students understand these relationships in a problem, they can generally work out a solution, perhaps by carrying out an algorithm, making a drawing, or doing mental arithmetic. Number models with variables can help students understand problems and, therefore, become better problem solvers.

- Number models familiarize students with the mathematical symbol system that is used in algebra and beyond. Students are not expected to manipulate the number models in order to solve problems, but through repeated exposures, they gradually learn the rudiments of a mathematical language that will eventually become a powerful tool for solving problems.

Informal Methods for Solving Equations

In *Kindergarten* through *Third Grade Everyday Mathematics*, children use simple strategies such as counting or informal *trial and error* in which they substitute a trial value for the variable in an open sentence to see if it makes the sentence true. If it's true, they have found a solution and the problem is solved. If the sentence is false, they pick a new trial value and check again, repeating until a solution is found. It might go something like this:

Example: Solve $37 + \_\_ = 83$ by trial and error.

Try 40. Does $37 + 40 = 83$? $37 + 40 = 77$. No.

Try 50. Does $37 + 50 = 83$? $37 + 50 = 87$. No.

Try 45. Does $37 + 45 = 83$? $37 + 45 = 82$. No.

Try 46. Does $37 + 46 = 83$? Yes.

So the solution to $37 + \_\_ = 83$ is 46.

Obviously, trial and error is not an algorithm for solving equations. But short-term efficiency is not the only goal, and the experience of solving equations by trial and error can develop students' number sense and their understanding of operations and equations. Trial

chapter 17

and error actually is a very powerful strategy in higher mathematics. When problems are too hard to be solved by direct methods, trial and error can be a practical way to make progress. Students use trial and error in all grades of *Everyday Mathematics*.

A more systematic informal approach to solving equations is called the *cover-up method*. Sixth graders use this method to solve complicated equations, but it is equally useful with even the simplest equations. For example, you might write $8 * (11 - c) = 72$ on the board, cover up the expression $11 - c$, and ask *What times 8 is 72? (9)* Then write $11 - c = 9$. Now cover up the c and ask *Eleven minus what number is 9? (2)* So $c = 2$.

The next three sections describe more systematic approaches to solving linear equations in one variable and proportions.

Pan-Balance Problems

Building on work with pan balances in earlier grades, *Fifth Grade Everyday Mathematics* introduces students to a pan-balance representation for equations. The problems are first presented concretely, with objects of different weights distributed on both sides of a pan balance. Students attempt to keep the pans balanced while removing weights. This leads to the idea of applying the same operation to both sides of an equation in order to write it in a form that is easy to solve.

For example, Figure 1 shows a pan-balance representation of the equation $3x + 14 = 23$. Each square represents x and each circle represents 1.

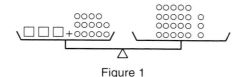

Figure 1

Removing 14 circles from each pan keeps them balanced and is equivalent to subtracting 14 from each side of the equation. Figure 2 shows that the pan balance now represents $3x = 9$.

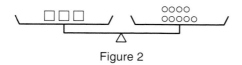

Figure 2

Finally, by equal sharing, each square in the left pan must balance three circles in the right pan. This is equivalent to division by 3. Figure 3 shows the pan balance representing $x = 3$.

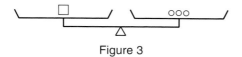

Figure 3

In *Fifth* and *Sixth Grade Everyday Mathematics,* students solve many pan-balance problems. The problems become progressively more complicated, leading to problems with two separate balances that are equivalent to systems of equations. Pictures of objects in the pans are eventually replaced by letter variables, so that students are essentially solving linear equations in one and two variables.

A Systematic Method for Solving Linear Equations

A *linear equation* is one in which all variables are to the first power and no two variables are in the same term. For example, the following are linear equations:

$$5x = 30 \qquad 16 = 8 - 4x \qquad 2x + 3y = 9 \qquad x = y$$

In *Sixth Grade Everyday Mathematics,* work with pan-balance problems leads to a systematic method for solving *linear equations in one unknown,* such as $3x + 8 = x + 24$ and the first two equations above. Building on their experience with pan-balance problems, students learn to solve an equation by transforming it into an equivalent equation in which the variable is equal to a constant. The method involves removing parentheses using the Distributive Property and combining like terms, as in the following example.

NOTE: *S 2b* for "Subtract 2b," *A 4* for "Add 4," and *D 2* for "Divide by 2" are called *abbreviated forms* of the operations performed in the steps of a solution. This shorthand helps some students make the connection between the purely abstract symbolic manipulation and a verbal description of the action.

Example: Solve $5(b + 3) - 3b + 5 = 4(b - 1)$.

Solution:

Step	Equation
1. Use the Distributive Property to remove parentheses.	$5(b + 3) - 3b + 5 = 4(b - 1)$ $5b + 15 - 3b + 5 = 4b - 4$
2. Combine like terms.	$2b + 20 = 4b - 4$
3. Subtract 2b from both sides. ($S\ 2b$)	$2b + 20 = 4b - 4$ $\underline{-\ 2b \qquad\qquad -\ 2b}$ $20 = 2b - 4$
4. Add 4 to both sides. ($A\ 4$)	$20 = 2b - 4$ $\underline{+\ 4 \qquad\qquad +\ 4}$ $24 = 2b$
5. Divide both sides by 2. ($D\ 2$)	$24 = 2b$ $24/2 = 2b/2$ $12 = b$

Solving an equation in this way involves transforming the original equation into a series of equivalent simpler equations. This requires a step-by-step undoing of the operations in the original equation. A major goal of algebra courses in middle school and high school is for students to become proficient at this process. Your students will find the equation solving in those courses easy because of the solid foundation provided in *Fifth* and *Sixth Grade Everyday Mathematics.*

Solving Proportions

A *proportion* is a number sentence equating two fractions. Proportions can be used to model a wide range of situations, including rate, ratio, and other multiplication and division situations. Students learn to model problems with proportions beginning in fifth grade. The following example illustrates the approach.

Example 1: Jack earned \$12. He bought a can of tennis balls that cost $\frac{1}{3}$ of his earnings. How much did he spend?

Solution: Write a proportion for the cost of the tennis balls and Jack's earnings.

$$\frac{\text{cost of tennis balls}}{\text{total earnings}} = \frac{1}{3}$$

Jack's total earnings were \$12. Substitute 12 for "total earnings" in the proportion.

$$\frac{\text{cost of tennis balls}}{12} = \frac{1}{3}$$

These two fractions are equivalent. To name $\frac{1}{3}$ as an equivalent fraction with a denominator of 12, multiply the numerator and the denominator of $\frac{1}{3}$ by 4.

$$\frac{\text{cost of tennis balls}}{12} = \frac{1 * 4}{3 * 4}$$

$$= \frac{4}{12}$$

So Jack spent \$4.

If you know any three numbers in a proportion, then you can find the fourth number. Finding a missing number in a proportion is called *solving the proportion*. Students in *Everyday Mathematics* learn to solve proportions using two general strategies: with multiplication and division rules for equivalent fractions as in the example above, and by cross multiplication.

- *Solve proportions using the multiplication and division rules for equivalent fractions.*

Example 2: Solve $\frac{2}{3} = \frac{n}{15}$.

The denominators, 3 and 15, are related by multiplication: $3 * 5 = 15$. The multiplication rule for equivalent fractions tells you that the numerators must be related in the same way.

$$\frac{2 * 5}{3 * 5} = \frac{n}{15}$$

$$\frac{10}{15} = \frac{n}{15}$$

So $10 = n$.

Example 3: Solve $\frac{6}{15} = \frac{x}{5}$.

The denominators, 5 and 15, are related by division: $5 = 15 \div 3$. The division rule for equivalent fractions tells you that the numerators must be related in the same way.

$$\frac{6 \div 3}{15 \div 3} = \frac{x}{5}$$

$$\frac{2}{5} = \frac{x}{5}$$

So $2 = x$.

For more information, see Sections 11.3.4: Fraction Multiplication and 11.3.5: Fraction Division.

- *Solve proportions using cross multiplication.*

  In *Fifth* and *Sixth Grade Everyday Mathematics,* students use *cross multiplication* to solve proportions. A *cross product* of two fractions is the product of the numerator of one fraction and the denominator of the other fraction. Every pair of fractions has two cross products.

Example 4: Find the cross products of $\frac{5}{6}$ and $\frac{10}{12}$.

The cross products are $5 * 12 = 60$ and $6 * 10 = 60$.

Example 5: Find the cross products of $\frac{2}{3}$ and $\frac{1}{4}$.

The cross products are $2 * 4 = 8$ and $3 * 1 = 3$.

The cross-multiplication method of solving proportions relies on the following fact, or *theorem:*

> If two fractions are equivalent, then their cross products are equal.

In the first example above, $\frac{5}{6}$ and $\frac{10}{12}$ are equivalent, and their cross products are equal ($60 = 60$).

In symbols, cross multiplication says that:

For fractions $\frac{a}{b}$ and $\frac{c}{d}$, where b and d are nonzero, if

$$\frac{a}{b} = \frac{c}{d},$$

then

$$ad = bc.$$

NOTE: It is also true that if two fractions are *not* equivalent, then the cross products are *not* equal. In Example 5, $\frac{2}{3}$ and $\frac{1}{4}$ are not equivalent, and their cross products are not equal ($8 \neq 3$). Comparing cross products is a handy way to compare fractions for equality.

chapter 17

Example 6: Solve $\frac{3}{4} = \frac{z}{20}$ using cross multiplication.

Multiply the denominator of the left side of the equation times the numerator of the right side, and the denominator of the right side times the numerator of the left side.

$$\frac{3}{4} = \frac{z}{20}$$

$$3 * 20 = 4 * z$$

Simplify each side of the equation. Note that shorthand for $4 * z$ is $4z$.

$$3 * 20 = 4 * z$$

$$60 = 4z$$

Solve the equation by dividing both sides by 4.

$$60 = 4z$$

$$60/4 = 4z/4$$

$$15 = z$$

Advanced students can develop the following proof that equal fractions have equal cross products. Suppose $\frac{a}{b}$ and $\frac{c}{d}$ are equivalent fractions, with b and d nonzero, then

$$\frac{a}{b} = \frac{c}{d}.$$

Multiply both sides by bd.

$$\frac{a}{b} * bd = \frac{c}{d} * bd$$

This simplifies to

$$ad = bc.$$

If some students are puzzled by the cross-multiplication step, you can have them do the second step of the proof with their equations. In the example above:

$$\frac{3}{4} = \frac{z}{20}$$

$$\frac{3}{4} * 4 * 20 = \frac{z}{20} * 4 * 20$$

The 4s on the left side of the equation divide to 1 and cancel, as do the 20s on the right side. What remains is the first step of cross multiplication. Students will use cross multiplication often in middle school and high school mathematics courses.

Interpreting Inequalities

Children began using the inequality symbols $<$ and $>$ in *Second Grade Everyday Mathematics* to compare numbers. They also see inequality number models for number stories. Students are introduced to open sentences with inequalities $>$, $<$, $\geq$, and $\leq$ in fourth grade and solve linear equations beginning in fifth grade. In sixth grade, students write open sentences and draw graphs to represent solutions to mathematical and real-life problems involving linear inequalities.

Students use the following guide for solving the problems that builds on a guide for solving number stories from earlier grades.

Step 1: List several values that solve the problem.

Step 2: Describe the set of all possible solutions in words.

Step 3: Write an inequality (or inequalities) to represent all possible values.

Step 4: Graph the set of possible values on a number line.

Step 5: Check whether the solutions make the inequality true and that they make sense in the problem context.

In *Everyday Mathematics*, the problems are limited to being represented by linear inequalities starting with the simple forms

$$x < a, \qquad x > a, \qquad x \leq a, \qquad x \geq a,$$

and graduating to the forms

$$ax + b < c, \qquad ax + b > c, \qquad ax + b \leq c, \qquad ax + b \geq c.$$

The next two examples illustrate how to use the problem-solving guide to represent inequality situations. Note that the solution sets can be *continuous* (all possible real numbers in an interval) or *discrete* (a possible subset of real numbers in an interval).

Example 1: An amusement park's rules state that a guest must be at least 4 feet tall to ride a roller coaster. Represent this situation with an inequality and a graph.

1: Possible solutions include 4 feet, 5 feet $2\frac{1}{2}$ inches, and 6 feet 1 inch.

2: Say, "All heights greater than or equal to 4 feet."

3: For height h, possible solutions are $h \geq 4$ or $4 \leq h$.

4:

5: Check: $4'$, $5'\, 2\frac{1}{2}''$, and $6'\, 1''$ all satisfy the inequality. However, numbers greater than $8'\, 11''$ are not realistic solutions to the problem because that's the height of Robert Pershing Wadlow, the tallest known human in history.

Example 2: A carton of avocados needs to weigh at least 16 kilograms (16,000 grams). The carton weighs about 1,000 grams and an avocado weighs an average of 300 grams. Write an inequality representing the number of avocados a in the carton. Graph the solution set.

1: Possible solutions include 50, 60, or 100 avocados.

2: Say, "All whole numbers greater than or equal to 50."

3: For whole-numbers of avocados a, possible solutions are $a \geq 50$ or $50 \leq a$.

4:

5: Check: 50, 60, and 100 all satisfy the inequality. However, it is most likely that the number will be as close to 50 as possible to meet the weight requirement.

The focus in *Sixth Grade Everyday Mathematics* is on representing problems and solution sets with inequalities and graphs, not learning formal algebraic techniques for solving the inequalities.

References and Resources for Patterns, Sequences, Functions, and Algebra

Coxford, A. F., and Shulte, A. P. (1988). *The Ideas of Algebra, K–12: 1988 Yearbook.* Reston, VA: National Council of Teachers of Mathematics.

Friedlander, A., and Tabach, M. (2001). "Promoting Multiple Representations in Algebra." In Cuoco, A. A., and Curcio, F. R. (Eds.) *The Roles of Representation in School Mathematics: 2001 Yearbook.* Reston, VA: National Council of Teachers of Mathematics.

Kalchman, M., and Koedinger, K. R. (2005). "Teaching and Learning Functions." In Donovan, M., and Bransford, J. (Eds.) *How Students Learn: History, Mathematics, and Science in the Classroom.* Washington, DC: The National Academies Press.

chapter 17

18 Problem Solving

In 1977, the National Council of Supervisors of Mathematics issued a position paper on basic skills. The first basic skill listed was *problem solving:* "Learning to solve problems is the principal reason for studying mathematics" (NCSM, 1977, p. 20). Ever since, problem solving has remained at the top of the school mathematics agenda.

This chapter is about problem solving and how *Everyday Mathematics* teaches it. It first examines different definitions of problem solving and explains what problem solving means in *Everyday Mathematics.* This is followed by a discussion of ways mathematical ideas can be represented (concretely, pictorially, verbally, and symbolically) and what such representations have to do with problem solving. Next is an explanation of what mathematical modeling is and its relationship to problem solving. The chapter closes with details about teaching problem solving in *Everyday Mathematics* and a list of resources to help you learn more about this important mathematical thread.

▶ 18.1 What Is Problem Solving?

In elementary school mathematics books, *problem solving* often refers only to finding answers to printed "word problems." But problem solving is much more than that. In the NCSM position paper cited above, problem solving is defined as "the process of applying previously acquired knowledge to new and unfamiliar situations." In *Principles and Standards for School Mathematics,* the National Council of Teachers of Mathematics (NCTM) states that problem solving "is finding a way to reach a goal that is not immediately attainable" (NCTM, 2000, p. 116). In his classic book *How to Solve It,* George Polya wrote, "Solving a problem is finding the unknown means to a distinctly conceived end" (1988, p. 1).

These broader definitions of problem solving are not restricted to arithmetic and certainly not to arithmetic "word problems." Central to all of them is the idea that solution methods are not known in advance. A problem is not a problem if the problem solver knows exactly what to do right away. "Problems" for which the solution method is known ahead of time are simply exercises.

In *Everyday Mathematics,* problem solving is broadly conceived. Number stories, the program's version of word problems, have their place, but problem solving permeates the entire curriculum. Students solve problems both in purely mathematical contexts, such as "What's My Rule?" tables, and in real situations from the classroom and everyday life. Students also create and solve problems using information from the materials, from you, and from their own experiences and imaginations.

Everyday Mathematics defines problem solving as "the process of modeling everyday situations to find solutions using tools from mathematics." Mathematical modeling is discussed in detail in Section 18.3; but, in a nutshell, it means that expert problem solvers generally do one or more of these things:

- Identify what the problem is;
- Analyze what is known and seek out further data as necessary;
- Play with the data to discover patterns and meaning;
- Identify and apply mathematical techniques to find a solution;
- Look back after finding a solution to ask whether it makes sense and whether the method can be applied to other problems.

18.2 Problem Representations

Often a key step in solving a problem is simply looking at it in the right way. Consider the problem *How many handshakes are there when five people shake hands with one another?* Some ways to solve this problem are listed here.

- Find five people and have them shake hands, being careful to count each handshake. This approach is, to say the least, not very convenient.
- Make a list. If the people are represented by the letters A, B, C, D, and E, the handshakes could be listed as follows: A-B, A-C, A-D, A-E, B-C, B-D, B-E, C-D, C-E, and D-E. Although this is practical for five people, it could be troublesome for larger numbers, as you might make a mistake in listing all the handshakes.
- Draw a picture of a pentagon with all its diagonals. Each corner stands for a person, and each line connecting two people stands for a handshake. Finding a mistake in such a figure may be easier than finding one in a long list, although it might be a nuisance to draw the figure for a large number of people.

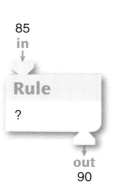

A "What's My Rule?" problem

in	out
55	60
85	90
103	108

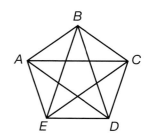

chapter 18

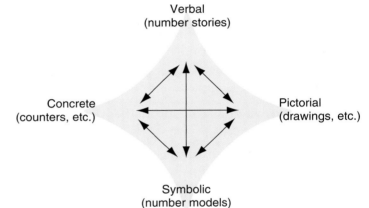

Each of these solutions to the handshake problem depends on a different way of approaching, or representing, the problem. One way used real people; another way involved a list; the third way made use of a drawing. Different ways of approaching a problem are called *problem representations*.

Everyday Mathematics focuses on four problem representations: *concrete, verbal, pictorial,* and *symbolic*. Suppose, for example, you need a dozen eggs to make egg salad, but when you take the eggs out of the refrigerator, you drop the carton on the floor. That's a *concrete* situation. A *verbal* description might make certain details explicit, such as *Oh no! I broke 7 of them!* A *pictorial* representation like the one in the margin could show the unfortunate eggs, and symbolically, you could write the number model $12 - 7 = 5$.

These varieties of problem representations are diagrammed below. Note that double-headed arrows connect each kind of representation with each of the other kinds. Students and adults are likely to use all of these representations at one time or another, depending on the situation at hand.

Verbal
(number stories)

Concrete
(counters, etc.)

Pictorial
(drawings, etc.)

Symbolic
(number models)

Four problem-solving representations

Representations are used both to give problems and to model solutions. Different students have different talents for, and preferences among, the representations, so all students benefit from repeated exposures to all four types. One of the aims of *Everyday Mathematics* is to increase students' facility with a variety of representations. In Grades 4 through 6, students extend their use of symbolic representations by writing and solving open sentences and their use of pictorial representations by drawing and interpreting coordinate graphs.

Another objective in *Everyday Mathematics* is to help students make easy translations among various ways of representing problems. Representations are closely related to solution strategies; translating a problem into another representation is often a key to solving it. Discussion of different representations and solutions exposes students to methods they may like to try and reinforces the important message that there are many ways to solve problems.

As you discuss problems and solutions with students, compare various representations and ask for translations from one to another.

For examples of four representations of functions, see Section 17.1.3: Functions.

NOTE: Individual differences are likely to lead some students, and even teachers, to favor some representations over others. For example, ELL or hearing-impaired students may be less likely to favor verbal representations. Be careful not to over-emphasize the need for all students to explore all the representations.

chapter 18

For example, consider the following options for the problem *If Jean rode her bike for 2.5 hours at an average speed of 8 miles per hour, how far did she travel?*

- You or a student present the problem orally or write it in a Math Message or on a journal page.
- Have different students make and share a rate diagram or graph (pictorial), write a number model (symbolic), or explain a mental solution (verbal).
- Ask a student who solved the problem mentally to write a number model.
- Ask students to compare a number model and a graph.

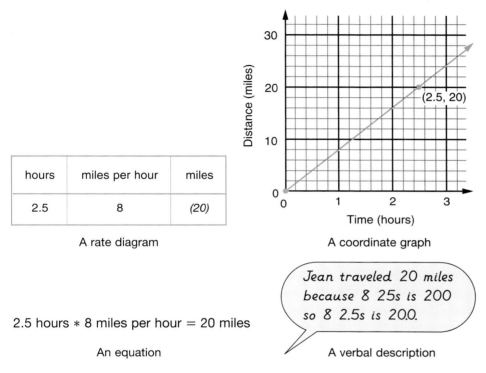

hours	miles per hour	miles
2.5	8	*(20)*

A rate diagram

A coordinate graph

2.5 hours * 8 miles per hour = 20 miles

An equation

Jean traveled 20 miles because 8 25s is 200 so 8 2.5s is 20.0.

A verbal description

By encouraging multiple representations and translations among representations, you can help students develop into more powerful problem solvers.

As you observe students working with various representations, you can also determine their problem-solving strengths and weaknesses. In turn, this can help you tailor activities to meet individual needs. For example, you might observe that a certain student never uses letter variables in number models, preferring blanks instead. This might lead you to suggest a number model such as "2.5 hours * 8 miles per hour = d miles" for the bicycle problem above. A student who is having difficulty understanding rate tables might benefit from a suggestion to try drawing a graph.

▶ 18.3 Mathematical Modeling

A *mathematical model* is something mathematical that corresponds to something in the real or imaginary world. A sphere is a model for a basketball. The number sentence $22 + 1 = 23$ is a model for the number

NOTE: Using pictures to represent problems and solutions can be especially helpful for students who are having difficulty with other representations. Use simple pictures and diagrams to illustrate classroom discussions as much as possible.

For more information on problem representations, see *The Roles of Representation in School Mathematics* edited by Cuoco and Curcio (2001). A full reference is on page 309.

chapter 18

NOTE: The word *model* can also refer to something in the real world that illustrates something mathematical. In this sense, a basketball is a model of a sphere. When people speak of mathematical modeling, however, the model is the mathematical object and the thing that is modeled is something in the real or hypothetical world.

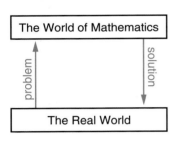

Mathematical modeling

of students in a classroom when a new student arrives. The equation $d = (5 \text{ hours}) * (50 \text{ miles/hour})$ is a model for the distance a car travels in 5 hours at 50 mph; and the formula $d = rt$ is a model linking distance, rate (speed), and time more generally. Specialists in science and industry spend much of their time building and testing mathematical models of real-world systems. Some people do mathematical modeling whenever they use mathematics to solve a problem.

Put another way, *mathematical modeling* is a process of translating a real or hypothetical situation into mathematical language. After the translation, a solution is found using mathematical techniques. Then the result is translated back into the real or hypothetical world as the answer to the original problem. This process is illustrated in the margin.

Yet the figure in the margin probably oversimplifies the process. Mathematical modeling is often more complicated and is likely to involve some or all of the following stages:

- *Formulate or confront a problem.* Try to understand your problem. What do you want to find out? Imagine what the answer would look like if you had one.
- *Study the information that is given and seek additional data as necessary.* Discard unnecessary information. Sort the data you have.
- *Explore the data.* Represent the data in various ways, perhaps by drawing a picture, making a graph, or writing a number model. Play with the data.
- *Do the math.* Do the arithmetic, algebra, geometry, data analysis, or whatever else is necessary to find an answer.
- *Check the answer to see if it makes sense.* Compare your answer to someone else's or to an answer you obtain in another way. Think about the method you used. Can the same method be used to solve other problems? Is there another method that would work for this problem? Compare various solutions and methods.

These stages of the mathematical-modeling process are summarized in the following diagram.

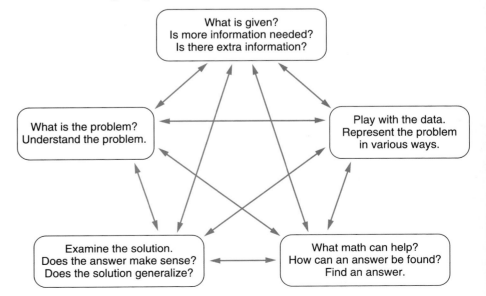

Stages in the mathematical-modeling process

The process of mathematical modeling can actually begin anywhere and go anywhere. The arrows in the figure on page 302 illustrate this. For example, mathematical modeling often begins with data. Suppose you are a baseball fan and are studying tables of baseball statistics. As you explore the data, you might notice that it appears that in inter-league games, National League teams win more often than American League teams. This might lead you to ask whether this is actually true. By finding the total number of wins for each league, you might find that the National League does win more often. If you wished, you could test your conclusion by making a prediction about the next set of inter-league games.

This baseball situation involves all five stages of the mathematical-modeling process. Sometimes, only a few of the stages are involved. An expert problem solver, or a child for that matter, might see a solution to a problem instantly and simply have to check that it's correct. Sometimes it may be necessary to cycle repeatedly among the stages—play with the data, find more data, and play with the new data, and so on—before finding a solution.

Mathematical modeling involves *abstraction.* For example, the number model $100 - 79 = 21$ is an abstraction of buying a 79¢ granola bar with a dollar bill. The modeling process involves both a real situation and an abstract mathematical model of that situation. Even a mathematical model that uses concrete physical objects, such as base-10 blocks, is abstract in the sense that it omits many details of the original situation. Because it is abstract, a single mathematical model can fit many different real-world situations. For example, the formula for the area of a rectangle, $A = lw$ (area A equals length l times width w), applies to all real-world rectangles. This versatility is part of what makes mathematics such a powerful problem-solving tool.

However, because they are abstract, mathematical models can become disconnected from the situation they are meant to model. Sometimes, students work their way through a mathematical process, arrive at an answer that makes no sense, and are completely unconcerned that they have produced nonsense. Making frequent connections between the real situation and the abstract model can help keep the process on track. Encourage students to ask themselves questions to keep the modeling process grounded: *What does this number refer to? What does this graph say about the problem situation? Does this solution make sense?*

One reason for making ballpark estimates is to keep the problem-solving process on track. If a solution doesn't agree with the estimate, then something is wrong either with the estimate or with the solution. Making ballpark estimates helps reinforce connections between mathematical abstractions and real-world situations.

▶ 18.4 Teaching Problem Solving

Often when you are trying to learn something complicated, it is a good idea to focus on just one part of the whole. A pianist might play a difficult passage over and over again; a chef might practice making

NOTE: In *Everyday Mathematics,* the problem-solving process often begins with information from a journal or *Student Reference Book* page. Students use the information to make up their own problems, which they or their classmates solve.

For more information on ballpark estimates, see Section 16.1.3: Estimates in Calculations.

a *roux* until it's just right; a golfer might spend hours working on 8-foot putts. Practicing just one part at a time helps develop component skills that are essential for mastery of the entire complex activity, whether it's piano playing, cooking, or golfing.

As the mathematical-modeling-process diagram illustrates, problem solving is a complicated activity that can be broken down into parts, such as formulating problems and playing with data, each of which students can practice separately. Many of the exercises in *Everyday Mathematics* aim to provide practice in specific parts of the problem-solving process. For example, students become skilled at counting, measuring, calculating, estimating, looking up information, and many other skills that are useful in solving problems. During their years in school, students thus learn how to be effective in each separate stage of the mathematical-modeling process.

Such instruction is effective in teaching students how to manage each individual stage of the process, but successful problem solving in real life requires experience in navigating among the stages, just as cooking a fine meal requires successfully orchestrating many separate steps. It may take years of experience to become proficient at navigating among the stages. Knowing when to abandon an approach that's not working and go back to playing with the data, for example, is a skill that develops with experience.

As students progress through *Everyday Mathematics,* they confront or pose problems that are more interesting and less routine, that make use of more sophisticated skills and concepts, and that require more complicated navigation through the mathematical-modeling process.

18.4.1 Number Stories

Everyday Mathematics aims to help students deal with real, age-appropriate problems. The authors' research shows that young students have impressive but largely untapped problem-solving abilities. One way *Everyday Mathematics* works to expand these abilities is through the use of number stories.

Number stories are stories that involve numbers and one or more explicit or implicit questions. For example:

- *I have 7 crayons in my desk. Carrie gave me 8 more crayons. How many crayons do I have in all? There are 15 crayons in all.*

- *I have 7 crayons in my desk. Carrie gave me 8 more crayons. Now I have 15 crayons in all.*

Number stories may be written, oral, pictorial, or even dramatic. They may be created by you or by the students. Stories may arise spontaneously from classroom situations or be designed to practice specific problem-solving techniques. For example, you might tell a rate story in order to introduce or practice using a rate diagram.

Starting with *Kindergarten Everyday Mathematics,* children create number stories based on everyday experiences. In Kindergarten through Grade 3, many of the children's stories are based on journal pages that present a range of numerical data related to real situations such as animal measures, shopping for groceries, and vending machines. Beginning in fourth grade, students also write and tell stories based on reference materials; sections of the *Student Reference Book,* including the World Tour and American Tour sections; and data from experiments they perform.

Problem posing, that is, making up problems, is a part of the problem-solving process that is often ignored in school mathematics; yet identifying and defining the problem is often the crucial first step toward a solution. Problem posing also leads to a high level of enthusiasm and involvement because students feel they have ownership of the problems they themselves create. Because the information presented tends to cover a wide range of difficulty, all members of the class have opportunities to participate.

Students enjoy hearing and telling number stories. You might consider devoting an occasional language arts lesson to working with number stories. Creating, sharing, and discussing number stories can help develop students' communication and listening skills as well as their problem-solving abilities. The careful reading required for solving number stories helps students develop skills that will serve them well when they deal with technical text in later years.

The following is a description of what Kindergarten and first-grade children do with number stories in *Everyday Mathematics.* It is included here in case you are interested in the backgrounds of your students or if you have students new to the program in Grades 4 through 6.

Number stories provide a bridge from natural to symbolic language. Children in Kindergarten and Grade 1 can be helped across that bridge if you follow these steps:

- Introduce number stories using a situation that is familiar to the children. Keep the stories short and the language simple. Be aware that when children tell their own stories, this is not always easy to do. Draw pictures or diagrams whenever possible to illustrate the stories. Modeling with concrete objects is effective with all ages and essential with younger children.

- Begin to include occasional mathematical terms in your comments on children's stories. For example, *You told an addition story. You had 5 candies and then you added 3 more.*

- Begin writing number models beneath your illustrations as you discuss the stories. Connect the numbers and relation symbols in the number models to quantities and actions in the stories. For example, *This 5 is for the candies you started with, + 3 means you got three more, 8 tells how many you ended up with, and = means that 8 is the same as 5 and 3 more.* Help children understand how the symbols fit the problem situation. Explain that symbols let them write a number story quickly and easily. *If you write it in words, it takes a long time and might fill the board.*

- Children may begin writing number models to fit stories. Often more than one number model can fit a given number story. Some first-grade children may begin to use diagrams for parts-and-total, change, and comparison stories, although this is not expected until second grade.

Many first-grade teachers report that children enjoy trying to put their stories into words. For many children, it appears that skill at writing stories develops later than the ability to write number models using +, −, and =. But by second grade, most children are able to write number stories. Younger children can tell or dictate stories before they can write them, or they can draw pictures and write a few words or numbers for their stories.

From third grade on, students write, swap, and solve stories for each other. By fourth grade, students should be using variables in number models for number stories. In fifth grade, students are encouraged to communicate with one another and with you using more writing than in previous grades. Writing provides opportunities for students to analyze their own thinking, to reflect upon their thoughts, and to organize information for themselves. It also gives you a great additional way to assess understanding of ideas and concepts.

Students use a variety of methods to solve one another's number stories, but *Everyday Mathematics* encourages using mental arithmetic whenever possible. This does not mean restricting students to doing the arithmetic entirely in their heads. Instead, students should develop a variety of flexible solution strategies that use whatever means are familiar and comfortable, such as manipulatives, jumps on a number line, doodles, diagrams, and calculators. The emphasis is on solving problems in the students' own ways, on being open to a variety of approaches, and on choosing the approach that is most appropriate for a particular problem situation.

18.4.2 Sharing Students' Strategies and Solutions

Research indicates that students develop a variety of problem-solving strategies if they are given the opportunity to share their ideas with their peers. If this sharing takes place in an open, receptive environment, students will learn that inventing creative, innovative ways of solving problems is acceptable in mathematics. The practice of gathering together to share solutions after individual or group problem solving continues throughout *Everyday Mathematics*.

Number stories are an excellent context for developing habits of sharing. Students can share their strategies, both correct and incorrect. They can record their solutions on the board, illustrating with pictures and number models. Students develop a better understanding of various mathematical processes when asked to think and strategize rather than when they are merely asked to repeat the steps of a standard written algorithm.

Discussing students' solutions can be extremely valuable, but care should be taken to ensure that students are not embarrassed if their

For more information, see "Exploring Mathematics through Talking and Writing" by Whitin and Whitin (2000). A full reference is on page 309.

efforts fall short. Students with correct answers are usually happy to share their models and strategies with the class, but discussing incorrect answers can also be very instructive. Here are several suggestions for dealing with wrong answers:

- Emphasize that it is OK to make mistakes. In fact, errors are inevitable. What is *not* OK is failing to learn from one's mistakes.

- Frame discussions of incorrect solutions by saying *Some students in last year's class did _____.* [Describe the incorrect approach.] *Why do you think they did that? How would you help them see their mistake?*

- Emphasize that answers obtained using different methods should agree, so if there is not agreement, something must be wrong. Encourage students to resolve the dilemma.

- Compare and contrast different strategies and help students see advantages and disadvantages of each. An incorrect method may have some good ideas that can be used to improve another method.

At the beginning of each school year, *Everyday Mathematics* includes specific occasions for students to share strategies and solutions. Many other opportunities materialize over the course of the year. With practice, students eventually become comfortable sharing their strategies and are able to talk about them freely and fluently, listen to one another attentively, and revise their own strategies and adopt new ones based on these discussions.

18.4.3 Basic Problem-Solving Strategies

The diagram of the mathematical-modeling process shown on page 302 fits what experts actually do when they solve problems but is too complicated to be of much help for beginners. On the other hand, many elementary school mathematics textbooks include long lists of strategies and tips; but these lists are often little help even with simple real-life problems and are essentially useless for dealing with complicated problems on public policy and the workplace.

Students need a guide that is more useful than a list of tips but simpler than a diagram of expert behavior. To this end, *Third* through *Sixth Grade Everyday Mathematics* includes general guidelines for managing problem solving, such as those in the margin, which are taken from the *Fourth Grade Student Reference Book*.

Because problems from everyday life are usually complicated, the first need is often to simplify the situation and figure out exactly what is known and what is to be found out. For example, problem situations in daily life often contain many irrelevant numbers. Sometimes relevant numbers are missing and must be inferred or derived from what is known. Often, the problem solver must deal not only with just a few counts or measures but also with large sets of data. Considerable effort may be required to make the data consistent in format and to devise a display that suggests useful patterns or interesting questions. The process seldom follows one predictable step after another.

A Guide to Number Stories

1. Understand the problem.
2. Plan what to do.
3. Carry out the plan.
4. Look back.

18.4.4 Results from *Everyday Mathematics* Teachers

Teachers who have used the approach to problem solving that is integrated into *Everyday Mathematics* report very positive results, as have researchers and program evaluators who have studied problem solving in the program. These teachers and researchers find that students develop strong, flexible, and independent calculation skills and problem-solving strategies. After using mental arithmetic with interesting number stories and relatively small numbers, students become able to operate with much larger numbers than they would typically have been able to handle. Students also develop an understanding of various mathematical processes that many students do not attain when using standard written algorithms.

Blair Chewning, an *Everyday Mathematics* teacher from Virginia, provides an example of the powerful results that this approach can yield. Ms. Chewning read an article in the *Richmond Times-Dispatch* with the headline "State, national math scores add up to poor report card." The picture painted was bleak, charging that on a recent national mathematics test, 40% of eighth-grade students failed to perform at even a basic level. The following problem was given as an example of a "basic" problem for grade 8:

> Jill needs to earn $45 for a class trip. She earns $2 each day on Mondays, Tuesdays, and Wednesdays. She earns $3 each day on Thursdays, Fridays, and Saturdays. She does not work on Sundays. How many weeks will it take her to earn $45?

Ms. Chewning was teaching second grade at the time, using *Everyday Mathematics,* and decided to see how her students would handle this problem. This is what she reported:

Every single student attempted the problem, which was presented as optional. Such risk-takers they have become! Two children, using mental math only, presented me with the correct answer by the time I had completed writing the number story on the board. A total of 82% of the children, using a variety of strategies (see page 309), successfully solved the problem in less than five minutes. Of the three children who struggled, two were right on track, making only minor computational errors, and the third achieved success after extensive trial and error.

Needless to say, I was astounded. While I had expected them to be successful to some extent, I had not anticipated the speed and comfort with which they approached the task.

Thank you, *Everyday Mathematics.* The skills your program fosters empowered my second graders to soar higher than they or their teacher thought possible. They wore the "hats" of eighth graders quite proudly that day and would seem to suggest that our math future is anything but bleak.

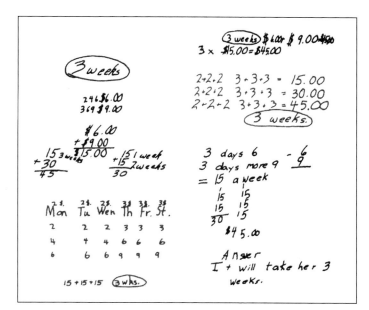

References and Resources on Problem Solving

Cuoco, A. A., and Curcio, F. R. (2001). *The Roles of Representation in School Mathematics: 2001 Yearbook.* Reston, VA: National Council of Teachers of Mathematics.

National Council of Supervisors of Mathematics. (1977). Position paper on basic skills. *Arithmetic Teacher 25(1):* pp. 19–22.

National Council of Supervisors of Mathematics. (1988). *Essential Mathematics for the 21st Century: The Position of the National Council of Supervisors of Mathematics.* Minneapolis, MN: Author.

National Council of Teachers of Mathematics. (1980). *An Agenda for Action: Recommendations for School Mathematics of the 1980s.* Reston, VA: Author.

National Council of Teachers of Mathematics. (1989). *Curriculum and Evaluation Standards for School Mathematics.* Reston, VA: Author.

National Council of Teachers of Mathematics. (2000). *Principles and Standards for School Mathematics.* Reston, VA: Author.

Polya, George. (1988). *How to Solve It.* Princeton, NJ: Princeton University Press.

Whitin, D. J., and Whitin, P. (2000). "Exploring Mathematics through Talking and Writing." In Burke, M., and Curcio, F. R. (Eds.) *Learning Mathematics for a New Century: 2000 Yearbook.* Reston, VA: National Council of Teachers of Mathematics.

Glossary

This glossary contains words and phrases from *Fourth* through *Sixth Grade Everyday Mathematics.* To place the definitions in broader mathematical contexts, most entries also refer to sections in this *Teacher's Reference Manual.* In a definition, terms in italics are defined elsewhere in the glossary.

A

absolute value The distance between a number and 0 on a *number line*. The absolute value of a positive number is the number itself, and the absolute value of a negative number is the *opposite* of the number. The absolute value of 0 is 0. The symbol for the absolute value of n is $|n|$.

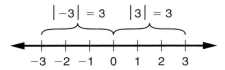

abundant number A *counting number* whose *proper factors* add to a number greater than itself. For example, 12 is an abundant number because $1 + 2 + 3 + 4 + 6 = 16$, and 16 is greater than 12. Compare to *deficient number* and *perfect number*. See Section 9.8.2: Perfect, Deficient, and Abundant Numbers.

account balance An amount of money that you have or that you owe. See *"in the black"* and *"in the red."*

accurate As correct as possible according to an accepted standard. For example, an accurate measure or count is one with little or no error. See *precise* and Section 16.2: Approximation and Rounding.

acre A U.S. customary unit of *area* equal to 43,560 square feet. An acre is roughly the size of a football field. A square mile is 640 acres. See the Tables of Measures and Section 14.4: Area.

acute angle An *angle* with a measure less than 90°. See Section 13.4.1: Angles and Rotations.

Acute angles

acute triangle A *triangle* with three acute angles. See Section 13.4.2: Polygons (*n*-gons).

An acute triangle

addend Any one of a set of numbers that are added. For example, in $5 + 3 + 1$, the addends are 5, 3, and 1.

addition fact Two 1-digit numbers and their sum, such as $9 + 7 = 16$. See *arithmetic facts* and Section 16.3.3: Fact Practice.

addition/subtraction use class In *Everyday Mathematics,* situations in which addition or subtraction is used. These include *parts-and-total, change,* and *comparison* situations. See Section 10.3.1: Addition and Subtraction Use Classes.

additive inverses Two numbers whose sum is 0. Each number is called the additive inverse, or *opposite,* of the other. For example, 3 and −3 are additive inverses because $3 + (-3) = 0$.

address A letter-number pair used to locate a spreadsheet *cell.* For example, A5 is the fifth cell in column A.

address box A place where the address of a spreadsheet *cell* is shown when the cell is selected.

adjacent angles Two *angles* with a common *side* and *vertex* that do not otherwise overlap. See Section 13.6.3: Relations and Orientations of Angles.

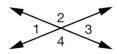

Angles 1 and 2, 2 and 3, 3 and 4, and 4 and 1 are pairs of adjacent angles.

adjacent sides Same as *consecutive sides.*

algebra (1) The use of letters of the alphabet to represent numbers in *equations, formulas,* and rules. (2) A set of rules and properties for a number system. (3) A school subject, usually first studied in eighth or ninth grade. See Section 17.2: Algebra and Uses of Variables.

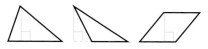

$$4 + x = 10$$
$$4 + ? = 10$$
$$4 + \underline{\quad} = 10$$
$$4 + \boxed{} = 10$$

$$a + b = b + a$$
$$a(b + c) = ab + ac$$

Formulas, equations, and properties using algebra

algebraic expression An *expression* that contains a *variable.* For example, if Maria is 2 inches taller than Joe and if the variable M represents Maria's height, then the algebraic expression $M - 2$ represents Joe's height. See *algebra* and Section 17.2: Algebra and Uses of Variables.

algebraic order of operations Same as *order of operations.*

algorithm A set of step-by-step instructions for doing something, such as carrying out a computation or solving a problem. The most common algorithms are those for basic arithmetic computation, but there are many others. Some mathematicians and many computer scientists spend a great deal of time trying to find more efficient algorithms for solving problems. See Chapter 11: Algorithms.

altitude (1) In *Everyday Mathematics,* same as *height* of a figure. (2) Distance above sea level. Same as *elevation.*

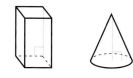

Altitudes of 2-D figures are shown in blue.

Altitudes of 3-D figures are shown in blue.

analog clock (1) A clock that shows the time by the positions of the hour and minute hands. (2) Any device that shows time passing in a continuous manner, such as a sundial. Compare to *digital clock.* See Section 15.2.1: Clocks.

An analog clock

-angle A suffix meaning *angle,* or corner.

angle A figure formed by two *rays* or two *line segments* with a common *endpoint* called the *vertex* of the angle. The rays or segments are called the *sides* of the angle. An angle is measured in degrees between 0 and 360. One side of an angle is the *rotation* image of the other side through a number of degrees. Angles are named after their vertex point alone as in $\angle A$ below; or by three points, one on each side and the vertex in the middle as in $\angle BCD$ below. See *acute angle, obtuse angle, reflex angle, right angle, straight angle,* and Section 13.4.1: Angles and Rotations.

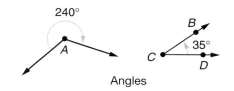

Angles

anthropometry The study of human body sizes and proportions.

apex In a *pyramid* or *cone,* the *vertex* opposite the *base.* In a pyramid, all the nonbase faces meet at the apex. See Section 13.5.2: Polyhedrons and Section 13.5.3: Solids with Curved Surfaces.

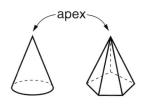

approximately equal to ($\approx$) A symbol indicating an *estimate* or approximation to an exact value. For example, $\pi \approx 3.14$. See Section 16.2: Approximation and Rounding.

Glossary

arc of a circle A part of a *circle* between and including two *endpoints* on the circle. For example, the endpoints of the *diameter* of a circle define an arc called a *semicircle*. An arc is named by its endpoints.

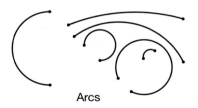

Arcs

area The amount of *surface* inside a *2-dimensional figure*. The figure might be a triangle or rectangle in a plane, the curved surface of a cylinder, or a state or country on Earth's surface. Commonly, area is measured in *square units* such as square miles, square inches, or square centimeters. See Section 14.4: Area.

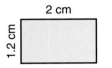

A rectangle with area
1.2 cm * 2 cm = 2.4 cm²

A triangle with area
21 square units

The area of the United States
is about 3,800,000 square miles.

area model (1) A model for multiplication in which the *length* and *width of a rectangle* represent the *factors,* and the *area* of the rectangle represents the *product.* See Section 10.3.2: Multiplication and Division Use Classes. (2) A model showing fractions as parts of a whole. The *whole* is a region, such as a circle or a rectangle, representing the *ONE,* or *unit whole.* See Section 9.3.2: Uses of Fractions.

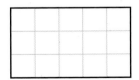

Area model for 3 * 5 = 15

Area model for $\frac{2}{3}$

arithmetic facts The addition facts (whole-number *addends* 9 or less); their inverse subtraction facts; multiplication facts (whole-number *factors* 9 or less); and their inverse division facts, except there is no division by zero. There are:

100 addition facts: $0 + 0 = 0$ through $9 + 9 = 18$;
100 subtraction facts: $0 - 0 = 0$ through $18 - 9 = 9$;
100 multiplication facts: $0 * 0 = 0$ through $9 * 9 = 81$;
90 division facts: $0/1 = 0$ through $81/9 = 9$.

See *extended facts, fact extensions, fact power,* and Section 16.3.2: Basic Facts and Fact Power.

arm span Same as *fathom.*

array (1) An arrangement of objects in a regular *pattern,* usually rows and columns. (2) A *rectangular array.* In *Everyday Mathematics,* an array is a rectangular array unless specified otherwise. See Section 10.3.2: Multiplication and Division Use Classes and Section 14.4: Area.

Associative Property of Addition A property of addition that three numbers can be added in any order without changing the sum. For example, $(4 + 3) + 7 = 4 + (3 + 7)$ because $7 + 7 = 4 + 10$.

In symbols:
For any numbers *a, b,* and *c,*
$(a + b) + c = a + (b + c)$.

Subtraction is not associative. For example, $(4 - 3) + 7 \neq 4 - (3 + 7)$ because $8 \neq -6$.

Associative Property of Multiplication A property of multiplication that three numbers can be multiplied in any order without changing the product. For example, $(4 * 3) * 7 = 4 * (3 * 7)$ because $12 * 7 = 4 * 21$.

In symbols:
For any numbers *a, b,* and *c,*
$(a * b) * c = a * (b * c)$.

Division is not associative. For example, $(8/2)/4 \neq 8/(2/4)$ because $1 \neq 16$.

astronomical unit The *average* distance from Earth to the sun. Astronomical units measure distances in space. One astronomical unit is about 93 million miles or 150 million kilometers.

attribute A feature of an object or common feature of a set of objects. Examples of attributes include size, shape, color, and number of sides. Same as *property.*

autumnal equinox The first day of autumn, when the sun crosses the plane of Earth's equator and day and night are about 12 hours each. "Equinox" is from the Latin *aequi-* meaning "equal" and *nox* meaning "night." Compare to *vernal equinox*.

average A typical value for a set of numbers. In everyday life, average usually refers to the *mean* of the set, found by adding all the numbers and dividing by the number of numbers. In statistics, several different averages, or *landmarks,* are defined, including *mean, median,* and *mode.* See Section 12.2.4: Data Analysis.

axis of a coordinate grid Either of the two *number lines* used to form a *coordinate grid.* Plural is axes. See Section 15.3: Coordinate Systems.

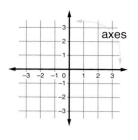

axis of rotation A line about which a solid figure rotates.

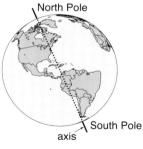

B

ballpark estimate A rough *estimate;* "in the ballpark." A ballpark estimate can serve as a check of the reasonableness of an answer obtained through some other procedure, or it can be made when an exact value is unnecessary or impossible to obtain. See Section 16.1: Estimation.

bank draft A written order for the exchange of money. For example, $1,000 bills are no longer printed so $1,000 bank drafts are issued. People can exchange $1,000 bank drafts for smaller bills, perhaps ten $100 bills.

bar graph A graph with horizontal or vertical bars that represent data. See Section 12.2.3: Organizing and Displaying Data.

Source: The Garbage Product

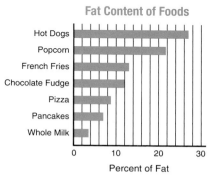

Source: The New York Public Library Desk Reference

base (in exponential notation) A number that is raised to a *power.* For example, the base in 5^3 is 5. See *exponential notation* and Section 10.1.2: Powers and Exponents.

base of a number system The foundation number for a *numeration system.* For example, our usual way of writing numbers uses a *base-ten place-value* system. In programming computers or other digital devices, bases of 2, 8, 16, or other powers of 2 are more common than base 10.

base of a parallelogram (1) The side of a *parallelogram* to which an *altitude* is drawn. (2) The length of this side. The area of a parallelogram is the base times the *altitude* or height perpendicular to it. See *height of a parallelogram* and Section 13.4.2: Polygons (*n*-gons).

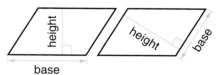

base of a prism or cylinder Either of the two parallel and congruent *faces* that define the shape of a *prism* or *cylinder*. In a cylinder, the base is a circle. See *height of a prism or cylinder*, Section 13.5.2: Polyhedrons, and Section 13.5.3: Solids with Curved Surfaces.

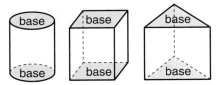

base of a pyramid or cone The *face* of a pyramid or cone that is opposite its *apex*. The base of a cone is a circle. See *height of a pyramid or cone*, Section 13.5.2: Polyhedrons, and Section 13.5.3: Solids with Curved Surfaces.

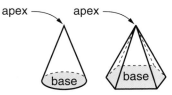

base of a rectangle (1) One of the sides of a *rectangle*. (2) The length of this side. The area of a rectangle is the base times the *altitude* or height. See *height of a rectangle* and Section 13.4.2: Polygons (*n*-gons).

base of a triangle (1) Any side of a *triangle* to which an *altitude* is drawn. (2) The length of this side. The area of a triangle is half the base times the altitude or height. See *height of a triangle* and Section 13.4.2: Polygons (*n*-gons).

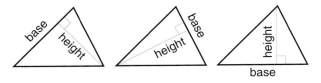

base ten Our system for writing numbers that uses only the 10 symbols 0, 1, 2, 3, 4, 5, 6, 7, 8, and 9, called *digits*. You can write any number using one or more of these 10 digits, and each digit has a value that depends on its place in the number (its *place value*). In the base-ten system, each place has a value 10 times that of the place to its right, and 1 tenth the value of the place to its left.

base-10 blocks A set of blocks to represent ones, tens, hundreds, and thousands in the *base-ten place-value* system. In *Everyday Mathematics,* the unit block, or *cube,* has 1-cm edges; the ten block, or *long,* is 10 unit blocks in length; the hundred block, or *flat,* is 10 longs in width; and the thousand block, or *big cube,* is 10 flats high. See *long, flat,* and *big cube* for photos of the blocks. See *base-10 shorthand* and Section 9.9.1: Base-10 Blocks.

base-10 shorthand In *Everyday Mathematics,* a written notation for *base-10 blocks*. See Section 9.9.1: Base-10 Blocks.

Base-10-Block Shorthand		
Name	**Block**	**Shorthand**
cube	◻	▪
long	▯		
flat	▦	☐
big cube	▨	◻◻

baseline A set of *data* used for comparison with subsequent data. Baseline data can be used to judge whether an experimental intervention is successful.

benchmark A count or measure that can be used to evaluate the reasonableness of other counts, measures, or estimates. A benchmark for land area is that a football field is about one acre. A benchmark for length is that the width of an adult's thumb is about one inch. See Section 14.1: Personal Measures.

biased sample A *sample* that does not fairly represent the total *population* from which it was selected. A sample is biased if every member of the population does not have the same chance of being selected for the sample. See *random sample* and Section 12.2.2: Collecting and Recording Data.

Glossary

big cube In *Everyday Mathematics,* a *base-10 block* cube that measures 10-cm by 10-cm by 10-cm. A big cube consists of one thousand 1-cm cubes. See Section 9.9.1: Base-10 Blocks.

A big cube

billion By U.S. custom, 1 billion is 1,000,000,000 or 10^9. By British, French, and German custom, 1 billion is 1,000,000,000,000 or 10^{12}.

bisect To divide a segment, angle, or figure into two parts of equal measure. See *bisector.*

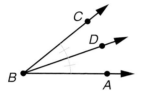
Ray *BD* bisects angle *ABC*.

bisector A *line, segment,* or *ray* that divides a segment, an angle, or a figure into two parts of equal measure. See *bisect.*

box-and-whiskers plot A plot displaying the spread, or distribution, of a data set using 5 *landmarks:* the *minimum, lower quartile, median, upper quartile,* and *maximum.* For example,

Landmark	Hair length (inches)
Minimum	14
Lower quartile	16
Median	20
Upper quartile	25
Maximum	32

the table above gives the landmarks for hair lengths, in inches, of a class of sixth graders. A box-and-whiskers plot using these landmarks is shown below. Also called a box plot. See Section 12.2.3: Organizing and Displaying Data.

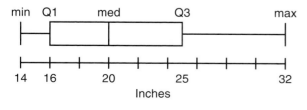

braces See *grouping symbols.*

brackets See *grouping symbols.*

broken-line graph Same as *line graph.*

C

calibrate (1) To divide or mark a measuring tool with gradations such as the degree marks on a thermometer. (2) To test and adjust the accuracy of a measuring tool.

calorie A unit for measuring the amount of energy a food will produce when it is digested by the body. One calorie is the amount of energy required to raise the temperature of 1 liter of water 1° Celsius. Technically, this is a "large calorie" or kilocalorie. A "small calorie" is 1 thousandth of the large calorie.

capacity (1) The amount of space occupied by a *3-dimensional figure.* Same as *volume.* (2) Less formally, the amount a container can hold. Capacity is often measured in units such as quarts, gallons, cups, or liters. See Section 14.5: Volume (Capacity). (3) The maximum weight a scale can measure. See Section 14.11.4: Scales and Balances.

cartographer A person who makes maps.

cell (1) In a *spreadsheet,* the box where a vertical *column* and a horizontal *row* intersect. The *address* of a cell is the column letter followed by the row number. For example, cell B3 in column B, row 3, is highlighted below. See Section 3.1.3: Spreadsheets. (2) The box where a column and row in a table intersect.

	A	B	C	D
1				
2				
3				
4				

Celsius A *temperature scale* on which pure water at sea level freezes at 0° and boils at 100°. The Celsius scale is used in the metric system. A less common name for this scale is centigrade because there are 100 units between the freezing and boiling points of water. Compare to *Fahrenheit.* See Section 15.1.1: Temperature Scales.

census An official count of population and the recording of other demographic data such as age, gender, income, and education.

cent A penny; $\frac{1}{100}$ of a dollar. From the Latin word *centesimus,* which means "a hundredth part." See Section 14.9: Money.

center of a circle The point in the plane of a *circle* equally distant from all points on the circle. See Section 13.4.3: Circles and Pi (π).

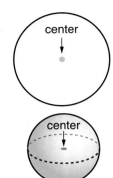

center of a sphere The point equally distant from all points on a *sphere*. See Section 13.5.3: Solids with Curved Surfaces.

centi- A prefix meaning 1 hundredth.

centimeter (cm) A metric unit of *length* equivalent to 10 millimeters, $\frac{1}{10}$ of a decimeter, and $\frac{1}{100}$ of a meter. See the Tables of Measures and Section 14.2.2: Metric System.

1 centimeter

0   1   2   3   4 cm

chance The possibility that an *outcome* will occur in an uncertain *event*. For example, in flipping a coin there is an equal chance of getting HEADS or TAILS. See Section 12.1.2: The Language of Chance.

change diagram A diagram used in *Everyday Mathematics* to model situations in which quantities are either increased or decreased by addition or subtraction. The diagram includes a starting quantity, an ending quantity, and an amount of change. See *situation diagram* and Section 10.3.1: Addition and Subtraction Use Classes.

A change diagram for $14 - 5 = 9$

change-to-less story A *number story* about a change situation in which the ending quantity is less than the starting quantity. For example, a story about spending money is a change-to-less story. Compare to *change-to-more story*. See Section 10.3.1: Addition and Subtraction Use Classes.

change-to-more story A *number story* about a change situation in which the ending quantity is more than the starting quantity. For example, a story about earning money is a change-to-more story. Compare to *change-to-less story*. See Section 10.3.1: Addition and Subtraction Use Classes.

circle The set of all points in a *plane* that are equally distant from a fixed point in the plane called the *center* of the circle. The distance from the center to the circle is the *radius* of the circle. The *diameter* of a circle is twice its radius. Points inside a circle are not part of the circle. A circle together with its interior is called a *disk* or a circular region. See Section 13.4.3: Circles and Pi (π).

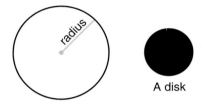

A disk

circle graph A graph in which a *circle* and its interior are divided into *sectors* corresponding to parts of a set of data. The whole circle represents the whole set of data. Same as *pie graph* and sometimes called a pie chart. See Section 12.2.3: Organizing and Displaying Data.

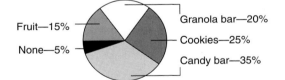

Fruit—15%
None—5%
Granola bar—20%
Cookies—25%
Candy bar—35%

circumference The distance around a circle; its *perimeter*. The circumference of a sphere is the circumference of a circle on the sphere with the same center as the sphere. See Section 13.4.3: Circles and Pi (π) and Section 13.5.3: Solids with Curved Surfaces.

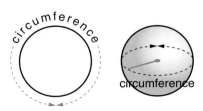

Class Data Pad In *Everyday Mathematics,* a large pad of paper used to store and recall data collected throughout the year. The data can be used for analysis, graphing, and generating number stories. See Section 5.2: Class Data Pad.

clockwise rotation The direction in which the hands move on a typical *analog clock;* a turn to the right.

coefficient The number, or *constant,* factor in a *variable term* in an expression. For example, in $3c + 8d,$ 3 and 8 are coefficients. See Section 17.2.2: Reading and Writing Open Sentences.

column (1) A vertical arrangement of objects or numbers in an *array* or a table.

(2) A vertical section of *cells* in a spreadsheet.

column addition An addition *algorithm* in which the addends' digits are first added in each place-value column separately, and then 10-for-1 trades are made until each column has only one digit. Lines may be drawn to separate the place-value columns. See Section 11.2.1: Addition Algorithms.

column division A division *algorithm* in which vertical lines are drawn between the digits of the dividend. As needed, trades are made from one column into the next column at the right. The lines make the procedure easier to carry out. See Section 11.2.4: Division Algorithms.

combine like terms To rewrite the sum or difference of *like terms* as a single term. For example, $5a + 6a$ can be rewritten as $11a,$ because $5a + 6a = (5 + 6)a = 11a.$ Similarly, $16t - 3t = 13t.$ See Section 17.2.3: Simplifying Expressions.

common denominator A nonzero number that is a multiple of the *denominators* of two or more fractions. For example, the fractions $\frac{1}{2}$ and $\frac{2}{3}$ have common denominators 6, 12, 18, and other multiples of 6. Fractions with the same denominator already have a common denominator. See Section 11.3.1: Common Denominators.

common factor A *factor* of each of two or more counting numbers. For example, 4 is a common factor of 8 and 12. See *factor of a counting number* and Section 9.8.1: Prime and Composite Numbers: Divisibility.

common fraction A *fraction* in which the *numerator* and the nonzero *denominator* are both *integers.*

Commutative Property of Addition A property of addition that two numbers can be added in either order without changing the sum. For example, $5 + 10 = 10 + 5.$ In *Everyday Mathematics,* this is called a *turn-around fact,* and the two Commutative Properties are called *turn-around rules.*

In symbols:

For any numbers a and $b,$ $a + b = b + a.$

Subtraction is not commutative. For example, $8 - 5 \neq 5 - 8$ because $3 \neq -3.$ See Section 16.3.3: Fact Practice.

Commutative Property of Multiplication A property of multiplication that two numbers can be multiplied in either order without changing the product. For example, $5 * 10 = 10 * 5.$ In *Everyday Mathematics,* this is called a *turn-around fact,* and the two Commutative Properties are called *turn-around rules.*

In symbols:

For any numbers a and $b,$ $a * b = b * a.$

Division is not commutative. For example, $10/5 \neq 5/10$ because $2 \neq \frac{1}{2}.$ See Section 16.3.3: Fact Practice.

comparison diagram A diagram used in *Everyday Mathematics* to model situations in which two quantities are compared by addition or subtraction. The diagram contains two quantities and their difference. See *situation diagram* and Section 10.3.1: Addition and Subtraction Use Classes.

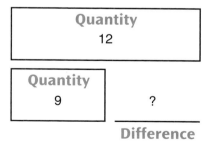

A comparison diagram for $12 = 9 + ?$

comparison story A *number story* about the difference between two quantities. Comparison situations can lead to either addition or subtraction depending on whether one of the compared quantities or the difference between them is unknown. See Section 10.3.1: Addition and Subtraction Use Classes.

compass (1) A tool used to draw *circles* and *arcs* and copy *line segments*. Certain geometric figures can be drawn with *compass-and-straightedge construction.* See Section 13.13.1: Compass-and-Straightedge Constructions. (2) A tool used to determine geographic direction.

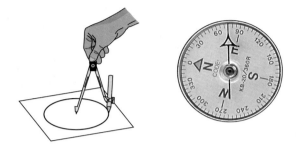

compass-and-straightedge construction A drawing of a geometric figure made using only a *compass* and a *straightedge* with no measurement allowed. See Section 13.13.1: Compass-and-Straightedge Constructions.

compass rose Same as *map direction symbol.*

complement of a number *n* (1) In *Everyday Mathematics,* the difference between *n* and the next higher multiple of 10. For example, the complement of 4 is $10 - 4 = 6$ and the complement of 73 is $80 - 73 = 7$. (2) The difference between *n* and the next higher power of 10. In this definition, the complement of 73 is $100 - 73 = 27$.

complementary angles Two *angles* whose measures add to 90°. Complementary angles do not need to be *adjacent.* Compare to *supplementary angles.* See Section 13.6.3: Relations and Orientations of Angles.

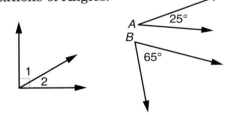

∠1 and ∠2; ∠A and ∠B
are pairs of complementary angles.

composite number A *counting number* greater than 1 that has more than two *factors.* For example, 10 is a composite number because it has four factors: 1, 2, 5, and 10. A composite number is *divisible by* at least three whole numbers. Compare to *prime number.* See Section 9.8.1: Prime and Composite Numbers: Divisibility.

compound unit A quotient or product of *units.* For example, miles per hour (mi/hr, mph), square centimeters (cm^2), and person-hours are compound units.

concave polygon A *polygon* on which there are at least two points that can be connected with a *line segment* that passes outside the polygon. For example, segment *AD* is outside the hexagon between *B* and *C.* Informally, at least one vertex appears to be "pushed inward." At least one interior angle has measure greater than 180°. Same as *nonconvex polygon.* Compare to *convex polygon.* See Section 13.4.2: Polygons (*n*-gons).

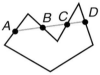

A concave polygon

concentric circles *Circles* that have the same center but radii of different lengths.

Concentric circles

cone A *geometric solid* with a circular *base,* a vertex *(apex)* not in the *plane* of the base, and all of the line segments with one endpoint at the apex and the other endpoint on the circumference of the base. See Section 13.5.3: Solids with Curved Surfaces.

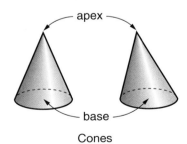

Cones

congruent figures (≅) Figures having the same size and shape. Two figures are congruent if they match exactly when one is placed on top of the other after a combination of slides, flips, and/or turns. In diagrams of congruent figures, the corresponding congruent sides may be marked with the same number of hash marks. The symbol ≅ means "is congruent to." See Section 13.6.2: Congruence and Similarity.

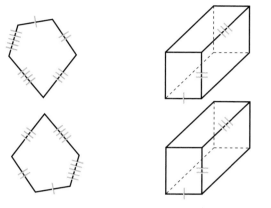

Congruent pentagons   Congruent prisms

consecutive Following one after another in an uninterrupted order. For example, A, B, C, and D are four consecutive letters of the alphabet; 6, 7, 8, 9, and 10 are five consecutive whole numbers.

consecutive angles Two *angles* in a *polygon* with a common side.

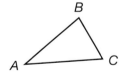

Angles *A* and *B*, *B* and *C*, and *C* and *A*
are pairs of consecutive angles.

consecutive sides (1) Two *sides* of a *polygon* with a common *vertex*. (2) Two sides of a *polyhedron* with a common *edge*. Same as *adjacent sides*. See Section 13.6.4: Other Geometric Relations.

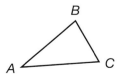

Sides *AB* and *BC*, *BC* and *CA*, and *CA* and *AB*
are pairs of consecutive sides.

consecutive vertices The vertices of *consecutive angles* in a polygon.

constant A quantity that does not change. For example, the ratio of the circumference of a circle to its diameter is the famous constant π. In *x* + 3 = *y*, 3 is a constant. See Section 17.2.2: Reading and Writing Open Sentences.

continuous model of area A way of thinking about *area* as sweeping one dimension of a plane figure across the other dimension. For example, the paint roller below shows how the area of a rectangle can be modeled continuously by sweeping the shorter side across the longer side. See Section 14.4.1: Discrete and Continuous Models of Area.

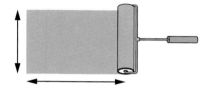

A continuous model of area

continuous model of volume A way of thinking about *volume* as sweeping a 2-dimensional cross section of a solid figure across the third dimension. For example, imagine filling the box below with water. The surface of the water would sweep up the height of the box. See Section 14.5.1: Discrete and Continuous Models of Volume.

contour line A curve on a map through places where a measurement such as temperature, elevation, air pressure, or growing season is the same. Contour lines often separate regions that have been differently colored to show a range of conditions. See *contour map* and Section 15.4.3: Contour Maps.

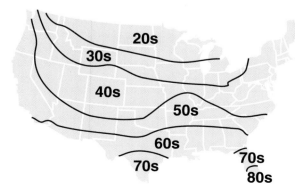

A temperature contour map

contour map A map that uses *contour lines* to indicate areas having a particular feature, such as elevation or temperature. See Section 15.4.3: Contour Maps.

conversion fact A fixed relationship such as 1 yard = 3 feet or 1 inch = 2.54 centimeters that can be used to convert measurements within or between systems of measurement. See Section 14.2.3: Converting between Measures.

convex polygon A *polygon* on which no two points can be connected with a *line segment* that passes outside the polygon. Informally, all vertices appear to be "pushed outward." Each angle in the polygon measures less than 180°. Compare to *concave polygon*. See Section 13.4.2: Polygons (*n*-gons).

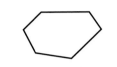

A convex polygon

coordinate (1) A number used to locate a point on a *number line;* a point's distance from an *origin*. (2) One of the numbers in an *ordered pair* or triple that locates a point on a *coordinate grid* or in coordinate space, respectively. See Section 9.9.2: Number Grids, Scrolls, and Lines and Section 15.3: Coordinate Systems.

coordinate grid (rectangular coordinate grid) A *reference frame* for locating points in a plane by means of *ordered pairs* of numbers. A rectangular coordinate grid is formed by two number lines that intersect at *right angles* at their *zero points*. See Section 15.3.2: 2- and 3-Dimensional Coordinate Systems.

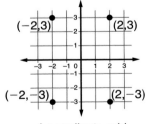

A coordinate grid

corner Same as *vertex*.

corresponding angles (1) *Angles* in the same relative position in *similar* or *congruent figures*. Pairs of corresponding angles are marked either by the same number of arcs or by the same number of hash marks per arc.

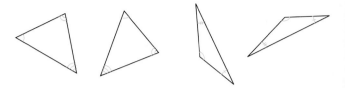

(2) Two angles in the same relative position when two lines are intersected by a *transversal*. In the diagram, $\angle a$ and $\angle e$, $\angle b$ and $\angle f$, $\angle d$ and $\angle h$, and $\angle c$ and $\angle g$ are pairs of corresponding angles. If any two corresponding angles in a pair are congruent, then the two lines are parallel.

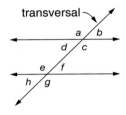

corresponding sides *Sides* in the same relative position in *similar* or *congruent figures*. Pairs of corresponding sides are marked with the same number of hash marks.

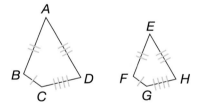

corresponding vertices Vertices in the same relative position in *similar* or *congruent figures*. Pairs of corresponding vertices can be identified by their *corresponding angles*. Sometimes corresponding vertices have the same letter name, but one has a "prime" symbol as in A and A'.

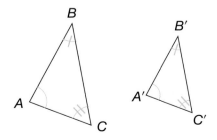

Glossary

counterclockwise rotation Opposite the direction in which the hands move on a typical *analog clock;* a turn to the left.

counting numbers The numbers used to count things. The set of counting numbers is {1, 2, 3, 4, . . .}. Sometimes 0 is included, but not in *Everyday Mathematics.* Counting numbers are in the sets of *whole numbers, integers, rational numbers,* and *real numbers,* but each of these sets include numbers that are not counting numbers. See Section 9.2.1: Counting.

counting-up subtraction A subtraction *algorithm* in which a difference is found by counting or adding up from the smaller number to the larger number. For example, to calculate $87 - 49$, start at 49, add 30 to reach 79, and then add 8 more to reach 87. The difference is $30 + 8 = 38$. See Section 11.2.2: Subtraction Algorithms.

cover-up method An informal method for finding a *solution of an open sentence* by covering up a part of the sentence containing a *variable.*

credit An amount added to an account balance; a deposit.

cross multiplication The process of rewriting a *proportion* by calculating *cross products.* Cross multiplication can be used in solving open proportions. In the example below, the cross products are 60 and $4z$. See Section 17.2.4: Solving Open Sentences.

$$3 * 20 = 60 \qquad 4 * z = 4z$$
$$\frac{3}{4} = \frac{z}{20}$$

To solve:
$$\frac{3}{4} = \frac{z}{20}$$
$$3 * 20 = 4 * z$$
$$60 = 4z$$
$$60/4 = 4z/4$$
$$15 = z$$

cross products The two *products* of the numerator of each fraction and the denominator of the other fraction in a *proportion.* The cross products of a proportion are equal. For example, in the proportion $\frac{2}{3} = \frac{6}{9}$, the cross products $2 * 9$ and $3 * 6$ are both 18.

$$2 * 9 = 18 \qquad 3 * 6 = 18$$
$$\frac{2}{3} = \frac{6}{9}$$

cross section A shape formed by the intersection of a *plane* and a *geometric solid.*

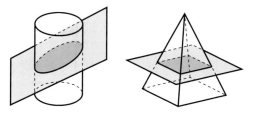

Cross sections of a cylinder and a pyramid

cube (1) A *regular polyhedron* with 6 square faces. A cube has 8 *vertices* and 12 *edges.* See Section 13.5.2: Polyhedrons.

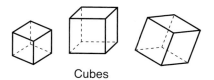

Cubes

(2) In *Everyday Mathematics,* the smaller cube of the *base-10 blocks,* measuring 1 cm on each edge. See Section 9.9.1: Base-10 Blocks.

cube of a number The product of a number used as a *factor* three times. For example, the cube of 5 is $5 * 5 * 5 = 5^3 = 125$. See Section 10.1.2: Powers and Exponents.

cubic centimeter (cc or cm³) A metric unit of *volume* or *capacity* equal to the volume of a cube with 1-cm edges. $1 \text{ cm}^3 = 1$ milliliter (mL). See the Tables of Measures and Section 14.5: Volume (Capacity).

cubic unit A unit such as cubic centimeters, cubic inches, cubic feet, and cubic meters used to measure *volume* or *capacity.* See Section 14.5: Volume (Capacity).

cubit An ancient unit of *length,* measured from the point of the elbow to the end of the middle finger. The cubit has been standardized at various times between 18 and 22 inches. The Latin word *cubitum* means "elbow." See Section 14.1: Personal Measures.

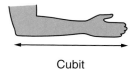

Cubit

cup (c) A U.S. customary unit of *volume* or *capacity* equal to 8 fluid ounces or $\frac{1}{2}$ pint. See the Tables of Measures and Section 14.5: Volume (Capacity).

curved surface A 2-dimensional surface that does not lie in a plane. *Spheres, cylinders,* and *cones* each have one curved surface. See Section 13.5.3: Solids with Curved Surfaces.

customary system of measurement In *Everyday Mathematics,* same as *U.S. customary system of measurement.*

cylinder A *geometric solid* with two congruent, parallel circular regions for *bases* and a curved *face* formed by all the segments with an endpoint on each circle that are parallel to a segment with endpoints at the centers of the circles. Also called a circular cylinder. See Section 13.5.3: Solids with Curved Surfaces.

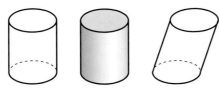

Cylinders

D

data Information that is gathered by counting, measuring, questioning, or observing. Strictly, data is the plural of *datum,* but data is often used as a singular word. See Section 12.2: Data Collection, Organization, and Analysis.

debit An amount subtracted from a bank balance; a withdrawal.

deca- A prefix meaning 10.

decagon A 10-sided polygon. See Section 13.4.2: Polygons (*n*-gons).

deci- A prefix meaning 1 tenth.

decimal (1) In *Everyday Mathematics,* a number written in standard *base-ten* notation containing a decimal point, such as 2.54. (2) Any number written in standard base-ten notation. See *repeating decimal, terminating decimal,* Section 9.3.1: Fraction and Decimal Notation, and Section 9.3.4: Rational Numbers and Decimals.

decimal notation In *Everyday Mathematics,* same as *standard notation.*

decimal point A mark used to separate the ones and tenths places in *decimals.* A decimal point separates dollars from cents in dollars-and-cents notation. The mark is a dot in the U.S. customary system and a comma in Europe and some other countries.

decimeter (dm) A metric unit of *length* equivalent to $\frac{1}{10}$ meter, or 10 centimeters.

deficient number A *counting number* whose *proper factors* add to less than the number itself. For example, 10 is a deficient number because the sum of its proper factors is $1 + 2 + 5 = 8$, and 8 is less than 10. Compare to *abundant number* and *perfect number.* See Section 9.8.2: Perfect, Deficient, and Abundant Numbers.

degree (°) (1) A unit of measure for *angles* based on dividing a *circle* into 360 equal parts. Lines of latitude and longitude are measured in degrees, and these degrees are based on angle measures. See Section 13.4.1: Angles and Rotations and Section 15.4.4: The Global Grid System. (2) A unit for measuring *temperature.* See *degree Celsius, degree Fahrenheit,* and Section 15.1.1: Temperature Scales.
The symbol ° means degrees of any type.

degree Celsius (°C) The *unit interval* on *Celsius* thermometers and a metric unit for measuring *temperatures.* Pure water at sea level freezes at 0°C and boils at 100°C. See Section 15.1.1: Temperature Scales.

degree Fahrenheit (°F) The *unit interval* on *Fahrenheit* thermometers and a U.S. customary unit for measuring *temperatures.* Pure water at sea level freezes at 32°F and boils at 212°F. A saturated salt solution freezes at 0°F. See Section 15.1.1: Temperature Scales.

denominator The nonzero divisor *b* in a fraction $\frac{a}{b}$ and *a/b.* In a *part-whole fraction,* the denominator is the number of equal parts into which the *whole,* or *ONE,* has been divided. Compare to *numerator.* See Section 9.3.1: Fraction and Decimal Notation.

density A *rate* that compares the *mass* of an object to its *volume.* For example, a ball with mass 20 grams and volume 10 cubic centimeters has a density of $\frac{20 \text{ g}}{10 \text{ cm}^3} = 2$ g/cm^3, or 2 grams per cubic centimeter.

dependent variable (1) A *variable* whose value is dependent on the value of at least one other variable in a *function.* (2) The *variable y* in a *function* defined by the set of *ordered pairs* (*x,y*). Same as the *output* of the function. Compare to *independent variable.* See Section 17.2.1: Uses of Variables.

diagonal (1) A *line segment* joining two nonconsecutive vertices of a *polygon*. See Section 13.4.2: Polygons (*n*-gons). (2) A segment joining two nonconsecutive vertices on different faces of a *polyhedron*.

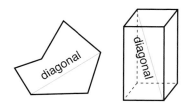

(3) A line of objects or numbers between *opposite corners* of an *array* or a table.

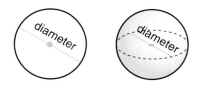

A diagonal of an array

diameter (1) A *line segment* that passes through the center of a *circle* or *sphere* and has endpoints on the circle or sphere. (2) The length of such a segment. The diameter of a circle or sphere is twice the *radius*. See Section 13.4.3: Circles and Pi (π) and Section 13.5.3: Solids with Curved Surfaces.

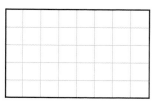

difference The result of subtracting one number from another. For example, the difference of 12 and 5 is $12 - 5 = 7$.

digit (1) Any one of the symbols 0, 1, 2, 3, 4, 5, 6, 7, 8, and 9 in the *base-ten* numeration system. For example, the numeral 145 is made up of the digits 1, 4, and 5. (2) Any one of the symbols in any number system. For example, A, B, C, D, E, and F are digits along with 0 through 9 in the base-16 notation used in some computer programming.

digital clock A clock that shows the time with numbers of hours and minutes, usually separated by a colon. This display is discrete, not continuous, meaning that the display jumps to a new time after a minute delay. Compare to *analog clock*. See Section 15.2.1: Clocks.

A digital clock

dimension (1) A measure along one direction of an object, typically length, width, or height. For example, the dimensions of a box might be 24-cm by 20-cm by 10-cm. (2) The number of *coordinates* necessary to locate a point in a geometric space. For example, a line has one dimension because one coordinate uniquely locates any point on the line. A plane has two dimensions because an *ordered pair* of two coordinates uniquely locates any point in the plane. See Section 13.1: Dimension.

discount The amount by which a price of an item is reduced in a sale, usually given as a fraction or percent of the original price, or as a "percent off." For example, a $4 item on sale for $3 is discounted to 75% or $\frac{3}{4}$ of its original price. A $10.00 item at "10% off" costs $9.00, or $\frac{1}{10}$ less than the usual price.

discrete model of area A way of thinking about *area* as filling a figure with unit squares and counting them. For example, the rectangle below has been filled with 40 square units. See Section 14.4.1: Discrete and Continuous Models of Area.

discrete model of volume A way of thinking about *volume* as filling a figure with unit cubes and counting them. For example, the box below will eventually hold 108 cubic units. See Section 14.5.1: Discrete and Continuous Models of Volume.

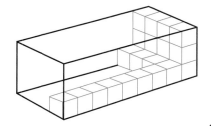

disk A *circle* and its interior region.

displacement method A method for estimating the *volume* of an object by submerging it in water and then measuring the volume of water it displaces. The method is especially useful for finding the volume of an irregularly shaped object. Archimedes of Syracuse (circa 287–212 B.C.) is famous for having solved a problem of finding the volume and density of a king's crown by noticing how his body displaced water in a bathtub and applying the method to the crown. He reportedly shouted "Eureka!" at the discovery, and so similar insights are today sometimes called Eureka moments. See Section 14.5: Volume (Capacity).

Distributive Property of Multiplication over Addition A property relating multiplication to a sum of numbers by distributing a *factor* over the terms in the sum. For example,
$2 * (5 + 3) = (2 * 5) + (2 * 3) = 10 + 6 = 16.$

In symbols:
> For any numbers *a, b,* and *c:*
> $a * (b + c) = (a * b) + (a * c)$
> or $a(b + c) = ab + ac$

See Section 17.2.3: Simplifying Expressions.

Distributive Property of Multiplication over Subtraction A property relating multiplication to a difference of numbers by distributing a *factor* over the terms in the difference. For example,
$2 * (5 - 3) = (2 * 5) - (2 * 3) = 10 - 6 = 4.$

In symbols:
> For any numbers *a, b,* and *c:*
> $a * (b - c) = (a * b) - (a * c)$
> or $a(b - c) = ab - ac$

See Section 17.2.3: Simplifying Expressions.

dividend The number in division that is being divided. For example, in 35/5 = 7, the dividend is 35.

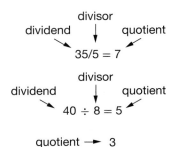

divisibility rule A shortcut for determining whether a counting number is *divisible by* another counting number without actually doing the division. For example, a number is divisible by 5 if the *digit* in the ones place is 0 or 5. A number is divisible by 3 if the sum of its digits is divisible by 3. See Section 9.8.1: Prime and Composite Numbers: Divisibility.

divisibility test A test to see if a *divisibility rule* applies to a particular number. See Section 9.8.1: Prime and Composite Numbers: Divisibility.

divisible by If the larger of two *counting numbers* can be divided by the smaller with no remainder, then the larger is divisible by the smaller. For example, 28 is divisible by 7, because 28/7 = 4 with no remainder. If a number *n* is divisible by a number *d,* then *d* is a *factor* of *n.* Every counting number is divisible by itself. See Section 9.8.1: Prime and Composite Numbers: Divisibility.

Division of Fractions Property A rule for dividing that says division by a *fraction* is the same a multiplication by the *reciprocal* of the fraction. Another name for this property is the "invert and multiply rule." For example,

$$5 \div 8 = 5 * \frac{1}{8} = \frac{5}{8}$$
$$15 \div \frac{3}{5} = 15 * \frac{5}{3} = \frac{75}{3} = 25$$
$$\frac{1}{2} \div \frac{3}{5} = \frac{1}{2} * \frac{5}{3} = \frac{5}{6}$$

In symbols:
> For any *a* and nonzero *b, c,* and *d:*
> $$\frac{a}{b} \div \frac{c}{d} = \frac{a}{b} * \frac{d}{c}$$

If $b = 1$, then $\frac{a}{b} = a$ and the property is applied as in the first two examples above. See Section 11.3.5: Fraction Division.

division symbols The number *a* divided by the number *b* is written in a variety of ways. In *Everyday Mathematics, a ÷ b, a/b,* and $\frac{a}{b}$ are the most common notations, while $b\overline{)a}$ is used to set up the traditional long-division algorithm. *a:b* is sometimes used in Europe, ÷ is common on calculators, and $\boxed{/}$ is common on computer keyboards. See Section 10.1.1: The Four Basic Arithmetic Operations.

divisor In division, the number that divides another number, the *dividend.* For example, in 35/7 = 5, the divisor is 7. See the diagram under the definition of *dividend.*

dodecahedron A *polyhedron* with 12 faces. If each face is a regular pentagon, it is one of the five *regular polyhedrons*. See Section 13.5.2: Polyhedrons.

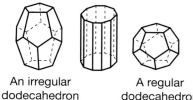

A decagonal prism

An irregular dodecahedron

A regular dodecahedron

doubles fact The sum (or product) of a 1-digit number added to (or multiplied by) itself, such as $4 + 4 = 8$ or $3 * 3 = 9$. A doubles fact does not have a *turn-around fact* partner.

double-stem plot A *stem-and-leaf plot* in which each stem is split into two parts. Numbers on the original stem ending in 0 through 4 are plotted on one half of the split, and numbers ending in 5 through 9 are plotted on the other half. Double-stem plots are useful if the original stem-and-leaf plot has many leaves falling on few stems. The following plot shows eruption duration in minutes of the Old Faithful Geyser. For example, the first two stems show one observation each of durations lasting 42, 44, 45, 48, and 49 minutes. See Section 12.2.3: Organizing and Displaying Data.

Eruption Duration of Old Faithful
(minutes)

Stems (10s)	Leaves (1s)
4	2 4
4	5 8 9
5	0 1 1 1 3 3 3 4
5	5 5 6 6 7 7 8
6	0 1 1
6	6 7 7 8 8 9
7	0 1 1 1 2 2 3 3 4 4
7	5 5 6 6 6 7 7 8 8 9 9 9
8	0 1 1 1 2 2 3 3 4 4 4
8	5 6 6 6 6 8 8 9
9	
9	

A double-stem plot

edge (1) Any *side* of a polyhedron's *faces*. (2) A line segment or curve where two surfaces of a geometric solid meet. See Section 13.5.2: Polyhedrons and Section 13.5.3: Solids with Curved Surfaces.

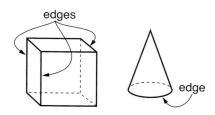

edges

edge

Egyptian multiplication A 4,000-year-old multiplication *algorithm* based on repeated doubling of one factor. See Section 11.2.3: Multiplication Algorithms.

elevation A height above sea level. Same as *altitude (2)*.

ellipse A closed, oval figure that is the set of points in a *plane,* the sum of whose distances from two fixed points is *constant.* Each of the fixed points is called a focus of the ellipse. You can draw an ellipse by attaching the ends of a string at the two focus points, and moving a pencil or pen taut against the string around the focus points. The length of the string is the constant.

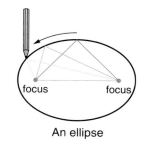

focus   focus

An ellipse

embedded figure A figure entirely enclosed within another figure.

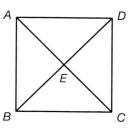

Triangle *ADE* is embedded in square *ADCB*.

endpoint A point at the end of a *line segment, ray,* or *arc*. These shapes are usually named using their endpoints. For example, the segment shown is "segment *TL*" or "segment *LT*."

endpoints

T   L

enlarge To increase the size of an object or a figure without changing its shape. Same as *stretch*. See *size-change factor* and Section 13.7.2: Size-Change Transformations

equal Same as *equivalent*.

equal-grouping story A *number story* in which a quantity is divided into equal groups. The total and size of each group are known. For example, *How many tables seating 4 people each are needed to seat 52 people?* is an equal-grouping story. Often division can be used to solve equal-grouping stories. Compare to *measurement division* and *equal-sharing story* and see Section 10.3.2: Multiplication and Division Use Classes.

equal groups Sets with the same number of elements, such as cars with 5 passengers each, rows with 6 chairs each, and boxes containing 100 paper clips each. See Section 10.3.2: Multiplication and Division Use Classes.

equal-groups notation In *Everyday Mathematics,* a way to denote a number of equal-size groups. The size of each group is shown inside square brackets and the number of groups is written in front of the brackets. For example, 3 [6s] means 3 groups with 6 in each group. In general, n [bs] means n groups with b in each group.

equal parts Equivalent parts of a *whole*. For example, dividing a pizza into 4 equal parts means each part is $\frac{1}{4}$ of the pizza and is equal in size to the other 3 parts. See Section 9.3.2: Uses of Fractions.

4 equal parts, each $\frac{1}{4}$ of a pizza

equal-sharing story A *number story* in which a quantity is shared equally. The total quantity and the number of groups are known. For example, *There are 10 toys to share equally among 4 children; how many toys will each child get?* is an equal-sharing story. Often division can be used to solve equal-sharing stories. Compare to *partitive division* and *equal-grouping story*. See Section 10.3.2: Multiplication and Division Use Classes.

equally likely outcomes *Outcomes* of a chance experiment or situation that have the same *probability* of happening. If all the possible outcomes are equally likely, then the probability of an *event* is equal to:

$$\frac{\text{number of favorable outcomes}}{\text{number of possible outcomes}}$$

See *favorable outcomes, random experiment,* and Section 12.1.2: The Language of Chance.

equation A *number sentence* that contains an equal sign. For example, $5 + 10 = 15$ and $P = 2l + 2w$ are equations. See Section 10.2: Reading and Writing Number Sentences and Section 17.2.2: Reading and Writing Open Sentences.

equator An imaginary circle around Earth halfway between the North Pole and the South Pole. The equator is the 0° line for *latitude*.

equidistant marks A series of marks separated by a constant space. See *unit interval*.

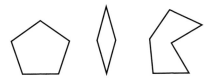
Equidistant marks

equilateral polygon A *polygon* in which all sides are the same length. See Section 13.4.2: Polygons (*n*-gons).

Equilateral polygons

equilateral triangle A *triangle* with all three sides equal in length. Each angle of an equilateral triangle measures 60°, so it is also called an equiangular triangle. See Section 13.4.2: Polygons (*n*-gons).

An equilateral triangle

equivalent Equal in value but possibly in a different form. For example, $\frac{1}{2}$, 0.5, and 50% are all equivalent. See Section 9.7.1: Equality.

Glossary

equivalent equations *Equations* with the same *solution*. For example, $2 + x = 4$ and $6 + x = 8$ are equivalent equations with the common solution 2. See Section 17.2.4: Solving Open Sentences.

equivalent fractions *Fractions* with different *denominators* that name the same number. See Section 9.3.3: Rates, Ratios, and Proportions.

equivalent names Different ways of naming the same number. For example, $2 + 6$, $4 + 4$, $12 - 4$, $18 - 10$, $100 - 92$, $5 + 1 + 2$, eight, VIII, and $\cancel{||||}\,|||$ are all equivalent names for 8. See *name-collection box*.

equivalent rates *Rates* that make the same comparison. For example, the rates $\frac{60 \text{ miles}}{1 \text{ hour}}$ and $\frac{1 \text{ mile}}{1 \text{ minute}}$ are equivalent. *Equivalent fractions* represent equivalent rates if the units for the rates are the same. For example $\frac{12 \text{ pages}}{4 \text{ minutes}}$ and $\frac{6 \text{ pages}}{2 \text{ minutes}}$ are equivalent rates because $\frac{12}{4}$ and $\frac{6}{2}$ are equivalent with the same unit of pages per minute.

equivalent ratios *Ratios* that make the same comparison. *Equivalent fractions* represent equivalent ratios. For example, $\frac{1}{2}$ and $\frac{4}{8}$ are equivalent ratios. See Section 9.3.3: Rates, Ratios, and Proportions.

estimate (1) An answer close to, or approximating, an exact answer. (2) To make an estimate. See Section 16.1: Estimation.

European subtraction A subtraction *algorithm* in which the subtrahend is increased when regrouping is necessary. The algorithm is commonly used in Europe and in certain parts of the United States. See Section 11.2.2: Subtraction Algorithms.

evaluate an algebraic expression To replace each *variable* in an algebraic *expression* with a number and then calculate a single value for the expression.

evaluate a formula To find the value of one *variable* in a *formula* when the values of the other variables are known.

evaluate a numerical expression To carry out the operations in a numerical *expression* to find a single value for the expression.

even number (1) A *counting number* that is *divisible by* 2. (2) An *integer* that is divisible by 2. Compare to *odd number* and see Section 17.1: Patterns, Sequences, and Functions.

event A set of possible *outcomes* to an experiment. For example, in an experiment flipping two coins, getting 2 HEADS is an event, as is getting 1 HEAD and 1 TAIL. The *probability* of an event is the chance that the event will happen. For example, the probability that a fair coin will land HEADS up is $\frac{1}{2}$. If the probability of an event is 0, the event is *impossible*. If the probability is 1, the event is *certain*. See Section 12.1: Probability.

expanded notation A way of writing a number as the sum of the values of each *digit*. For example, 356 is $300 + 50 + 6$ in expanded notation. Compare to *standard notation, scientific notation,* and *number-and-word notation*.

expected outcome The *average outcome* over a large number of repetitions of a *random experiment*. For example, the expected outcome of rolling one die is the average number of spots landing up over a large number of rolls. Because each face of a fair die has equal *probability* of landing up, the expected outcome is $\frac{(1 + 2 + 3 + 4 + 5 + 6)}{6} = \frac{21}{6} = 3\frac{1}{2}$. This means that the average of many rolls of a fair die is expected to be about $3\frac{1}{2}$. More formally, the expected outcome is defined as an average over infinitely many repetitions.

exponent A small raised number used in *exponential notation* to tell how many times the *base* is used as a *factor*. For example, in 5^3, the base is 5, the exponent is 3, and $5^3 = 5 * 5 * 5 = 125$. Same as *power*. See Section 10.1.2: Powers and Exponents.

exponential notation A way of representing repeated multiplication by the same factor. For example, 2^3 is exponential notation for $2 * 2 * 2$. The *exponent* 3 tells how many times the *base* 2 is used as a factor. See Section 10.1.2: Powers and Exponents.

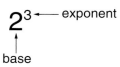

expression (1) A mathematical phrase made up of numbers, *variables, operation symbols,* and/or *grouping symbols.* An expression does not contain *relation symbols* such as =, >, and ≤. (2) Either side of an *equation* or *inequality.* See Section 10.2: Reading and Writing Number Sentences and Section 17.2.2: Reading and Writing Open Sentences.

$$2 + 3$$
$$\sqrt{2ab}$$
$$\pi r^2$$
$$9x - 2$$

Expressions

extended facts Variations of basic *arithmetic facts* involving multiples of 10, 100, and so on. For example, $30 + 70 = 100$, $40 * 5 = 200$, and $560/7 = 80$ are extended facts. See *fact extensions* and Section 16.3: Mental Arithmetic.

F

face (1) In *Everyday Mathematics,* a flat *surface* on a *3-dimensional figure.* Some special faces are called *bases.* (2) More generally, any 2-dimensional surface on a 3-dimensional figure. See Section 13.5: Space and 3-D Figures.

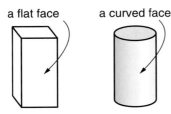

a flat face   a curved face

fact extensions Calculations with larger numbers using knowledge of basic *arithmetic facts.* For example, knowing the addition fact $5 + 8 = 13$ makes it easier to solve problems such as $50 + 80 = ?$ and $65 + ? = 73$. Fact extensions apply to all four basic arithmetic operations. See *extended facts* and Section 16.3.3: Fact Practice.

fact family A set of related *arithmetic facts* linking two inverse operations. For example,

$5 + 6 = 11$	$6 + 5 = 11$
$11 - 5 = 6$	$11 - 6 = 5$

are an addition/subtraction fact family. Similarly,

$5 * 7 = 35$	$7 * 5 = 35$
$35/7 = 5$	$35/5 = 7$

are a multiplication/division fact family. Same as *number family.* See Section 16.3.3: Fact Practice.

fact habits Same as *fact power.*

fact power In *Everyday Mathematics,* the ability to automatically recall basic *arithmetic facts.* Automatically knowing the facts is as important to arithmetic as knowing words by sight is to reading. Same as *fact habits.* See Section 16.3.2: Basic Facts and Fact Power.

Fact Triangle In *Everyday Mathematics,* a triangular flash card labeled with the numbers of a *fact family* that students can use to practice addition/subtraction and multiplication/division facts. The two 1-digit numbers and their sum or product (marked with a dot) appear in the corners of each triangle. See Section 1.3.1: Fact Families/Fact Triangles.

factor (1) Each of the two or more numbers in a *product.* For example, in $6 * 0.5$, 6 and 0.5 are factors. Compare to *factor of a counting number* n. (2) To represent a number as a product of factors. For example, factor 21 by rewriting as $7 * 3$. See Section 9.8.1: Prime and Composite Numbers: Divisibility.

factor of a counting number *n* A *counting number* whose product with some other counting number equals *n.* For example, 2 and 3 are factors of 6 because $2 * 3 = 6$. But 4 is not a factor of 6 because $4 * 1.5 = 6$, and 1.5 is not a counting number.

factor pair Two *factors of a counting number* n whose product is *n.* A number may have more than one factor pair. For example, the factor pairs for 18 are 1 and 18, 2 and 9, and 3 and 6. See Section 9.8.1: Prime and Composite Numbers: Divisibility.

factor rainbow A way to show *factor pairs* in a list of all the factors of a number. A factor rainbow can be used to check whether a list of factors is correct.

A factor rainbow for 24

factor string A *counting number* written as a product of two or more of its counting-number *factors* other than 1. The length of a factor string is the number of factors in the string. For example, 2 * 3 * 4 is a factor string for 24 with length 3. By convention, 1 * 2 * 3 * 4 is not a factor string for 24 because it contains the number 1.

factor tree A way to get the *prime factorization* of a counting number. Write the original number as a product of *factors*. Then write each of these factors as a product of factors, and continue until the factors are all prime numbers. A factor tree looks like an upside-down tree, with the root (the original number) at the top and the leaves (the factors) beneath it. See *tree diagram* and Section 9.8.1: Prime and Composite Numbers: Divisibility.

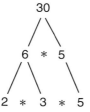

factorial (!) A *product* of a counting number and all smaller counting numbers. The symbol ! means "factorial." For example, 3! is read "three factorial" and 3! = 3 * 2 * 1 = 6. Similarly, 4! = 4 * 3 * 2 * 1 = 24.

In symbols:

For any counting number n,
$n! = n * (n - 1) * (n - 2) * \ldots * 1$.

By convention, 0! = 1.

facts table A chart showing *arithmetic facts*. An addition/subtraction facts table shows addition and subtraction facts. A multiplication/division facts table shows multiplication and division facts.

Fahrenheit A *temperature scale* on which pure water at sea level freezes at 32° and boils at 212°. The Fahrenheit scale is widely used in the United States but in few other places. Compare to *Celsius*. See *degree Fahrenheit* and Section 15.1.1: Temperature Scales.

fair Free from bias. Each side of a fair die or coin will land up about equally often. Each region of a fair spinner will be landed on in proportion to its area.

fair game A game in which every player has the same chance of winning. See Section 12.1.2: The Language of Chance.

false number sentence A *number sentence* that is not true. For example, 8 = 5 + 5 is a false number sentence. Compare to *true number sentence*. See Section 10.2: Reading and Writing Number Sentences.

fathom A unit of *length* equal to 6 feet, or 2 yards. It is used mainly by people who work with boats and ships to measure depths underwater and lengths of cables. Same as *arm span*. See Section 14.1: Personal Measures.

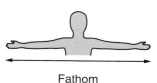

Fathom

favorable outcome An *outcome* that satisfies the conditions of an *event* of interest. For example, suppose a 6-sided die is rolled and the event of interest is "roll an even number." There are six possible outcomes: roll 1, 2, 3, 4, 5, or 6. Of these, 3 are favorable: roll 2, 4, or 6. See *equally likely outcomes* and Section 12.1.2: The Language of Chance.

figurate numbers Numbers that can be illustrated by specific geometric *patterns*. *Square numbers* and *triangular numbers* are figurate numbers. See Section 17.1.2: Sequences.

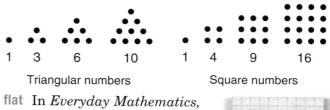

Triangular numbers   Square numbers

flat In *Everyday Mathematics*, the *base-10 block* consisting of one hundred 1-cm cubes. See Section 9.9.1: Base-10 Blocks.

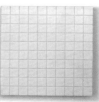

A flat

flat surface A *surface* contained entirely in one *plane*. See Section 13.4: Planes and Plane Figures and Section 13.5: Space and 3-D Figures.

flip An informal name for a *reflection* transformation. See Section 13.7.1: Reflections, Rotations, and Translations.

flowchart A diagram that shows a series of steps to complete a task. A typical flowchart is a network of frames and symbols connected by arrows that provides a guide for working through a problem step by step.

fluid ounce (fl oz) A U.S. customary unit of *volume* or *capacity* equal to $\frac{1}{16}$ of a pint, or about 29.573730 milliliters. Compare to *ounce*. See the Tables of Measures and Section 14.5: Volume (Capacity).

foot (ft) A U.S. customary unit of *length* equivalent to 12 inches, or $\frac{1}{3}$ of a yard. See the Tables of Measures and Section 14.3: Length.

formula A general rule for finding the value of something. A formula is usually an *equation* with quantities represented by letter *variables*. For example, a formula for distance traveled d at a rate r over a time t is $d = r * t$. The area A of a triangle with base length b and height h is given at right. See the Tables of Formulas and Section 17.2.1: Uses of Variables.

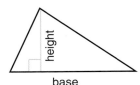

$$A = \frac{1}{2} * b * h$$

fraction (primary definition) A number in the form $\frac{a}{b}$ or a/b, where a and b are *whole numbers* and b is not 0. A fraction may be used to name part of an object or part of a collection of objects, to compare two quantities, or to represent division. For example, $\frac{12}{6}$ might mean 12 eggs divided into 6 groups of 2 eggs each, a ratio of 12 to 6, or 12 divided by 6. See Section 9.3: Fractions, Decimals, Percents, and Rational Numbers.

fraction (other definitions) (1) A fraction that satisfies the previous definition and includes a *unit* in both the *numerator* and *denominator*. For example, the *rates*

$$\frac{50 \text{ miles}}{1 \text{ gallon}} \quad \text{and} \quad \frac{40 \text{ pages}}{10 \text{ minutes}}$$

are fractions. (2) A number written using a fraction bar, where the fraction bar is used to indicate division. For example,

$$\frac{2.3}{6.5}, \quad \frac{1\frac{4}{5}}{12}, \quad \text{and} \quad \frac{\frac{3}{4}}{\frac{5}{8}}.$$

fraction stick In *Fifth* and *Sixth Grade Everyday Mathematics,* a diagram used to represent simple fractions. See Section 9.9.4: Fraction-Stick Charts and Fraction Sticks.

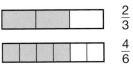

fractional part Part of a *whole. Fractions* represent fractional parts of numbers, sets, or objects. See Section 9.3.2: Uses of Fractions.

Frames and Arrows In *Everyday Mathematics,* diagrams consisting of frames connected by arrows used to represent number *sequences*. Each frame contains a number, and each arrow represents a rule that determines which number goes in the next frame. There may be more than one rule, represented by different-color arrows. Frames-and-Arrows diagrams are also called chains. See Section 17.1.2: Sequences.

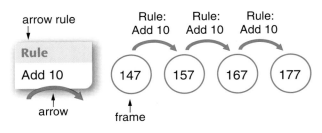

frequency (1) The number of times a value occurs in a set of data. See Section 12.2.3: Organizing and Displaying Data. (2) A number of repetitions per unit of time. For example, the vibrations per second in a sound wave.

frequency graph A graph showing how often each value occurs in a data set. See Section 12.2.3: Organizing and Displaying Data.

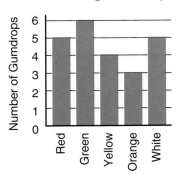

Colors in a Bag of Gumdrops

frequency table A table in which data are *tallied* and organized, often as a first step toward making a *frequency graph*. See Section 12.2.3: Organizing and Displaying Data.

Color	Number of Gumdrops
red	卌
green	卌 /
yellow	////
orange	///
white	卌

fulcrum (1) The point on a mobile at which a rod is suspended. (2) The point or place around which a lever pivots. (3) The center support of a *pan balance*.

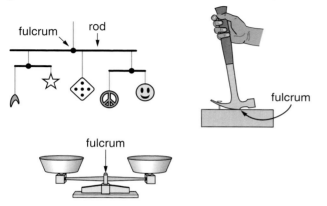

function A set of *ordered pairs* (x, y) in which each value of x is paired with exactly one value of y. A function is typically represented in a table, by points on a coordinate graph, or by a rule such as an *equation*. For example, for a function with the rule "Double," 1 is paired with 2, 2 is paired with 4, 3 is paired with 6, and so on. In symbols, $y = 2 * x$ or $y = 2x$. See Section 17.1.3: Functions.

function machine In *Everyday Mathematics,* an imaginary device that receives *inputs* and pairs them with *outputs*. For example, the function machine below pairs an input number with its double. See *function* and Section 17.1.3: Functions.

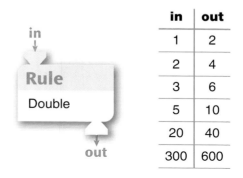

in	out
1	2
2	4
3	6
5	10
20	40
300	600

A function machine and function table

furlong A unit of *length* equal to 1 eighth of a mile. Furlongs are commonly used in horse racing.

G

gallon (gal) A U.S. customary unit of *volume* or *capacity* equal to 4 quarts. See the Tables of Measures and Section 14.5: Volume (Capacity).

general pattern In *Everyday Mathematics,* a number model for a *pattern* or *rule*.

generate a random number To produce a *random number* by such methods as drawing a card without looking from a shuffled deck, rolling a fair die, and flicking a fair spinner. In *Everyday Mathematics,* random numbers are commonly generated in games. See Section 12.4.1: Random-Number Generators.

genus In *topology,* the number of holes in a geometric shape. Shapes with the same genus are topologically equivalent. For example, a donut and a teacup are topologically equivalent because both are genus 1. See Section 13.11: Topology.

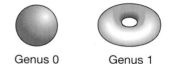

Genus 0   Genus 1

geoboard A manipulative *2-dimensional coordinate system* made with nails or other posts at equally-spaced intervals relative to both axes. Children loop rubber bands around the posts to make polygons and other shapes.

geometric solid The *surface* or surfaces that make up a *3-dimensional figure* such as a prism, pyramid, cylinder, cone, or sphere. Despite its name, a geometric solid is hollow; that is, it does not include the points in its interior. Informally, and in some dictionaries, a solid is defined as both the surface and its interior. See Section 13.5.1: "Solid" Figures.

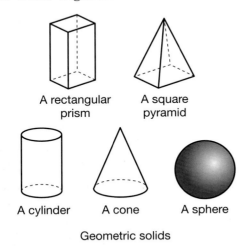

A rectangular prism

A square pyramid

A cylinder

A cone

A sphere

Geometric solids

Geometry Template A *Fourth* through *Sixth Grade Everyday Mathematics* tool that includes a millimeter ruler, a ruler with $\frac{1}{16}$-inch intervals, half-circle and full-circle *protractors,* a *percent circle,* pattern-block shapes, and other geometric figures. The template can also be used as a *compass (1)*. See Section 13.13.2: Pattern-Block and Geometry Templates.

girth The distance around a 3-dimensional object.

Golden Ratio The *ratio* of the length of the long side to the length of the short side of a *Golden Rectangle,* approximately equal to 1.618 to 1. The Greek letter ϕ (phi) sometimes stands for the Golden Ratio. The Golden Ratio is an *irrational number* equal to $\frac{1 + \sqrt{5}}{2}$.

See Section 9.3.3: Rates, Ratios, and Proportions.

Golden Rectangle A rectangle prized for its pleasing proportions in which the longer side is constructed with compass and straightedge from the shorter side. The ratio of these sides is the *Golden Ratio,* about 1.618 to 1. A 5-inch by 3-inch index card is roughly similar to a Golden Rectangle, as are the front faces of many ancient Greek buildings.

A Golden Rectangle

-gon A suffix meaning *angle.* For example, a *hexagon* is a plane figure with six angles.

gram (g) A metric unit of *mass* equal to $\frac{1}{1,000}$ of a kilogram. See the Tables of Measures and Section 14.6: Weight and Mass.

graph key An annotated list of the symbols used in a graph explaining how to read the graph. Compare to *map legend.*

greatest common factor (GCF) The largest *factor* that two or more *counting numbers* have in common. For example, the common factors of 24 and 36 are 1, 2, 3, 4, 6, and 12, and their greatest common factor is 12.

great span The distance from the tip of the thumb to the tip of the little finger (pinkie), when the hand is stretched as far as possible. The great span averages about 9 inches for adults. Same as *hand span.* Compare to *normal span* and see Section 14.1: Personal Measures.

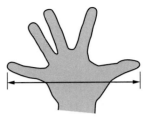

Great span

grouping symbols Parentheses ( ), brackets [ ], braces { }, and similar symbols that define the order in which operations in an *expression* are to be done. *Nested* grouping symbols are groupings within groupings, and the innermost grouping is done first. For example, in $(3 + 4) * [(8 + 2)/5]$, the group $(8 + 2)$ is nested within $[(8 + 2)/5]$ and is done first. So $(3 + 4) * [(8 + 2)/5]$ simplifies as follows:

$$(3 + 4) * [(8 + 2)/5]$$
$$(3 + 4) * [10/5]$$
$$7 * 2$$
$$14$$

See Section 10.2.1: Grouping Symbols.

hand span Same as *great span*.

height (1) A perpendicular segment from one *side* of a geometric figure to a parallel side or from a *vertex* to the *opposite side*. (2) The length of this segment. In *Everyday Mathematics*, same as *altitude*. See *height of a parallelogram, height of a rectangle, height of a prism or cylinder, height of a pyramid or cone, height of a triangle*, Section 13.4.2: Polygons (*n*-gons), Section 13.5.2: Polyhedrons, and Section 13.5.3: Solids with Curved Surfaces.

Heights/altitudes of 2-D figures are shown in blue.

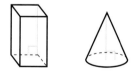

Heights/altitudes of 3-D figures are shown in blue.

height of a parallelogram (1) The *length* of the shortest line segment between a *base of a parallelogram* and the line containing the *opposite side*. The height is perpendicular to the base. (2) The line segment itself. See *altitude, base of a parallelogram*, and Section 13.4.2: Polygons (*n*-gons).

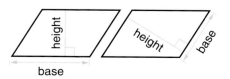

height of a prism or cylinder The *length* of the shortest line segment from a *base of a prism or cylinder* to the plane containing the opposite base. The height is perpendicular to the bases. (2) The line segment itself. See *altitude, base of a prism or cylinder*, Section 13.5.2: Polyhedrons, and Section 13.5.3: Solids with Curved Surfaces.

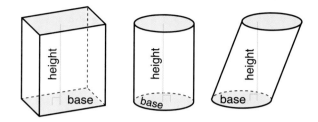

height of a pyramid or cone The *length* of the shortest line segment from the *apex* of a pyramid or cone to the plane containing the *base*. The height is perpendicular to the base. (2) The line segment itself. See *altitude, base of a pyramid or cone*, Section 13.5.2: Polyhedrons, and Section 13.5.3: Solids with Curved Surfaces.

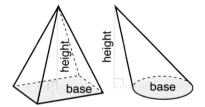

height of a rectangle The *length* of a side perpendicular to a *base of a rectangle*. Same as *altitude* of a rectangle. See Section 13.4.2: Polygons (*n*-gons).

height of a triangle The *length* of the shortest segment from a *vertex* of a triangle to the line containing the opposite *side*. The height is perpendicular to the base. (2) The line segment itself. See *altitude, base of a triangle*, and Section 13.4.2: Polygons (*n*-gons).

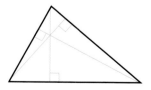

The heights of the triangle are shown in blue.

hemisphere (1) Half of Earth's surface. (2) Half of a *sphere*.

hepta- A prefix meaning seven.

heptagon A 7-sided *polygon*. See Section 13.4.2: Polygons (*n*-gons).

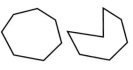

Heptagons

hexa- A prefix meaning six.

hexagon A 6-sided *polygon*. See Section 13.4.2: Polygons (*n*-gons).

A hexagon

horizon Where the earth and sky appear to meet, if nothing is in the way. The horizon looks like a line when you look out to sea.

horizontal In a left-to-right orientation. Parallel to the *horizon*.

hypotenuse In a *right triangle,* the *side* opposite the *right angle*. See Section 13.4.2: Polygons (*n*-gons).

icon A small picture or diagram sometimes used to represent quantities. For example, an icon of a stadium might be used to represent 100,000 people on a *pictograph*. Icons are also used to represent functions or objects in computer operating systems and applications.

icosahedron A *polyhedron* with 20 faces. An icosahedron with equilateral triangle faces is one of the five *regular polyhedrons*. See Section 13.5.2: Polyhedrons.

An irregular icosahedron

A regular icosahedron

image A figure that is produced by a *transformation* of another figure called the *preimage*. See Section 13.7: Transformations.

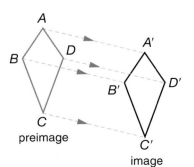

preimage

image

improper fraction A *fraction* with a *numerator* that is greater than or equal to its *denominator*. For example, $\frac{4}{3}, \frac{5}{2}, \frac{4}{4}$, and $\frac{24}{12}$ are improper fractions. In *Everyday Mathematics,* improper fractions are sometimes called "top-heavy" fractions.

inch (in.) A U.S. customary unit of *length* equal to $\frac{1}{12}$ of a foot and 2.54 centimeters. See the Tables of Measures and Section 14.3: Length.

independent variable (1) A *variable* whose value does not rely on the values of other variables. (2) The *variable* x in a *function* defined by the set of *ordered pairs* (x,y). Same as the *input* of the function. Compare to *dependent variable*. See Section 17.2.1: Uses of Variables.

index of locations A list of places together with a *reference frame* for locating them on a map. For example, "Billings, D3," means that Billings is in the rectangle to the right of D and above 3 on the map below. See Section 15.4.1: Map Coordinates.

Section of Map of Montana

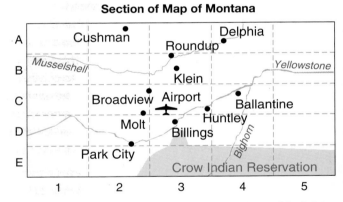

indirect measurement The determination of heights, distances, and other quantities that cannot be measured directly.

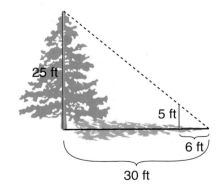

Indirect measurement lets you calculate the height of the tree from the other measures.

inequality A *number sentence* with a *relation symbol* other than =, such as >, <, ≥, ≤, ≠, or ≈. See Section 9.7: Numeric Relations.

input (1) A number inserted into an imaginary *function machine,* which applies a rule to pair the input with an *output.* (2) The values for *x* in a *function* consisting of ordered pairs (*x,y*). See Section 17.1.3: Functions. (3) Numbers or other information entered into a calculator or computer.

inscribed polygon A *polygon* whose vertices are all on the same *circle.*

An inscribed square

instance of a pattern Same as *special case.*

integer A number in the set {. . ., −4, −3, −2, −1, 0, 1, 2, 3, 4, . . .}. A *whole number* or its *opposite,* where 0 is its own opposite. Compare to *rational number, irrational number,* and *real number.* See Section 9.4: Positive and Negative Numbers.

interest A charge for using someone else's money. Interest is usually a percentage of the amount borrowed.

interior of a figure (1) The set of all points in a *plane* bounded by a closed *2-dimensional figure* such as a *polygon* or *circle.* (2) The set of all points in space bounded by a closed *3-dimensional figure* such as a *polyhedron* or *sphere.* The interior is usually not considered to be part of the figure. See Section 13.4: Planes and Plane Figures and Section 13.5: Space and 3-D Figures.

interpolate To *estimate* an unknown value of a function between known values. Graphs are useful tools for interpolation. See Section 17.1.3: Functions.

interquartile range (IQR) (1) The *length* of the *interval* between the *lower* and *upper quartiles* in a data set. (2) The *interval* itself. The middle half of the data is *in* the interquartile range. See Section 12.2.3: Organizing and Displaying Data.

intersect To share a common point or points.

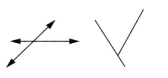

Intersecting lines and segments   Intersecting planes

interval (1) The set of all numbers between two numbers *a* and *b*, which may include one or both of *a* and *b*. (2) The points and their coordinates on a segment of a number line. The interval between 0 and 1 on a number line is the *unit interval.*

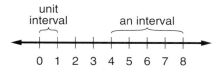

"in the black" Having a positive *account balance;* having more money than is owed.

"in the red" Having a negative *account balance;* owing more money than is available.

irrational numbers Numbers that cannot be written as *fractions* where both the *numerator* and *denominator* are *integers* and the denominator is not zero. For example, $\sqrt{2}$ and π are irrational numbers. An irrational number can be written as a nonterminating, nonrepeating decimal. For example, $\pi = 3.141592653$ . . . continues forever without any known pattern. The number 1.10100100010000 . . . is irrational because its pattern does not repeat. See Section 9.5: Irrational Numbers.

isometry transformation A *transformation* in which the *preimage* and *image* are *congruent. Reflections* (flips), *rotations* (turns), and *translations* (slides) are isometry transformations, while a *size change* (stretch or shrink) is not. Although the size and shape of the figures in an isometry transformation are the same, their orientations may be different. From the Greek *isometros* meaning "of equal measure." See Section 13.7.1: Reflections, Rotations, and Translations.

A reflection (flip)   A rotation (turn)   A translation (slide)

isosceles trapezoid A *trapezoid* whose nonparallel sides are the same length. Pairs of base angles have the same measure. See Section 13.4.2: Polygons (*n*-gons).

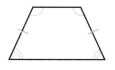

An isosceles trapezoid

isosceles triangle A *triangle* with at least two sides equal in length. Angles opposite the congruent sides are congruent to each other. See Section 13.4.2: Polygons (*n*-gons).

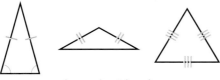
Isosceles triangles

J

juxtapose To represent multiplication in an *expression* by placing *factors* side by side without a multiplication symbol. At least one factor is a *variable*. For example, 5*n* means 5 * *n*, and *ab* means *a* * *b*. See Section 10.1.1: The Four Basic Arithmetic Operations.

K

key sequence The order in which calculator keys are pressed to perform a calculation. See Section 3.1.1: Calculators.

kilo- A prefix meaning 1 thousand.

kilogram A metric unit of *mass* equal to 1,000 grams. The international standard kilogram is a 39 mm diameter, 39 mm high *cylinder* of platinum and iridium kept in the International Bureau of Weights and Measures in Sèvres, France. A kilogram is about 2.2 pounds. See the Tables of Measures and Section 14.6: Weight and Mass.

kilometer A metric unit of *length* equal to 1,000 meters. A kilometer is about 0.62 mile. See the Tables of Measures and Section 14.3: Length.

kite A *quadrilateral* with two distinct pairs of adjacent sides of equal length. In *Everyday Mathematics,* the four sides cannot all have equal length; that is, a *rhombus* is not a kite. The diagonals of a kite are *perpendicular.* See Section 13.4.2: Polygons (*n*-gons).

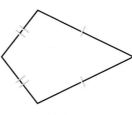
A kite

L

label (1) A descriptive word or phrase used to put a number or numbers in context. Labels encourage students to associate numbers with real objects. Flags, snowballs, and scary monsters are examples of labels. See Section 10.3: Use Classes and Situation Diagrams. (2) In a *spreadsheet* or graph, words or numbers providing information such as the title of the spreadsheet, the heading for a row or column, or the variable on an axis.

landmark In *Everyday Mathematics,* a notable feature of a *data* set. Landmarks include the *median, mode, mean, maximum, minimum,* and *range.* See Section 12.2.4: Data Analysis.

latitude A *degree* measure locating a place on Earth north or south of the *equator.* A location at 0° latitude is on the equator. The North Pole is at 90° north latitude, and the South Pole is at 90° south latitude. Compare to *longitude.* See *lines of latitude* and Section 15.4.4: The Global Grid System.

lattice multiplication A very old *algorithm* for multiplying multidigit numbers that requires only basic multiplication facts and addition of 1-digit numbers in a lattice diagram. See Section 11.2.3: Multiplication Algorithms.

least common denominator (LCD) The *least common multiple* of the denominators of every fraction in a given collection. For example, the least common denominator of $\frac{1}{2}$, $\frac{4}{5}$, and $\frac{3}{8}$ is 40. See Section 11.3: Algorithms for Fractions.

least common multiple (LCM) The smallest number that is a *multiple* of two or more given numbers. For example, common multiples of 6 and 8 include 24, 48, and 72. The least common multiple of 6 and 8 is 24. See Section 11.3: Algorithms for Fractions.

left-to-right subtraction A subtraction *algorithm* that works from the left decimal place to the right in several steps. For example, to solve 94 − 57, first calculate 94 − 50 to obtain 44 and then calculate 44 − 7 to obtain 37. The method is especially suited to mental arithmetic. See Section 11.2.2: Subtraction Algorithms.

leg of a right triangle Either *side* of the *right angle* in a *right triangle*; a side that is not the *hypotenuse*. See Section 13.4.2: Polygons (*n*-gons).

length The distance between two points on a *1-dimensional figure*. For example, the figure might be a line segment, an arc, or a curve on a map modeling a hiking path. Length is measured in units such as inches, kilometers, and miles. See Section 14.3: Length.

length of a factor string The number of factors in a *factor string*.

length of a rectangle Typically, but not necessarily, the longer dimension of a *rectangle*.

letter-number pair An *ordered pair* in which one of the coordinates is a letter. Often used to locate places on maps. See Section 15.4.1: Map Coordinates.

like fractions *Fractions* with equal *denominators*.

like terms In an *algebraic expression,* either the *constant terms* or any terms that contain the same variable(s) raised to the same power(s). For example, $4y$ and $7y$ are like terms in the expression $4y + 7y - z$. See *combine like terms* and Section 17.2.3: Simplifying Expressions.

line In *Everyday Mathematics*, a 1-dimensional straight path that extends forever in opposite directions. A line is named using two points on it or with a single, italicized lower-case letter such as *l*. In formal Euclidean geometry, line is an undefined geometric term. See Section 13.3: Lines, Segments, and Rays.

Line *PR* or $\overleftrightarrow{PR}$

line graph A graph in which *data* points are connected by *line segments*. Same as *broken-line graph*. See Section 12.2.3: Organizing and Displaying Data.

line of reflection (mirror line) (1) In *Everyday Mathematics,* a line halfway between a figure and its *reflection* image in a plane. (2) The *perpendicular bisector* of the line segments connecting points on a figure with their corresponding points on its reflection image. Compare to *line of symmetry*. See Section 13.7.1: Reflections, Rotations, and Translations.

line of symmetry A line that divides a figure into two parts that are *reflection* images of each other. A figure may have zero, one, or more lines of symmetry. For example, the numeral 2 has no lines of symmetry, a square has four lines of symmetry, and a circle has infinitely many lines of symmetry. Also called a symmetry line. See Section 13.8.1: Line Symmetry.

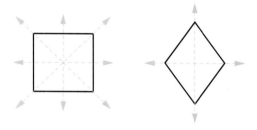

Lines of symmetry are shown in blue.

line plot A sketch of data in which check marks, Xs, or other symbols above a labeled line show the frequency of each value. See Section 12.2.3: Organizing and Displaying Data.

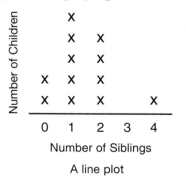

A line plot

line segment A part of a *line* between and including two points called *endpoints* of the segment. Same as *segment*. A line segment is often named by its endpoints. See Section 13.3: Lines, Segments, and Rays.

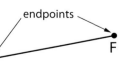

Segment *EF* or $\overline{EF}$

line symmetry A figure has line symmetry if a line can be drawn that divides it into two parts that are *reflection* images of each other. See *line of symmetry* and Section 13.7.1: Reflections, Rotations, and Translations.

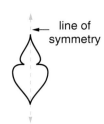

line of symmetry

lines of latitude Lines of constant *latitude* drawn on a 2-dimensional map or circles of constant latitude drawn on a globe. Lines of latitude are also called parallels because they are parallel to the equator and to each other. On a globe, latitude lines (circles) are intersections of planes parallel to the plane through the equator. Compare to *lines of longitude*. See Section 15.4.4: The Global Grid System.

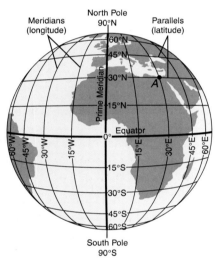

Point *A* is located at 30°N, 30°E.

lines of longitude Lines of constant *longitude* drawn on a 2-dimensional map or semicircles of constant longitude drawn on a globe connecting the North and South Poles. Lines of longitude are also called meridians. Compare to *lines of latitude*. See Section 15.4.4: The Global Grid System.

liter (L) A metric unit of *volume* or *capacity* equal to the volume of a cube with 10-cm-long edges. 1 L = 1,000 mL = 1,000 cm³. A liter is a little larger than a quart. See the Tables of Measures and Section 14.5: Volume (Capacity).

long In *Everyday Mathematics*, the *base-10 block* consisting of ten 1-cm cubes. Sometimes called a rod. See Section 9.9.1: Base-10 Blocks.

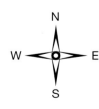

A long

long-term memory *Memory in a calculator* used by keys with an M on them, such as [M-] and [M+]. Numbers in long-term memory are not affected by calculations with keys without an M, which use *short-term memory*. See Section 3.1.1: Calculators.

longitude A degree measure locating a place on Earth east or west of the *prime meridian*. A location at 0° longitude is on the prime meridian. A location at 180° east or west longitude is on or near the international date line, which is based on the imaginary semicircle opposite the prime meridian. Compare to *latitude*. See *lines of longitude* and Section 15.4.4: The Global Grid System.

lower quartile In *Everyday Mathematics*, in an ordered data set, the middle value of the *data* below the *median*. Data values at the median are not included when finding the lower quartile. Compare to *upper quartile*. See Section 12.2.3: Organizing and Displaying Data.

lowest terms of a fraction Same as *simplest form of a fraction*.

M

magnitude estimate A rough *estimate* of whether a number is in the tens, hundreds, thousands, or other powers of 10. For example, the U.S. national debt per person is in the tens of thousands of dollars. In *Everyday Mathematics,* students give magnitude estimates for problems such as *How many dimes are in $200?* or *How many halves are in 30?* Same as *order-of-magnitude estimate*. See Section 16.1.3: Estimates in Calculations.

map direction symbol A symbol on a map that identifies north, south, east, and west. Sometimes only north is indicated. See Section 15.4: Maps.

map legend (map key) A diagram that explains the symbols, markings, and colors on a map.

map scale The *ratio* of a distance on a map, globe, or drawing to an actual distance. For example, 1 inch on a map might correspond to 1 real-world mile. A map scale may be shown on a segment of a number line, given as a ratio of distances such as $\frac{1}{63,360}$ or 1:63,360 when an inch represents a mile, or by an informal use of the = symbol such as 1 inch = 1 mile. See Section 15.4.2: Map and Model Scales.

0   1 mile
1 inch : 1 mile

mass A measure of the amount of matter in an object. Mass is not affected by gravity, so it is the same on Earth, the moon, or anywhere else in space. Mass is usually measured in grams, kilograms, and other metric units. Compare to *weight*. See Section 14.6: Weight and Mass.

Math Boxes In *Everyday Mathematics,* a collection of problems to practice skills. Math Boxes for each lesson are in the *Math Journal.* See Section 1.2.3: Math Boxes.

Math Journal In *Everyday Mathematics,* a place for students to record their mathematical discoveries and experiences. Journal pages give models for conceptual understanding, problems to solve, and directions for individual and small-group activities.

Math Master In *Everyday Mathematics,* a page ready for duplicating. Most masters support students in carrying out suggested activities. Some masters are used more than once during the school year.

Math Message In *Everyday Mathematics,* an introductory activity to the day's lesson that students complete before the lesson starts. Messages may include problems to solve, directions to follow, sentences to complete or correct, review exercises, or reading assignments. See Section 1.2.4: Math Messages.

maximum The largest amount; the greatest number in a set of data. Compare to *minimum.* See Section 12.2.4: Data Analysis.

mean For a set of numbers, their sum divided by the number of numbers. Often called the *average* value of the set. Compare to other data *landmarks median* and *mode.* See Section 12.2.4: Data Analysis.

mean absolute deviation (m.a.d.) In a data set, the *average* distance between individual *data* values and the *mean* of those values. See Section 12.2.3: Organizing and Displaying Data.

measurement division A term for the type of division used to solve an *equal-grouping story* such as *How many tables seating 4 people each are needed for 52 people?* Same as *quotitive division.* Compare to *partitive division.* See Section 10.3.2: Multiplication and Division Use Classes.

measurement unit The reference unit used when measuring. Examples of basic units include inches for *length,* grams for *mass* or *weight,* cubic inches for *volume* or *capacity,* seconds for elapsed time, and degrees Celsius for change of *temperature.* Compound units include square centimeters for area and miles per hour for speed. See Section 14.2: Measurement Systems.

median The *middle value* in a set of data when the data are listed in order from smallest to largest or vice versa. If there is an even number of data points, the median is the *mean* of the two middle values. Compare to other data *landmarks mean* and *mode.* See Section 12.2.4: Data Analysis.

memory in a calculator Where numbers are stored in a calculator for use in later calculations. Most calculators have both a *short-term memory* and a *long-term memory.* See Section 3.1.1: Calculators.

mental arithmetic Computation done by people "in their heads," either in whole or in part. In *Everyday Mathematics,* students learn a variety of mental-calculation strategies to develop automatic recall of basic facts and *fact power.* See Section 16.3: Mental Arithmetic.

Mental Math and Reflexes In *Everyday Mathematics,* exercises at three levels of difficulty at the beginning of lessons for students to get ready to think about math, warm-up skills they need for the lesson, continually build mental-arithmetic skills, and help you assess individual strengths and weaknesses. See Section 1.2.5: Mental Math and Reflexes.

meridian bar A device on a globe that shows degrees of *latitude* north and south of the equator. It's called a meridian bar because it is in the same orientation as *meridians.*

meridians Same as *lines of longitude*.

meter (m) The basic metric unit of *length* from which other metric units of length are derived. Originally, the meter was defined as $\frac{1}{10,000,000}$ of the distance from the North Pole to the equator along a meridian passing through Paris. From 1960 to 1983, the meter was redefined as 1,630,763.73 wavelengths of orange-red light from the element krypton. Today, the meter is defined as the distance light travels in a vacuum in $\frac{1}{299,792,458}$ second. One meter is equal to 10 decimeters, 100 centimeters, or 1,000 millimeters. See Section 14.3: Length.

metric system A measurement system based on the *base-ten* (decimal) numeration system and used in most countries and by virtually all scientists around the world. Units for *length* include millimeter, centimeter, meter, and kilometer; units for *mass* and *weight* include gram and kilogram; units for *volume* and *capacity* include milliliter and liter; and the unit for *temperature* change is degrees Celsius. See the Tables of Measures and Section 14.2.2: Metric System.

middle value Same as *median*.

midpoint A point halfway between two other points. The midpoint of a line segment is the point halfway between the endpoints.

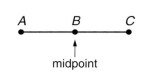

Length of $\overline{AB}$ = length of $\overline{BC}$

mile (mi) A U.S. customary unit of *length* equal to 5,280 feet, or 1,760 yards. A mile is about 1,609 meters.

milli- A prefix meaning 1 thousandth.

milliliter (mL) A metric unit of *volume* or *capacity* equal to $\frac{1}{1,000}$ of a liter, or 1 cubic centimeter. See Section 14.5: Volume (Capacity).

millimeter (mm) A metric unit of *length* equal to $\frac{1}{10}$ of a centimeter, or $\frac{1}{1,000}$ of a meter. See Section 14.3: Length.

millisecond (ms or msec) A unit of time equal to $\frac{1}{1,000}$ of a second.

minimum The smallest amount; the smallest number in a set of data. Compare to *maximum*. See Section 12.2.4: Data Analysis.

minuend In subtraction, the number from which another number is subtracted. For example, in $19 - 5 = 14$, the minuend is 19. Compare to *subtrahend*.

mirror image Same as *reflection* image.

mixed number A number that is written using both a *whole number* and a *fraction*. For example, $2\frac{1}{4}$ is a mixed number equal to $2 + \frac{1}{4}$.

Möbius strip (Möbius band) A *3-dimensional figure* with only one side and one edge, named for the German mathematician August Ferdinand Möbius (1790–1868).

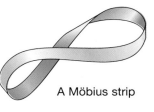

A Möbius strip

modal Of or relating to the *mode*.

mode The value or values that occur most often in a set of data. Compare to other *landmarks median* and *mean*. See Section 12.2.4: Data Analysis.

modified repeated addition A multiplication *algorithm* based on adding a to itself b times to find $a * b$. One of the factors is separated into parts and the partial products of the other factor and those parts are then added. For example, to compute $67 * 53$, think of 10 [67s] as 670 and add five of them to get $50 * 67$. Then add the remaining 3 [67s] to the result. See Section 11.2.3: Multiplication Algorithms.

modified U.S. traditional multiplication A multiplication *algorithm* in which the traditional algorithm is enhanced by introducing 0s into the blanks to maintain the logic of the process and to help avoid sloppy alignment of partial products. See Section 11.2.3: Multiplication Algorithms.

multiple of a number n (1) A product of n and a *counting number*. For example, the multiples of 7 are 7, 14, 21, 28, ... (2) A product of n and an *integer*. For example, the multiples of 7 are . . ., $-21, -14, -7, 0, 7, 14, 21, ...$

multiples of equal groups A *multiple* of a rate in an *equal-grouping* situation. For example, *How many balloons are there altogether in 6 packages with 20 balloons per package?* is a multiples-of-equal-groups problem. See Section 10.3.2: Multiplication and Division Use Classes.

multiplication counting principle A way of determining the total number of possible *outcomes* for two or more separate choices. For example, suppose you roll a typical die and then flip a coin. There are 6 choices for which number on the die lands up (1, 2, 3, 4, 5, or 6) and 2 choices for which side of the coin lands up (HEADS H or TAILS T). So there are $6 * 2 = 12$ possible outcomes all together: $(1,H), (1,T), (2,H), (2,T), (3,H),$ $(3,T), (4,H), (4,T), (5,H) (5,T), (6,H), (6,T).$

multiplication/division diagram A diagram used in *Everyday Mathematics* to model situations in which a total number is made up of equal-size groups. The diagram contains a number of groups, a number in each group, and a total number. Also called a multiplication diagram for short. See *situation diagram* and Section 10.3.2: Multiplication and Division Use Classes.

rows	chairs per row	total chairs
15	25	?

A multiplication/division diagram

multiplication/division use class In *Everyday Mathematics,* a situation in which multiplication or division is used. These include *equal grouping/sharing, arrays and area, rates and ratio, scaling,* and *Cartesian product* situations. See Section 10.3.2: Multiplication and Division Use Classes.

multiplication fact The product of two 1-digit numbers, such as $6 * 7 = 42$. See *arithmetic facts* and Section 16.3.2: Basic Facts and Fact Power.

Multiplication Property of −1 A property of multiplication that says multiplying any number by −1 gives the opposite of a number. For example, $-1 * 5 = -5$ and $-1 * -3 = -(-3) = 3$. In symbols:

For any number a, $-1 * a = -a$.

Some calculators apply this property with a $\boxed{+/-}$ key that *toggles* between a positive and negative value in the display.

multiplication symbols The number a multiplied by the number b is written in a variety of ways. Many mathematics textbooks and *Second* and *Third Grade Everyday Mathematics* use × as in $a \times b$. Beginning in fourth grade, *Everyday Mathematics* uses * as in $a * b$. Other common symbols are a dot as in $a \bullet b$ and by *juxtaposition* as in $ab,$ which is common in formulas and in algebra courses. See Section 10.1.1: The Four Basic Arithmetic Operations.

multiplicative inverses Same as *reciprocals*.

N

name-collection box In *Everyday Mathematics,* a diagram that is used for collecting *equivalent names* for a number. See Section 9.9.3: Name-Collection Boxes.

name of a tessellation A numerical description of a *tessellation* listing the number of sides of the polygons that meet at each *vertex point,* in order from the smallest. See Section 13.10.1: Classifying Tessellations.

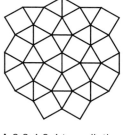

A 4.4.4.4 tessellation   A 3.3.4.3.4 tessellation

natural numbers In *Everyday Mathematics,* same as *counting numbers.*

negative numbers Numbers less than 0; the opposites of the *positive numbers,* commonly written as a positive number preceded by a −. Negative numbers are plotted left of 0 on a horizontal number line or below 0 on a vertical number line. See Section 9.4: Positive and Negative Numbers.

negative power of 10 A number that can be written in the form 10^{-a}, which is shorthand for $\frac{1}{10^a}$ where a is a counting number. For example, $10^{-2} = \frac{1}{10^2}$. Negative powers of 10 can be written as fractions or in standard decimal notation: $10^{-2} = \frac{1}{10^2} = \frac{1}{100} = 0.01$. Compare to *positive power of 10*. See Section 10.1.2: Powers and Exponents.

negative rational numbers *Rational numbers* less than 0; the opposites of the *positive rational numbers*. For example, -24, $-2.333\ldots$, and $-\frac{5}{8}$ are negative rational numbers. See Section 9.4: Positive and Negative Numbers.

nested parentheses Parentheses within parentheses in an *expression*. Expressions are evaluated from within the innermost parentheses outward. See *grouping symbols* for an example and Section 10.2.1: Grouping Symbols.

net score The final score of a turn or game after all calculations have been completed.

net weight The *weight* of the contents of a container, excluding the weight of the container.

n-gon Same as *polygon,* where n is the number of sides. Polygons that do not have special names like squares and pentagons are usually named using n-gon notation, such as 13-gon or 100-gon.

nona- A prefix meaning nine.

nonagon A 9-sided *polygon*.

nonconvex polygon Same as *concave polygon*.

normal span The distance from the end of the thumb to the end of the index (first) finger of an outstretched hand. For estimating lengths, many people can adjust this distance to approximately 6 inches or 15 centimeters. Same as *span*. Compare to *great span*. See Section 14.1: Personal Measures.

n-to-1 ratio A ratio of a number to 1. Every ratio $a{:}b$ can be converted to an n-to-1 ratio by dividing a by b. For example, a ratio of 3 to 2 is a ratio of $3/2 = 1.5$ or a 1.5-to-1 ratio.

number-and-word notation A notation consisting of the *significant digits* of a number and words for the place value. For example, 27 billion is number-and-word notation for 27,000,000,000.

number family Same as *fact family*.

number grid In *Everyday Mathematics,* a table in which *consecutive* numbers are arranged in *rows,* usually 10 *columns* per row. A move from one number to the next within a *row* is a change of 1; a move from one number to the next within a *column* is a change of 10. See Section 9.9.2: Number Grids, Scrolls, and Lines.

−9	−8	−7	−6	−5	−4	−3	−2	−1	0
1	2	3	4	5	6	7	8	9	10
11	12	13	14	15	16	17	18	19	20
21	22	23	24	25	26	27	28	29	30
31	32	33	34	35	36	37	38	39	40
41	42	43	44	45	46	47	48	49	50
51	52	53	54	55	56	57	58	59	60
61	62	63	64	65	66	67	68	69	70
71	72	73	74	75	76	77	78	79	80
81	82	83	84	85	86	87	88	89	90
91	92	93	94	95	96	97	98	99	100
101	102	103	104	105	106	107	108	109	110

A number grid

number-grid puzzle In *Everyday Mathematics,* a piece of a *number grid* in which some, but not all, of the numbers are missing. Students use number-grid puzzles to practice place-value concepts.

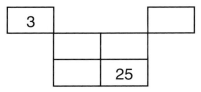

A number-grid puzzle

number line A line on which points are indicated by *tick marks* that are usually at regularly spaced intervals from a starting point called the *origin*, the *zero point*, or simply 0. Numbers are associated with the tick marks on a *scale* defined by the *unit interval* from 0 to 1. Every *real number* locates a point on the line, and every point corresponds to a real number. See Section 9.9.2: Number Grids, Scrolls, and Lines.

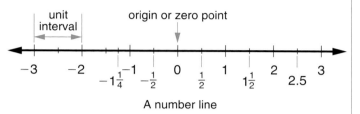

A number line

number model *A number sentence, expression,* or other representation that models a *number story* or situation. For example, the story *Sally had $5, and then she earned $8* can be modeled as the number sentence $5 + 8 = 13$, as the expression $5 + 8$, or by

$$\begin{array}{r} 5 \\ + \ 8 \\ \hline 13 \end{array}$$

See Section 10.2: Reading and Writing Number Sentences and Section 18.3: Mathematical Modeling.

number scroll In *Everyday Mathematics,* a series of *number grids* taped together. See Section 9.9.2: Number Grids, Scrolls, and Lines.

A number scroll

number sentence Two *expressions* with a *relation symbol*.

$$5 + 5 = 10 \qquad 16 \leq a * b$$
$$2 - \ ? = 8 \qquad a^2 + b^2 = c^2$$

Number sentences

number sequence A list of numbers, often generated by a rule. In *Everyday Mathematics*, students explore number sequences using *Frames-and-Arrows* diagrams. See Section 17.1.2: Sequences.

$$1, 2, 3, 4, 5, \dots \qquad 1, 4, 9, 16, 25, \dots$$
$$1, 2, 1, 2, 1, \dots \qquad 1, 3, 5, 7, 9, \dots$$

Number sequences

number story A story that involves numbers and one or more explicit or implicit questions. For example, *I have 7 crayons in my desk. Carrie gave me 8 more crayons. Now I have 15 crayons in all* is a number story. See Section 18.4.1: Number Stories.

numeral A word, symbol, or figure that represents a number. For example, six, VI, ⫴⃒, and 6 are all numerals that represent the same number.

numeration A method of numbering or of reading and writing numbers. In *Everyday Mathematics,* numeration activities include counting, writing numbers, identifying equivalent names for numbers in *name-collection boxes,* exchanging coins such as 5 pennies for 1 nickel, and renaming numbers in computation.

numerator The dividend a in a fraction $\frac{a}{b}$ or a/b. In a part-whole *fraction,* in which the *whole* (the ONE or *unit whole*) is divided into a number of equal parts, the numerator is the number of equal parts being considered. Compare to *denominator*. See Section 9.3.1: Fraction and Decimal Notation.

O

obtuse angle An *angle* with measure between 90° and 180°. See Section 13.4.1: Angles and Rotations.

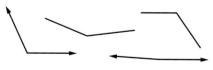

Obtuse angles

obtuse triangle A *triangle* with an angle measuring more than 90°. See Section 13.4.2: Polygons (*n*-gons).

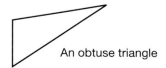

An obtuse triangle

Glossary

octa- A prefix meaning eight.

octagon An 8-sided *polygon*. See Section 13.4.2: Polygons (*n*-gons).

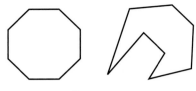
Octagons

octahedron A *polyhedron* with 8 faces. An octahedron with 8 *equilateral triangle* faces is one of the five *regular polyhedrons*. See Section 13.5.2: Polyhedrons.

odd number A *counting number* that is not *divisible by* 2. Compare to *even number*. See Section 17.1.1: Number Patterns.

ONE In *Everyday Mathematics,* same as *whole* or *unit whole.*

1-dimensional (1-D) coordinate system A *reference frame* in which any point on a *1-dimensional figure* can be located with one *coordinate* relative to the origin of a number line. Compare to *2-dimensional* and *3-dimensional coordinate systems*. See Section 15.3.1: 1-Dimensional Coordinate Systems.

1-dimensional (1-D) figure A figure such as a *line segment, arc,* or part of a curve that has length but no width or depth. Compare to *2-* and *3-dimensional figures*. See Section 13.1: Dimension.

open proportion A *proportion* with one or more *variables*. An open proportion is an *open sentence* and is neither true nor false. For example, $\frac{2}{3} = \frac{a}{5}$ and $\frac{z}{15} = \frac{y}{3}$ are open proportions. See Section 17.2.4: Solving Open Sentences.

open sentence A *number sentence* with one or more *variables*. An open sentence is neither true nor false. For example, $9 + \underline{} = 15$, $? - 24 < 10$, and $7 = x + y$ are open sentences. See Section 17.2.2: Reading and Writing Open Sentences.

operation A rule performed on one or more mathematical objects such as numbers, *variables,* or *expressions* to produce another mathematical object. Addition, subtraction, multiplication, and division are the four basic arithmetic operations. Taking a square root, squaring a number, and multiplying both sides of an *equation* by the same number are also operations. In *Everyday Mathematics,* students learn about many operations along with several procedures, or *algorithms,* for carrying them out. See Chapter 10: Arithmetic Operations.

operation symbol A symbol used in *expressions* and *number sentences* to stand for a particular mathematical operation. Symbols for common arithmetic operations are:

addition	$+$
subtraction	$-$
multiplication	$\times, *, \bullet$
division	$\div, /$
powering	$\wedge$

See Section 10.1: Arithmetic Symbols.

OPP(*n*) In *Everyday Mathematics,* same as *opposite of a number* n.

opposite angle in a triangle The *angle* opposite a *side* of a *triangle* that is not one of the sides of the angle.

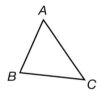
Angle *C* is opposite side *AB*.

opposite angles Same as *vertical angles*.

opposite angles in a quadrilateral Two *angles* in a *quadrilateral* that do not share a side.

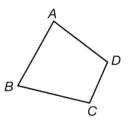
Angles *A* and *C*; angles *B* and *D* are pairs of opposite angles.

opposite-change rule for addition An addition *algorithm* in which a number is added to one *addend* and subtracted from the other addend. Compare to *same-change rule for subtraction*. See Section 11.2.1: Addition Algorithms.

opposite of a number *n* A number that is the same distance from 0 on a number line as *n*, but on the opposite side of zero. In symbols, the opposite of a number *n* is −*n*, and, in *Everyday Mathematics*, OPP(*n*). If *n* is a negative number, −*n* is a positive number. For example, the opposite of −5 is 5. The sum of a number *n* and its opposite is zero; $n + -n = 0$. Same as *additive inverse*. See Section 9.4: Positive and Negative Numbers.

opposite side in a triangle The *side* opposite an *angle* of a *triangle* that is not a side of the angle.

opposite sides in a quadrilateral Two *sides* in a *quadrilateral* that do not share a *vertex*.

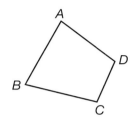

Sides *AB* and *DC*; sides *BC* and *AD* are pairs of opposite sides.

order-of-magnitude estimate Same as *magnitude estimate*.

order-of-magnitude increase A 10-times change in a value. Sometimes simply called a magnitude increase. See Section 10.1.2: Powers and Exponents and Section 16.1.2: Extreme Numbers.

order of operations Rules that tell the order in which operations in an *expression* should be carried out. The conventional order of operations is:

1. Do operations inside *grouping symbols*. Work from the innermost set of grouping symbols outward. Inside grouping symbols, follow Rules 2–4.
2. Calculate all expressions with *exponents*.
3. *Multiply* and *divide* in order from left to right.
4. *Add* and *subtract* in order from left to right.

For example:

$$5^2 + (3 * 4 - 2)/5 = 5^2 + (12 - 2)/5$$
$$= 5^2 + 10/5$$
$$= 25 + 10/5$$
$$= 25 + 2$$
$$= 27$$

Same as *algebraic order of operations*. See Section 10.2.3: The Order of Operations.

order of rotation symmetry The number of times a *rotation* image of a figure coincides with the figure before completing a 360° rotation. See Section 13.8.2: Rotation and Point Symmetries.

A figure with order 5 rotation symmetry

ordered pair (1) Two numbers, or *coordinates,* used to locate a point on a *rectangular coordinate grid.* The first coordinate *x* gives the position along the horizontal axis of the grid, and the second coordinate *y* gives the position along the vertical axis. The pair is written (*x,y*). See Section 15.3.2: 2- and 3-Dimensional Coordinate Systems. (2) Any pair of objects or numbers in a particular order, as in letter-number *spreadsheet cell* names or map coordinates. See Section 15.4.1: Map Coordinates.

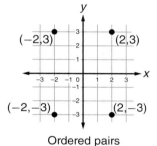

Ordered pairs

orders of magnitude Positive powers of 10 including 10, 100, 1,000, and so on. See *order-of-magnitude increase,* Section 10.1.2: Powers and Exponents and Section 16.1.2: Extreme Numbers.

ordinal number The position or order of something in a *sequence,* such as first, third, or tenth. Ordinal numbers are commonly used in dates, as in "May fifth" instead of "May five." See Section 9.2.2: Ordinal Numbers.

origin The *zero point* in a *coordinate system*. On a number line, the origin is the point at 0. On a coordinate grid, the origin is the point (0,0) where the two axes intersect. See Section 15.3: Coordinate Systems.

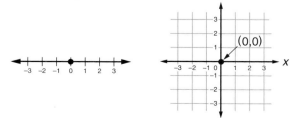

The points at 0 and (0,0) are origins.

ounce (oz) A U.S. customary unit of *weight* equal to $\frac{1}{16}$ of a pound or about 28.35 grams. Compare to *fluid ounce.* See the Tables of Measures and Section 14.6: Weight and Mass.

outcome A possible result of a chance experiment or situation. For example, HEADS and TAILS are the two possible outcomes of flipping a coin. See *event, equally likely outcomes,* and Section 12.1.2: The Language of Chance.

outlier A value far from most of the others in a data set. Commonly, outliers are much larger or smaller than other values. See Section 12.2.4: Data Analysis.

output (1) A number paired to an *input* by an imaginary *function machine* applying a rule. (2) The values for *y* in a *function* consisting of ordered pairs (*x,y*). See Section 17.1.3: Functions. (3) Numbers or other information displayed by calculator or computer.

P

pan balance A device used to weigh objects or compare their *weights.* See Section 14.11.4: Scales and Balances.

pan-balance problems In *Fifth* and *Sixth Grade Everyday Mathematics,* problems in which pan balances represent linear equations. One weight (real or symbolic) represents the variable, and another weight represents a single unit. Exchanges that keep the pans balanced correspond to mathematical operations on both sides of an equation until, eventually, a single variable weight balances with a number of units representing the solution. See Section 17.2.4: Solving Open Sentences.

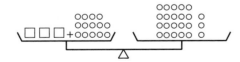

A pan-balance problem

parabola (1) The curve formed by the *intersection* of a right circular *cone* and a *plane* parallel to the lateral edge of the cone. (2) In a plane, the set of points that are the same distance from a line and a point not on the line.

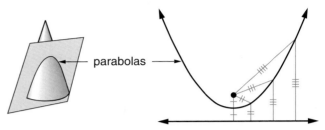

parabolas

parallel lines *Lines* in a *plane* that never meet. Two parallel lines are always the same distance apart. *Line segments* or *rays* on parallel lines are parallel to each other. See Section 13.6.1: Perpendicular and Parallel.

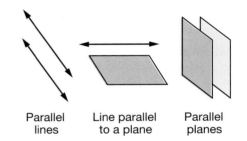

Parallel lines   Line parallel to a plane   Parallel planes

parallel planes *Planes* in space that never meet. Two parallel planes are always the same distance apart. A figure in one plane is parallel to the other plane. Polygons in one plane are said to be parallel to polygons in the other plane. However, 1-dimensional shapes such as lines, segments, and rays in one plane are not necessarily parallel to 1-dimensional shapes in a parallel plane. See *skew lines* and Section 13.6.1: Perpendicular and Parallel.

parallelogram A *quadrilateral* with two pairs of parallel sides. *Opposite sides* of a parallelogram have the same length and *opposite angles* have the same measure. All rectangles are parallelograms, but not all parallelograms are rectangles because parallelograms do not necessarily have right angles. See Section 13.4.2: Polygons (*n*-gons).

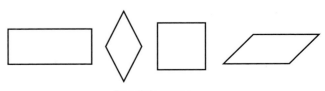

Parallelograms

parallels Same as *lines of latitude.*

parentheses See *grouping symbols.*

partial-differences subtraction A subtraction *algorithm* in which separate differences are computed for each place value of the numbers and then added to get a final difference. See Section 11.2.2: Subtraction Algorithms.

partial-products multiplication A multiplication *algorithm* in which partial products are computed by multiplying the value of each digit in one factor by the value of each digit in the other factor. The final product is the sum of the partial products. See Section 11.2.3: Multiplication Algorithms.

partial-quotients division A division *algorithm* in which a partial quotient is computed in each of several steps. The final quotient is the sum of the partial quotients. See Section 11.2.4: Division Algorithms.

partial-sums addition An addition *algorithm* in which separate sums are computed for each place value of the numbers and then added to get a final sum. See Section 11.2.1: Addition Algorithms.

partitive division A term for the type of division used to solve an *equal-sharing story* such as *If $10 is shared by 4 people, how much does each person get?* Compare to *measurement division.* See Section 10.3.2: Multiplication and Division Use Classes.

parts-and-total diagram In *Everyday Mathematics,* a diagram used to model problems in which two or more quantities (parts) are combined to get a total quantity. See *situation diagram* and Section 10.3.1: Addition and Subtraction Use Classes.

	13	
8	:	?

Total	
13	
Part :	Part
8 :	?

Parts-and-total diagrams for 13 = 8 + ?

parts-and-total story A *number story* in which a whole is made up of distinct parts. For example, *There are 15 girls and 12 boys in Mrs. Dorn's class. How many students are there in all?* is a parts-and-total story. In other stories, the total and one or more parts may be known and the last part unknown. See Section 10.3.1: Addition and Subtraction Use Classes.

part-to-part ratio A *ratio* that compares a part of a whole to another part of the same whole. For example, *There are 8 boys for every 12 girls* is a part-to-part ratio with a whole of 20 students. Compare to *part-to-whole ratio.* See Section 10.3.2: Multiplication and Division Use Classes.

part-to-whole ratio A *ratio* that compares a part of a whole to the whole. For example, *8 out of 20 students are boys* and *12 out of 20 students are girls* are part-to-whole ratios. Compare to *part-to-part ratio.* See Section 10.3.2: Multiplication and Division Use Classes.

part-whole fraction A *fraction* that describes dividing an object or collection into equal parts. In *Everyday Mathematics,* the object or collection is called the *whole,* or the *ONE,* and is the *denominator* of the fraction. The *numerator* is the number of parts of the whole. For example, in the situation *Padma ate $\frac{3}{5}$ of the pizza,* the ONE is 5 pieces of pizza (a whole pizza divided into 5 parts) and Padma ate 3 of the 5 parts. See Section 9.3.2: Uses of Fractions.

pattern A repetitive order or arrangement. In *Everyday Mathematics,* students mainly explore visual and number patterns in which elements are arranged so that what comes next can be predicted. Compare to *general pattern.* See Section 17.1: Patterns, Sequences, and Functions.

penta- A prefix meaning five.

pentagon A 5-sided *polygon.* See Section 13.4.2: Polygons (*n*-gons).

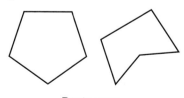

Pentagons

per For each, as in *ten chairs per row* or *six tickets per family.*

per capita For each person. Often used to describe an *average* of a data set, as in *The per-capita debt for U.S. citizens in July 2005 was $26,451.95.*

percent (%) Per hundred, for each hundred, or out of a hundred. $1\% = \frac{1}{100} = 0.01$. For example, *48% of the students in the school are boys* means that, on average, 48 of every 100 students in the school are boys. See Section 9.3.5: Percents.

Percent Circle A tool on the *Geometry Template* that is used to measure and draw figures that involve percents, such as *circle graphs*. See Section 14.11.2: Protractors and the Percent Circle.

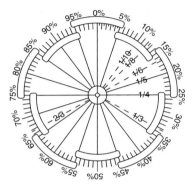

perfect number A *counting number* that equals the sum of its *proper factors*. For example, 6 is a perfect number because the sum of its proper factors is $1 + 2 + 3 = 6$. Compare to *abundant number* and *deficient number*. See Section 9.8.2: Perfect, Deficient, and Abundant Numbers.

perimeter The distance around the boundary of a *2-dimensional figure*. The perimeter of a *circle* is called its *circumference*. A formula for the perimeter P of a *rectangle* with length l and width w is $P = 2 * (l + w)$. Perimeter comes from the Greek words for "around measure." See the Tables of Formulas and Section 14.3: Length.

perpendicular (⊥) Two *lines* or two *planes* that intersect at *right angles*. *Line segments* or *rays* that lie on perpendicular lines are perpendicular to each other. The symbol ⊥ means "is perpendicular to." See Section 13.6.1: Perpendicular and Parallel.

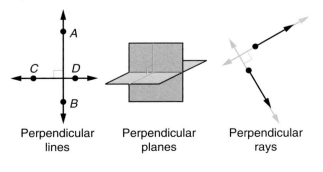

Perpendicular lines   Perpendicular planes   Perpendicular rays

perpendicular bisector A *line, ray,* or *segment* that *bisects* a line segment at a *right angle*. See Section 13.6.1: Perpendicular and Parallel and Section 13.13.1: Compass-and-Straightedge Constructions.

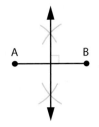

Construction of a perpendicular bisector of $\overline{AB}$

perpetual calendar A table that can be used to determine the correct day of the week for any date in a wide range of years.

personal-measurement reference A convenient approximation for a standard unit of measurement. For example, many people have thumbs that are approximately one inch wide. See Section 14.1: Personal Measures.

perspective drawing A drawing that realistically represents a 3-dimensional object on a 2-dimensional surface. See Section 13.5.4: Connecting 2-D and 3-D.

per-unit rate A *rate* with 1 unit of something in the denominator. Per-unit rates tell how many of one thing there are for 1 unit of another thing. For example, *3 dollars per gallon, 12 miles per hour,* and *1.6 children per family* are per-unit rates.

pi (π) The ratio of the *circumference* of a circle to its *diameter*. Pi is also the ratio of the area of a circle to the square of its radius. Pi is the same for every circle and is an *irrational number* that is approximately equal to 3.14. The symbol π is the 16th letter of the Greek alphabet. See Section 13.4.3: Circles and Pi (π).

pictograph A graph constructed with pictures or symbols. See Section 12.2.3: Organizing and Displaying Data.

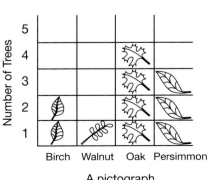

A pictograph

pie graph Same as *circle graph*.

pint (pt) A U.S. customary unit of *volume* or *capacity* equal to 2 cups, or 16 fluid ounces. A handy saying to remember is *A pint's a pound the world around,* meaning that a pint of water weighs about 1 pound. See the Tables of Measures and Section 14.5: Volume (Capacity).

place value A system that gives a *digit* a value according to its position, or place, in a number. In our standard, *base-ten* (decimal) system for writing numbers, each place has a value 10 times that of the place to its right and 1 tenth the value of the place to its left.

thousands	hundreds	tens	ones	.	tenths	hundredths

A place-value chart

plane In *Everyday Mathematics*, a *2-dimensional* flat surface that extends forever in all directions. In formal Euclidean geometry, plane is an undefined geometric term. See Section 13.4: Planes and Plane Figures.

A plane

plane figure A *2-dimensional figure* that is entirely contained in a single *plane*. For example, triangles, squares, pentagons, circles, and parabolas are plane figures; lines, rays, cones, cubes, and prisms are not. See Section 13.4: Planes and Plane Figures.

point In *Everyday Mathematics,* an exact location in space. Points are usually labeled with capital letters. In formal Euclidean geometry, point is an undefined geometric term. See Section 13.2: Points.

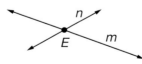

Lines *m* and *n* intersect at point *E*.

point symmetry (1) A figure has point symmetry if it is a *reflection* image of itself through a center of symmetry *C*. A line through *C* and a point *M* on the figure intersects the reflection image at point *M'* where the length of $\overline{CM}$ equals the length of $\overline{CM'}$. (2) Point symmetry is the same as *rotation symmetry* around point *C* through a 180° turn.

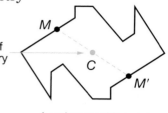

A polygon with point symmetry through *C*.

poly- A prefix meaning many.

polygon A *2-dimensional figure* formed by three or more line segments *(sides)* that meet only at their endpoints *(vertices)* to make a closed path. The sides may not cross one another. See Section 13.4.2: Polygons *(n-gons)*.

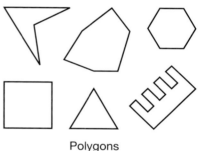

Polygons

polyhedron A *3-dimensional figure* formed by *polygons* with their interiors *(faces)* and having no holes. Plural is polyhedrons or polyhedra. See Section 13.5.2: Polyhedrons.

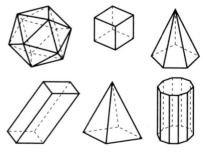

Polyhedrons

population (1) The total number of people living within a defined geographic region. (2) In data collection, the group of people or objects that is the focus of study. Large populations are often studied by picking a representative *random sample* from the population. See Section 12.2.2: Collecting and Recording Data.

population density The number of people living in a defined geographic region, usually given as a *rate,* such as *876 people per square mile.*

positive numbers Numbers greater than 0; the opposites of the *negative numbers.* Positive numbers are plotted to the right of 0 on a horizontal number line or above 0 on a vertical number line. See Section 9.4: Positive and Negative Numbers.

positive power of 10 A number that can be written in the form 10^a, where a is a *counting number.* That is, the numbers 10, 100, 1,000, and so on, that can be written using only 10s as factors. Compare to *negative power of 10.* See Section 10.1.2: Powers and Exponents.

positive rational numbers *Rational numbers* greater than 0; the opposites of the *negative rational numbers.* For example, 7, $\frac{4}{3}$, $\frac{1}{1,000}$, 0.01, 8.125, and 5.111 . . . are positive rational numbers. See Section 9.4: Positive and Negative Numbers.

poster In *Everyday Mathematics,* a page displaying a collection of illustrated numerical data. A poster may be used as a source of data for developing *number stories.*

pound (lb) A U.S. customary unit of *weight* equal to 16 ounces and defined as 0.45359237 kilograms. See the Tables of Measures and Section 14.6: Weight and Mass.

power Same as *exponent.*

power of a number A *product* of *factors* that are all the same; the result of a^b for any numbers a and b. For example, $5^3 = 5 * 5 * 5 = 125$ is read "5 to the third power" or "the third power of 5" because 5 is a factor three times. See *exponential notation* and Section 10.1.2: Powers and Exponents.

power of 10 (1) In *Everyday Mathematics,* a number that can be written in the form 10^a, where a is a *counting number.* That is, the numbers $10 = 10^1$, $100 = 10^2$, $1,000 = 10^3$, and so on, that can be written using only 10s as factors. Same as *positive power of 10.* (2) More generally, a number that can be written in the form 10^a, where a is an *integer.* That is, all the *positive* and *negative powers of 10* together, along with $10^0 = 1$. See Section 10.1.2: Powers and Exponents.

precise Exact or accurate.

precise calculations The more accurate measures or other data are, the more *precise* any calculations using those numbers can be. See *significant digits* and Section 16.2: Approximation and Rounding.

precise measures The smaller the *scale* of a measuring tool, the more *precise* a measurement can be. For example, a measurement to the nearest inch is more precise than a measurement to the nearest foot. A ruler with $\frac{1}{16}$-inch markings can be more precise than a ruler with only $\frac{1}{4}$-inch markings, depending on the skill of the person doing the measuring.

predict In mathematics, to say what will happen in the future based on experimental data or theoretical calculation.

prediction line A *line* on a graph of *data* that is used to predict values that are not in the data set. In statistics, prediction lines can be fit to data using a technique called regression analysis. In elementary school, prediction lines are usually drawn "by eye" to pass as close as possible to plotted data points.

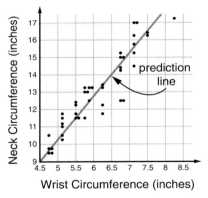

preimage The original figure in a *transformation.* Compare to *image.* See Section 13.7: Transformations.

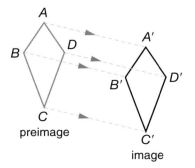

prime factorization A *counting number* written as a product of *prime-number* factors. Every counting number greater than 1 has a unique prime factorization. For example, the prime factorization of 24 is 2 * 2 * 2 * 3. See Section 9.8.1: Prime and Composite Numbers: Divisibility.

prime meridian An imaginary *semicircle* on Earth that connects the North and South Poles through Greenwich, England. See *lines of longitude* and Section 15.4.4: The Global Grid System.

prime number A *counting number* greater than 1 that has exactly two whole-number factors, 1 and itself. For example, 7 is a prime number because its only factors are 1 and 7. The first five prime numbers are 2, 3, 5, 7, and 11. Also simply called primes. Compare to *composite number*. See Section 9.8.1: Prime and Composite Numbers: Divisibility.

prism A *polyhedron* with two parallel and congruent polygonal regions for *bases* and lateral *faces* formed by all the line segments with endpoints on corresponding edges of the bases. The lateral faces are all parallelograms. Lateral faces intersect at lateral *edges*. In a *right prism,* the lateral faces are rectangular. Prisms get their names from the shape of their bases. See Section 13.5.2: Polyhedrons.

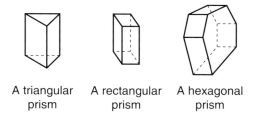

A triangular   A rectangular   A hexagonal
prism   prism   prism

probability A number from 0 through 1 giving the likelihood that an *event* will happen. The closer a probability is to 1, the more likely the event is to happen. The closer a probability is to 0, the less likely the event is to happen. For example, the probability that a fair coin will show HEADS is $\frac{1}{2}$. See Section 12.1: Probability.

Probability Meter In *Fifth* and *Sixth Grade Everyday Mathematics,* a tool used to show probabilities as fractions, decimals, and percents. See Section 12.4.2: Probability Meter.

probability tree diagram A drawing used to analyze a *probability* situation that consists of two or more choices or stages. For example, the branches of the probability tree diagram below represent the four *equally likely outcomes* of HEADS H and TAILS T when one coin is flipped two times. See Section 12.4.3: Tree Diagrams.

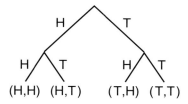

product The result of multiplying two numbers, called *factors*. For example, in 4 * 3 = 12, the product is 12.

program a calculator To instruct a calculator to repeat a calculation using its *memory* instead of having the user enter a key sequence over and over. In *Everyday Mathematics,* students program their calculators to skip count using the machines' built-in constant operation feature. See Section 3.1.1: Calculators.

Project In *Everyday Mathematics,* a thematic activity to be completed in one or more days by small groups or by a whole class. Projects often involve collecting and analyzing data and are usually cross-curricular in nature. See Section 1.2.7: Projects.

proper factor Any *factor* of a counting number except the number itself. For example, the factors of 10 are 1, 2, 5, and 10, and the proper factors of 10 are 1, 2, and 5. See Section 9.8.1: Prime and Composite Numbers: Divisibility.

proper fraction A *fraction* in which the numerator is less than the denominator. A proper fraction is between −1 and 1. For example, $\frac{3}{4}$, $-\frac{2}{5}$, and $\frac{12}{24}$ are proper fractions. Compare to *improper fraction*. *Everyday Mathematics* does not emphasize these distinctions.

property (1) A generalized statement about a mathematical relationship such as the *Distributive Property of Multiplication over Addition*. (2) Same as *attribute*.

proportion A *number model* equating two *fractions*. Often the fractions in a proportion represent rates or ratios. For example, the problem *Alan's speed is 12 miles per hour. At the same speed, how far can he travel in 3 hours?* is modeled by the proportion

$$\frac{12 \text{ miles}}{1 \text{ hour}} = \frac{n \text{ miles}}{3 \text{ hours}}.$$

See Section 9.3.3: Rates, Ratios, and Proportions and Section 17.2.4: Solving Open Sentences.

protractor A tool used for measuring or drawing *angles*. A half-circle protractor can be used to measure and draw angles up to 180°. A full-circle protractor can be used to measure and draw angles up to 360°. One of each type is on the *Geometry Template*. See Section 14.11.2: Protractors and the Percent Circle.

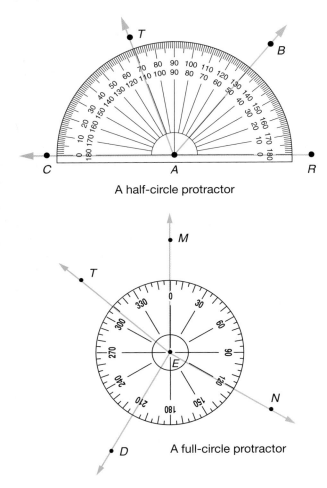

A half-circle protractor

A full-circle protractor

pyramid A *polyhedron* made up of any polygonal region for a *base,* a vertex *(apex)* not in the plane of the base, and all of the line segments with one endpoint at the apex and the other on an edge of the base. All faces except perhaps the base are triangular. Pyramids get their name from the shape of their base. See Section 13.5.2: Polyhedrons.

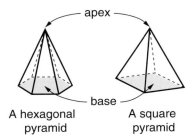

A hexagonal pyramid   A square pyramid

Pythagorean theorem If the *legs of a right triangle* have lengths a and b and the *hypotenuse* has length c, then $a^2 + b^2 = c^2$. See Section 13.4.2: Polygons (*n*-gons).

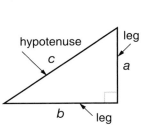

Q

quad- A prefix meaning four.

quadrangle Same as *quadrilateral*.

quadrant One of the four sections into which a *rectangular coordinate grid* is divided by the two axes. The quadrants are typically numbered I, II, III, and IV counterclockwise beginning at the upper right.

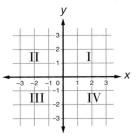

quadrilateral A 4-sided *polygon*. See *square, rectangle, parallelogram, rhombus, kite, trapezoid,* and Section 13.4.2: Polygons (*n*-gons).

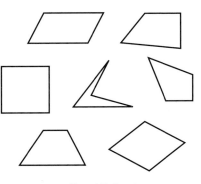

Quadrilaterals

quart A U.S. customary unit of *volume* or *capacity* equal to 32 fluid ounces, 2 pints, or 4 cups. See the Tables of Measures and Section 14.5: Volume (Capacity).

quick common denominator The *product* of the *denominators* of two or more *fractions*. For example, the quick common denominator of $\frac{3}{4}$ and $\frac{5}{6}$ is $4 * 6 = 24$. In general, the quick common denominator of $\frac{a}{b}$ and $\frac{c}{d}$ is $b * d$. As the name suggests, this is a quick way to get a *common denominator* for a collection of fractions, but it does not necessarily give the *least common denominator*. See Section 11.3.5: Fraction Division.

quotient The result of dividing one number by another number. For example, in $10/5 = 2$, the quotient is 2.

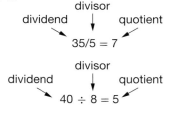

quotitive division Same as *measurement division.*

R

radius (1) A *line segment* from the center of a *circle* (or *sphere*) to any point on the circle (or sphere). (2) The length of this line segment. The length of a radius is half the length of a *diameter*. Plural is radiuses or radii. See Section 13.4.3: Circles and Pi (π).

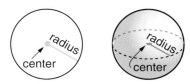

random draw Taking an object from a set of objects in which each object has an *equally likely* chance of being chosen. For example, drawing a card from a deck and drawing a domino from a bag of dominoes are random draws. See Section 12.1.2: The Language of Chance.

random experiment An experiment in which all *outcomes* are *equally likely.* No one outcome is more predictable than any other. See Section 12.1.2: The Language of Chance.

random number A number produced by a *random experiment,* such as rolling a die or spinning a spinner. For example, rolling a fair die produces random numbers because each of the six possible numbers 1, 2, 3, 4, 5, and 6 has the same chance of coming up. See Section 12.1.2: The Language of Chance.

random sample A *sample* that gives all members of the *population* the same chance of being selected. See Section 12.2.2: Collecting and Recording Data.

range The *difference* between the *maximum* and the *minimum* in a set of data. Used as a measure of the spread of the data. See Section 12.2.4: Data Analysis.

rank (1) To put in order by size; to sort from smallest to largest or vice versa. (2) A row in an *array.* In the military, rows and columns of rectangular formations are sometimes called rank and file, respectively.

rate A comparison by division of two quantities with different *units.* For example, traveling 100 miles in 2 hours is an average rate of $\frac{100 \text{ mi}}{2 \text{ hr}}$, or 50 miles per hour. Compare to *ratio.* See Section 9.3.3: Rates, Ratios, and Proportions and Section 10.3.2: Multiplication and Division Use Classes.

rate diagram A diagram used in *Everyday Mathematics* to model *rate* situations. The diagram includes two quantities and the rate comparing them. See *situation diagram* and Section 10.3.2: Multiplication and Division Use Classes.

rows	chairs per row	chairs
6	4	?

A rate diagram

rate-multiplication story A *number story* in which one quantity is a *rate* times another quantity. A typical rate is *speed,* which multiplied by a time traveled gives distance traveled. There are many other rates such as price per pound or hours per person. For example, *8 people work a total of 20 hours. What is the average number of work hours per person?* is a rate-multiplication story. See Section 10.3.2: Multiplication and Division Use Classes.

rate table A display of *rate* information. In a rate table, the fractions formed by the two numbers in each column are *equivalent fractions*. For example, $\frac{35}{1} = \frac{70}{2}$ in the table below. See Section 10.3.2: Multiplication and Division Use Classes.

miles	35	70	105	140	175	210
gallons	1	2	3	4	5	6

rate unit A compound *unit* for a *rate*. For example, *miles per hour, dollars per pound,* and *words per minute* are rate units. See Section 9.3.3: Rates, Ratios, and Proportions.

ratio A comparison by division of two quantities with the same *units*. Ratios can be fractions, decimals, percents, or stated in words. Ratios can also be written with a colon between the two numbers being compared. For example, if a team wins 3 games out of 5 games played, the ratio of wins to total games is $\frac{3}{5}$, 3/5, 0.6, 60%, 3 to 5, or 3:5 (read "three to five"). Compare to *rate*. See Section 9.3.3: Rates, Ratios, and Proportions.

rational numbers Numbers that can be written in the form $\frac{a}{b}$, where a and nonzero b are *integers*. The decimal form of a rational number either terminates or repeats. For example, $\frac{2}{3}$, $-\frac{2}{3}$, 0.5, 20.5, and 0.333 . . . are rational numbers. See Section 9.3: Fractions, Decimals, Percents, and Rational Numbers.

ray A part of a *line* starting at the ray's *endpoint* and continuing forever in one direction. A ray is often named by its endpoint and another point on it. See Section 13.3: Lines, Segments, and Rays.

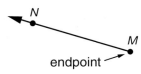

Ray *MN* or $\overrightarrow{MN}$

r-by-c array A rectangular arrangement of elements with r rows and c elements per row. Among other things, an r-by-c array models r sets with c objects per set. Although listing rows before columns is arbitrary, it is in keeping with the order used in matrix notation, which students will study later in school.

real numbers All *rational* and *irrational numbers;* all numbers that can be written as decimals. For every real number there is a corresponding point on a number line, and for every point on the number line there is a real number. See Section 9.6: Real Numbers.

recall survey A *survey* in which data are gathered by asking people what they remember about a particular topic. For example, a recall survey might ask people to list what soft drinks they consumed in the previous week.

reciprocals Two numbers whose product is 1. For example, 5 and $\frac{1}{5}$, $\frac{3}{5}$ and $\frac{5}{3}$, and 0.2 and 5 are pairs of reciprocals. Same as *multiplicative inverses*.

rectangle A *parallelogram* with all *right angles*. See Section 13.4.2: Polygons (*n*-gons).

rectangle method A strategy for finding the *area* of a *polygon* in which one or more *rectangles* are drawn around all or parts of the polygon though its vertices. The sides of the drawn rectangle(s), together with the sides of the original figure, define regions that are either rectangles or triangular halves of rectangles. Add and/or subtract the areas of these rectangular and triangular regions to get the area of the original polygon. For example, rectangle *RYSX* was drawn around the original triangle *XYZ* below.

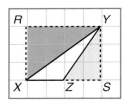

Area of △*XYZ* = area of rectangle *RYSX* −
area of △*XYR* − area of △*YZS*

rectangular array An arrangement of objects in *rows* and *columns* that form a *rectangle*. All rows have the same number of objects, and all columns have the same number of objects. See r-*by*-c *array* and Section 10.3.2: Multiplication and Division Use Classes.

A rectangular array

rectangular coordinate grid (1) In *Everyday Mathematics,* same as *coordinate grid*. (2) A coordinate grid with perpendicular *axes*. See Section 15.3.2: 2- and 3-Dimensional Coordinate Systems.

rectangular prism A *prism* with rectangular *bases.* The four faces that are not bases are either *rectangles* or *parallelograms*. For example, a shoe box models a rectangular prism in which all sides are rectangles. See Section 13.5.2: Polyhedrons.

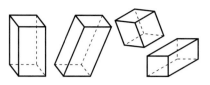
Rectangular prisms

rectangular pyramid A *pyramid* with a rectangular *base*. See Section 13.5.2: Polyhedrons.

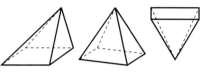
Rectangular pyramids

rectilinear figure (1) In *Everyday Mathematics,* a closed *2-dimensional* shape having *line segments* for *sides* and only 90° or 270° *angles*. (2) Any shape made up of *line segments*.

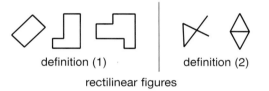
definition (1)   definition (2)
rectilinear figures

reduce To decrease the size of an object or figure without changing its shape. Same as *shrink*. See *size-change factor* and Section 13.7.2: Size-Change Transformations.

reduce a fraction To rewrite a fraction in a *simpler form*. See *simplest form of a fraction* and Section 9.3.1: Fraction and Decimal Notation.

reference frame A system for locating numbers within a given context, usually with reference to an *origin* or *zero point*. For example, number lines, clocks, calendars, temperature scales, and maps are reference frames. See Chapter 15: Reference Frames.

reflection A point A' is a reflection *image* of a point A over a *line of reflection l* if A' and A are the same distance from l on a line perpendicular to l. If all points on one figure are 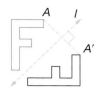 reflection images of all the points on another figure over the same line, the figures are reflection images. Informally called a *flip*. See Section 13.7.1: Reflections, Rotations, and Translations.

A reflection

reflex angle An *angle* with a measure between 180° and 360°. See Section 13.4.1: Angles and Rotations.

A reflex angle

regular polygon A *polygon* in which all *sides* are the same length and all *angles* have the same measure. See Section 13.4.2: Polygons (*n*-gons).

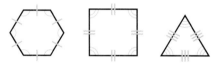
Regular polygons

regular polyhedron A *polyhedron* whose faces are all *congruent regular polygons* and in which the same number of faces meet at each *vertex*. The five regular polyhedrons, known as the Platonic solids, are shown below.

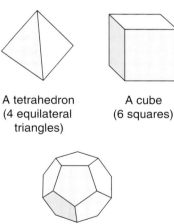

A tetrahedron (4 equilateral triangles)   A cube (6 squares)   An octahedron (8 equilateral triangles)

A dodecahedron (12 regular pentagons)   An icosahedron (20 equilateral triangles)

Glossary

regular tessellation A *tessellation* of one *regular polygon*. The only three regular tessellations are shown below. See Section 13.10: Tessellations.

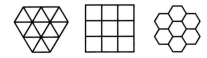

Samples of the three regular tessellations

relation symbol A symbol used to express a relationship between two quantities. See Section 10.2: Reading and Writing Number Sentences.

Relation	Meaning
=	is equal to
≠	is not equal to
<	is less than
>	is greater than
≤	is less than or equal to
≥	is greater than or equal to
≈	is approximately equal to

remainder An amount left over when one number is divided by another number. For example, in $16/3 \rightarrow 5$ R1, the *quotient* is 5 and the remainder R is 1. See Section 10.1.1: The Four Basic Arithmetic Operations.

repeating decimal A *decimal* in which one *digit* or a group of digits is repeated without end. For example, 0.3333. . . and $0.\overline{147}$ are repeating decimals. Compare to *terminating decimal*. See Section 9.3.1: Fraction and Decimal Notation.

revolution Movement on a circle or other closed curve around some point. The planets revolve around the sun in nearly-circular elliptical orbits.

rhombus A *parallelogram* with all sides the same length. All rhombuses are parallelograms. Every square is a rhombus, but not all rhombuses are squares. Also called a diamond. Plural is rhombuses or rhombi. See Section 13.4.2: Polygons (*n*-gons).

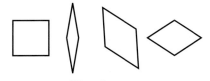

Rhombuses

right angle A 90° *angle*. See Section 13.4.1: Angles and Rotations.

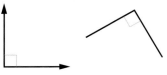

Right angles

right cone or pyramid A *cone* or *pyramid* whose *base* is perpendicular to the line segment joining the *apex* and the center of the base. See Section 13.5.2: Polyhedrons and Section 13.5.3: Solids with Curved Surfaces.

A right cone

right cylinder A *cylinder* whose *bases* are perpendicular to the line segment joining the centers of the bases. See Section 13.5.3: Solids with Curved Surfaces.

A right cylinder

right prism A *prism* whose *bases* are perpendicular to all of the *edges* that connect the two bases. See Section 13.5.2: Polyhedrons.

A right triangular prism

right triangle A *triangle* with a *right angle*. See Section 13.4.2: Polygons (*n*-gons).

Right triangles

Roman numerals Letters that are used alone and in combination to represent numbers in an ancient Roman system of *numeration*. Roman numerals are found on clocks, building cornerstones, preliminary pages in books, movie copyright dates, and other places.

Roman Numerals		
I = 1	X = 10	C = 100
II = 2	XX = 20 (2 tens)	CC = 200
III = 3	XXX = 30 (3 tens)	CCC = 300
IV = 4	XL = 40 (50 less 10)	CD = 400
V = 5	L = 50	D = 500
VI = 6	LX = 60 (50 plus 10)	CM = 900
VII = 7	LXX = 70 (50 plus 20)	M = 1,000
VIII = 8	LXXX = 80 (50 plus 30)	$\overline{X}$ = 10,000
IX = 9	XC = 90 (100 less 10)	$\overline{C}$ = 100,000
		∞ = 100,000,000 or infinity

rotation (1) A point P' is a rotation *image* of a point P around a center of rotation C if P' is on the *circle* with center C and radius CP. If all the points in one figure are rotation images of all the points in another figure around the same center of rotation and with the same angle of rotation, the figures are rotation images. The center can be inside or outside of the original image. Informally called a *turn*. See Section 13.7.1: Reflections, Rotations, and Translations. (2) If all points on the image of a *3-dimensional figure* are rotation images around a point on a line called the axis of rotation, then the image is a rotation image of the original figure.

C

A rotation

rotation symmetry A figure has rotation symmetry if it is the *rotation* image of itself after less than a 360° turn around a center or axis of rotation. See Section 13.8.2: Rotation and Point Symmetries.

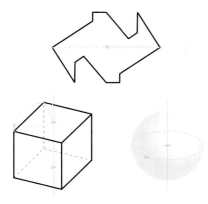

Shapes with rotation symmetry

round (1) To approximate a number to make it easier to work with, or to make it better reflect the precision of the data. "Rounding up" means to approximate larger than the actual value. "Rounding down" means to approximate smaller than the actual value. See *round to the nearest* and Section 16.2: Approximation and Rounding. (2) Circular in shape.

round to the nearest To *round* a number up or down in a particular decimal place, depending on which approximation is closer to the actual value. See Section 16.2: Approximation and Rounding.

row (1) A horizontal arrangement of objects or numbers in an *array* or table. (2) A horizontal section of *cells* in a *spreadsheet*. See Section 3.1.3: Spreadsheets.

rubber-sheet geometry Same as *topology*.

S

same-change rule for subtraction A subtraction *algorithm* in which the same number is added to or subtracted from both numbers. See Section 11.2.2: Subtraction Algorithms.

sample A part of a *population* intended to represent the whole population. See *random sample* and Section 12.2.2: Collecting and Recording Data.

scale (1) The relative size of something. (2) Same as *scale factor*. (3) A tool for measuring *weight*. See Section 14.6: Weight and Mass.

scale of a map Same as *map scale*.

scale of a number line The *unit interval* on a number line or measuring device. The scales on this ruler are 1 millimeter on the left side and $\frac{1}{16}$ inch on the right side. See Section 9.9.2: Number Grids, Scrolls, and Lines.

scale drawing A drawing of an object in which all parts are drawn to the same *scale* to the object. For example, architects and builders use scale drawings traditionally called blueprints. A map is a scale drawing of a geographical region. See *scale factor* and Section 15.4.2: Map and Model Scales.

A woodpecker (8 in.) to $\frac{1}{4}$ scale

scale factor (1) The *ratio* of lengths on an *image* and corresponding lengths on a *preimage* in a *size change*. Same as *size-change factor*. See Section 13.7.2: Size-Change Transformations. (2) The ratio of lengths in a *scale drawing* or *scale model* to the corresponding lengths in the object being drawn or modeled. See Section 15.4.2: Map and Model Scales.

scale model A model of an object in which all parts are made to the same *scale* to the object. For example, many model trains or airplanes are scale models of actual vehicles. See *scale factor* and Section 15.4.2: Map and Model Scales.

scalene triangle A *triangle* with sides of three different lengths. The three angles of a scalene triangle have different measures. See Section 13.4.2: Polygons (*n*-gons).

scientific calculator A calculator that can display numbers using *scientific notation*. Scientific calculators follow the *algebraic order of operations* and can calculate a *power of a number,* a *square root,* and several other functions beyond simple 4-function calculators. Some scientific calculators let you enter and do arithmetic with *fractions.* See Section 3.1.1: Calculators.

scientific notation A way of writing a number as the product of a *power of 10* and a number that is at least 1 and less than 10. Scientific notation allows you to write large and small numbers with only a few symbols. For example, in scientific notation, 4,300,000 is $4.3 * 10^6$, and 0.00001 is $1 * 10^{-5}$. *Scientific calculators* display numbers in scientific notation. Compare to *standard notation* and *expanded notation*. See Section 10.1.2: Powers and Exponents.

second (s or sec) (1) A unit of time defined as $\frac{1}{31,556,925.9747}$ of the tropical year at midnight Eastern Time on New Year's Day, 1900. There are 60 seconds in a minute. (2) An *ordinal number* in the sequence *first, second, third, ...*

sector A region bounded by and including an *arc* and two *radii* of a circle. A sector resembles a slice of pizza. *Circle graphs* are made with sectors corresponding to parts of a data set. Also called a wedge.

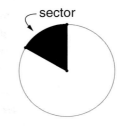

segment Same as *line segment*.

semicircle (1) Half of a *circle*. (2) Half of a circle and the *diameter* between the endpoints of the arc. Sometimes the interior of this closed figure is also included. See *circle* and Section 13.4.3: Circles and Pi (π).

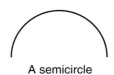

A semicircle

Glossary

semiregular tessellation A *tessellation* made with *congruent* copies of two or more different *regular polygons*. The same combination of polygons must meet in the same order at each *vertex point,* and the angles at each vertex point must add up to 360°. There are eight semiregular tessellations. Compare to *regular tessellation*. See *name of a tessellation* and Section 13.10.1: Classifying Tessellations.

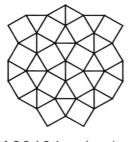

A 3.3.4.3.4 semiregular tessellation

sequence A list of numbers, often with an underlying rule that may be used to generate subsequent numbers in the list. *Frames-and-Arrows* diagrams are used to represent sequences. See Section 17.1.2: Sequences.

set A collection or group of objects, numbers, or other items.

short-term memory *Memory* in a calculator used to store values for immediate calculation. Short-term memory is usually cleared with a (C), (AC), (Clear), or similar key. Compare to *long-term memory*. See Section 3.1.1: Calculators.

shrink Same as *reduce*.

side (1) One of the *line segments* that make up a *polygon*. (2) One of the *rays* or *segments* that form an *angle*. (3) One of the *faces* of a *polyhedron*.

side-by-side bar graph A *bar graph* that uses pairs of bars to compare two related data sets. The graph below compares road miles and air miles from Los Angeles to different cities. See Section 12.2.3: Organizing and Displaying Data.

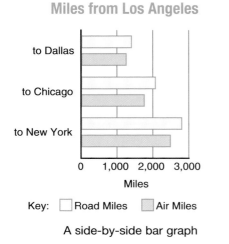

Miles from Los Angeles

Key: ☐ Road Miles ▨ Air Miles

A side-by-side bar graph

Sieve of Eratosthenes A method for identifying *prime numbers* named for Eratosthenes (circa 276–194 B.C.), a mathematician and head librarian at the Great Library in Alexandria, Egypt.

To find all prime numbers less than *n:*

1. List all the counting numbers from 2 to *n*.
2. Circle 2. Cross out all the multiples of 2 greater than 2.
3. Circle the first number that is not crossed out. Cross out all the multiples of that number.
4. Repeat Step 3 until the first uncircled and uncrossed number is greater than $\sqrt{n}$. At this point, the numbers that are not crossed out are all the prime numbers less than or equal to *n*.

②	③	4̸	⑤
6̸	7	8̸	9̸
1̸0̸	11	1̸2̸	13
1̸4̸	1̸5̸	1̸6̸	17
1̸8̸	19	2̸0̸	2̸1̸
2̸2̸	23	2̸4̸	2̸5̸

Sieve of Eratosthenes for primes less than 25

significant digits The *digits* in a number that convey useful and reliable information. A number with more significant digits is more *precise* than a number with fewer significant digits. In general, calculations should not produce results with more significant digits than the original numbers. See *scientific notation* and Section 16.2: Approximation and Rounding.

similar figures Figures that have the same shape, but not necessarily the same size. Compare to *congruent*. See Section 13.6.2: Congruence and Similarity.

Similar polygons

simpler form of a fraction A *fraction* renamed as an *equivalent fraction* with a smaller numerator and smaller denominator. To put a fraction in simpler form, divide both the numerator and the denominator by a common factor greater than 1. For example, divide the numerator and the denominator of $\frac{18}{24}$ by 2 to get the simpler form $\frac{9}{12}$.

simplest form of a fraction A *fraction* that cannot be renamed in *simpler form*. Same as *lowest terms of a fraction*. A *mixed number* is in simplest form if its fractional part is in simplest form.

simplify a fraction To write a fraction in *simplest form*.

simplify an expression To rewrite an *expression* by clearing grouping symbols and combining *like terms* and *constants*. For example, $7y + 4 + 5 + 3y$ simplifies to $10y + 9$ and $3(2k + 5) - k$ simplifies to $5k + 15$. Equations with simplified expressions are often easier to solve. For example, $2(a + 4) = 4a + 1 + 3$ simplifies to $2a + 8 = 4a + 4$. This step is sometimes called "simplifying the equation," although a completely simplified equation is the solution $2 = a$. See Section 17.2.3: Simplifying Expressions.

situation diagram A diagram used to organize information in a problem situation in one of the *addition/subtraction* or *multiplication/division use classes*. See Section 10.3: Use Classes and Situation Diagrams.

size change A *transformation* in which the *image* of a figure is a an enlargement *(stretch)* or reduction *(shrink)* of the original figure by a given *scale factor*. See Section 13.7.2: Size-Change Transformations.

size-change factor Same as *scale factor*.

skew lines *Lines* in space that do not lie in the same *plane*. Skew lines do not *intersect* and are not *parallel*. An east-west line on the floor and a north-south line on the ceiling are skew. See Section 13.6.1: Perpendicular and Parallel.

Skew lines can be modeled with two pencils.

slanted (oblique) cylinder, cone, prism, or pyramid A *cylinder, cone, prism,* or *pyramid* that is not a *right cylinder, right cone, right prism,* or *right pyramid*.

A slanted (oblique) cylinder, cone, prism, and pyramid

slate A lap-size (about 8-inch by 11-inch) chalkboard or whiteboard that children use in *Everyday Mathematics* for recording responses during group exercises and informal group assessments. See Section 1.2.8: Slates.

slide An informal name for a *translation*. See Section 13.7.1: Reflections, Rotations, and Translations.

slide rule An *Everyday Mathematics* tool for adding and subtracting integers and fractions.

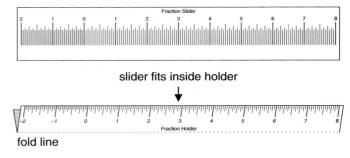

An *Everyday Mathematics* slide rule

solution of an open sentence A value or values for the *variable(s)* in an *open sentence* that make the sentence true. For example, 7 is a solution of $5 + n = 12$. Although equations are not necessarily open sentences, the solution of an open sentence is commonly referred to as a solution of an equation. See Section 17.2.4: Solving Open Sentences.

solution of a problem (1) The method by which an answer to a problem is obtained. (2) The answer to a problem. See Chapter 18: Problem Solving.

solution set The set of all *solutions of an open sentence*. For example, the solution set of $x^2 = 25$ is $\{5, -5\}$ because substituting either 5 or -5 for x makes the sentence true.

span Same as *normal span*.

special case In *Everyday Mathematics*, a specific example of a *general pattern*. For example, $6 + 6 = 12$ is a special case of $y + y = 2y$ and $9 = 4.5 * 2$ is a special case of $A = l * w$. Same as *instance of a pattern*.

speed A *rate* that compares distance traveled with the time taken to travel that distance. For example, if a car travels 100 miles in 2 hours, then its average speed is $\frac{100 \text{ mi}}{2 \text{ hr}}$, or 50 miles per hour. See Section 9.3.3: Rates, Ratios, and Proportions.

sphere The set of all points in space that are an equal distance from a fixed point called the *center of the sphere*. The distance from the center to the sphere is the *radius* of the sphere. The *diameter* of a sphere is twice its radius. Points inside a sphere are not part of the sphere. See Section 13.5.3: Solids with Curved Surfaces.

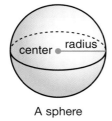

A sphere

spreadsheet program A computer application in which numerical information is arranged in *cells* in a grid. The computer can use the information in the grid to perform mathematical operations and evaluate *formulas*. When a value in a cell changes, the values in all other cells that depend on it are automatically changed. The name spreadsheet comes from ledger worksheets for financial records. Such sheets were often taped together and then spread out for examination. See Section 3.1.3: Spreadsheets.

	A	B	C	D
		Class Picnic ($$)		
1		budget for class picnic		
2				
3	quantity	food items	unit price	cost
4	6	packages of hamburgers	2.79	16.74
5	5	packages of hamburger buns	1.29	6.45
6	3	bags of potato chips	3.12	9.36
7	3	quarts of macaroni salad	4.50	13.50
8	4	bottles of soft drinks	1.69	6.76
9			subtotal	52.81
10			8% tax	4.22
11			total	57.03

A spreadsheet

square A *rectangle* with all sides of equal length. All angles in a square are *right angles*. See Section 13.4.2: Polygons (*n*-gons).

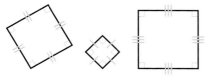

Squares

square array A rectangular *array* with the same number of *rows* as *columns*. For example, 16 objects will form a square array with 4 objects in each row and 4 objects in each column. See Section 10.3.2: Multiplication and Division Use Classes.

A square array

square corner Same as a *right angle*.

square numbers *Figurate numbers* that are the product of a *counting number* and itself. For example, 25 is a square number because $25 = 5 * 5$. A square number can be represented by a square *array* and as a number squared, such as $25 = 5^2$. See Section 10.1.2: Powers and Exponents and Section 17.1.2: Sequences.

square of a number *n* The product of *n* and itself, commonly written n^2. For example, $81 = 9 * 9 = 9^2$ and $3.5^2 = 3.5 * 3.5 = 12.25$. See Section 10.1.2: Powers and Exponents.

square pyramid A *pyramid* with a square *base*. See Section 13.5.2: Polyhedrons.

square root of a number *n* A number that multiplied by itself is *n*, commonly written $\sqrt{n}$. For example, 4 is a square root of 16, because $4 * 4 = 16$. Normally, square root refers to the positive square root, but the *opposite* of a positive square root is also a square root. For example, -4 is also a square root of 16 because $-4 * -4 = 16$.

square unit A unit to measure *area*. A model of a square unit is a square with each side a related unit of *length*. For example, a square inch is the area of a square with 1-inch sides. Square units are often labeled as the length unit squared. For example, 1 cm^2 is read "1 square centimeter" or "1 centimeter squared." See Section 14.4: Area.

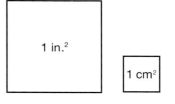

Square units

stacked bar graph A *bar graph* in which the bars are sub-divided to show additional information. A stacked bar graph shows how a total is made up of several parts. In this example, of all the boys, 30% are on 0 teams, about 45% are on 1 team, and the rest are on 2 or more teams. Compare to *side-by-side bar graph*. See Section 12.2.3: Organizing and Displaying Data.

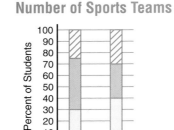

Number of Sports Teams

Key:
□ 0 teams
▨ 1 team
▧ 2 or more teams

A stacked bar graph

standard notation Our most common way of representing *whole numbers, integers,* and *decimals.* Standard notation is *base-ten place-value* numeration. For example, standard notation for three hundred fifty-six is 356. Same as *decimal notation.* See Section 9.3.1: Fraction and Decimal Notation.

standard unit A unit of measure that has been defined by a recognized authority, such as a government or a standards organization. For example, *inches, meters, miles, seconds, pounds, grams,* and *acres* are all standard units. See Section 14.2: Measurement Systems.

stem-and-leaf plot A display of data values in which *digits* with larger place values are "stems" and digits with smaller place values are "leaves." See Section 12.2.3: Organizing and Displaying Data.

Data List: 24, 24, 25, 26, 27, 27, 31, 31, 32, 32, 36, 36, 41, 41, 43, 45, 48, 50, 52.

Stems (10s)	Leaves (1s)
2	4 4 5 6 7 7
3	1 1 2 2 6 6
4	1 1 3 5 8
5	0 2

step graph A *2-dimensional coordinate* graph that looks like steps because the vertical values of points are the same over an interval of horizontal values, and then change, or "step," for another interval. Horizontal values in a step graph often represent time. See Section 12.2.3: Organizing and Displaying Data.

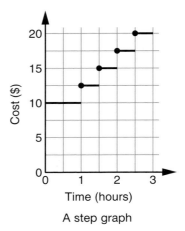

A step graph

straight angle A 180° *angle.* See Section 13.4.1: Angles and Rotations.

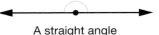

A straight angle

straightedge A tool used to draw *line segments.* Strictly speaking, a straightedge does not have a measuring *scale* on it, so ignore the marks if you use a ruler as a straightedge. Together, a *compass* and straightedge are used to construct geometric figures. See Section 13.13.1: Compass-and-Straightedge Constructions.

stretch Same as *enlarge.*

Study Links In *Fourth* through *Sixth Grade Everyday Mathematics,* a suggested follow-up or enrichment activity to be completed at home. See Section 1.2.10: Study Links.

substitute (1) To replace one thing with another. (2) To replace *variables* with numbers in an *expression* or *formula.* For example, substituting $b = 4.5$ and $h = 8.5$ in the formula $A = b * h$ gives $A = 4.5 * 8.5 = 38.25$. See Section 17.2.1: Uses of Variables.

subtrahend The number being taken away in a subtraction problem. For example, in $15 - 5 = 10$, the subtrahend is 5.

sum The result of adding two or more numbers. For example, in $5 + 3 = 8$, the sum is 8. Same as *total.*

Glossary

summer solstice The longest day of the year, when the sun is farthest north of Earth's equator. The number of hours of daylight depends on the latitude of a location. In Colorado, the summer solstice averages a little less than 16 hours of daylight. Compare to *winter solstice*.

supplementary angles Two angles whose measures add to 180°. Supplementary angles do not need to be *adjacent*. Compare to *complementary angles*. See Section 13.6.3: Relations and Orientations of Angles.

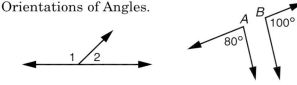

∠1 and ∠2; ∠A and ∠B
are two pairs of supplementary angles.

surface (1) The boundary of a 3-dimensional object. The part of an object that is next to the air. Common surfaces include the top of a body of water, the outermost part of a ball, and the topmost layer of ground that covers Earth. See Section 13.5: Space and 3-D Figures. (2) Any 2-dimensional layer, such as a *plane* or a face of a *polyhedron*.

surface area The *area* of the *surface* of a *3-dimensional figure*. The surface area of a polyhedron is the sum of the areas of its faces. See the Tables of Formulas and Section 14.4.2: Area Formulas.

survey A study that collects *data*. Surveys are commonly used to study "demographics" such as people's characteristics, behaviors, interests, and opinions. See Section 12.2.2: Collecting and Recording Data.

symmetric figure A figure that exactly matches with its *image* under a *reflection* or *rotation*. See *line symmetry, point symmetry, rotation symmetry,* and Section 13.8: Symmetry.

symmetry The balanced distribution of points over a line or around a point in a *symmetric figure*. See *line symmetry, point symmetry, rotation symmetry,* and Section 13.8: Symmetry.

A figure with line symmetry   A figure with rotation symmetry

T

tally (1) To keep a record of a count, commonly by making a mark for each item as it is counted. (2) The mark used in a count. Also called tally mark and tick mark. See Section 12.2.2: Collecting and Recording Data.

tally chart A table to keep track of a *tally*, typically showing how many times each value appears in a set of data.

Number of Pull-Ups	Number of Children
0	⊬⊬⊬ /
1	⊬⊬⊬
2	////
3	//

A tally chart

tangent A *line, segment, ray,* or curve that *intersects* a curve or curved surface at exactly one point.

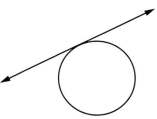

A line tangent to a circle

tangent circles Two *circles* with exactly one point in common.

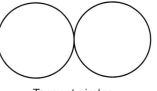

Tangent circles

temperature How hot or cold something is relative to another object or as measured on a standardized *scale* such as *degrees Celsius* or *degrees Fahrenheit*. See Section 15.1: Temperature.

template In *Everyday Mathematics,* a sheet of plastic with geometric shapes cut out of it, used to draw patterns and designs. See Section 13.13.2: Pattern-Block and Geometry Templates.

term (1) In an *algebraic expression,* a number or a product of a number and one or more *variables.* For example, in the equation $5y + 3k = 8$, the terms are $5y$, $3k$, and 8. The 8 is a *constant* term, or simply a *constant,* because it has no variable part. See Section 17.2.2: Reading and Writing Open Sentences. (2) An element in a *sequence.* In the sequence of square numbers, the terms are 1, 4, 9, 16, and so on.

terminating decimal A *decimal* that ends. For example, 0.5 and 0.125 are terminating decimals. See Section 9.3.1: Fraction and Decimal Notation and Section 9.3.4: Rational Numbers and Decimals.

tessellate To make a *tessellation;* to tile a surface.

tessellation A pattern of shapes that covers a surface completely without overlaps or gaps. Same as a *tiling.* See Section 13.10: Tessellations.

A tessellation

test number A number used to replace a *variable* when solving an equation using the *trial-and-error method.* Test numbers are useful for "closing in" on an exact solution. See Section 17.2.4: Solving Open Sentences.

tetrahedron A *polyhedron* with 4 faces. A tetrahedron is a *triangular pyramid.* See Section 13.5.2: Polyhedrons.

theorem A mathematical statement that can be proven to be true. For example, the Pythagorean theorem states that if the *legs of a right triangle* have lengths a and b and the *hypotenuse* has length c, then $a^2 + b^2 = c^2$. The Pythagorean theorem has been proven in hundreds of ways over the past 2,500 years.

3-dimensional (3-D) coordinate system A *reference frame* in which any point on a *3-dimensional figure* can be located with three *coordinates* relative to the *origin* of three axes intersecting perpendicularly at their origins in space. Compare to *1-* and *2-dimensional coordinate systems.* See Section 15.3.2: 2- and 3-Dimensional Coordinate Systems.

3-dimensional (3-D) figure A figure whose points are not all in a single *plane.* Examples include *prisms, pyramids,* and *spheres,* all of which have length, width, and height. See Section 13.1: Dimension.

tick marks (1) Marks showing the *scale* of a number line or ruler. (2) Same as *tally (2).*

tile A shape used in a *tessellation.* A tessellation of only one tile is called a same-tile tessellation.

tiling Same as *tessellation.*

time graph A graph representing a story that takes place over time. The units on the horizontal axis are time units.

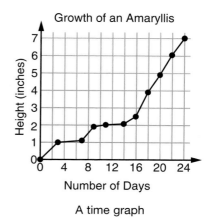

A time graph

timeline A *number line* showing when events took place. In some timelines the *origin* is based on the context of the events being graphed, such as the birth date of the child's life graphed below. The origin can also come from another reference system, such as the year A.D., in which case the scale below might cover the years 2000 through 2005. See Section 15.2.3: Timelines.

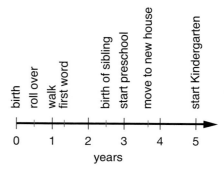

A timeline of a child's milestones

toggle A key on a calculator that changes back and forth between two displays each time it is pressed. For example, on some calculators ⊞⁄⊟ toggles between a number and its *opposite*. See Section 3.1.1: Calculators.

top-heavy fraction Same as *improper fraction*.

topological transformation A *transformation* that pairs a figure with its *image* after shrinking, stretching, twisting, bending, or turning inside out. Tearing, breaking, and sticking together are not allowed. Shapes that can be changed into one another by a topological transformation are called topologically equivalent shapes. For example, a donut is topologically equivalent to a coffee cup. See *topology, genus,* and Section 13.11: Topology.

topology The study of the properties of shapes that are unchanged by shrinking, stretching, twisting, bending, and turning inside out. Tearing, breaking, and sticking together are not allowed. Same as *rubber-sheet geometry*. See *topological transformation* and Section 13.11: Topology.

trade-first subtraction A subtraction *algorithm* in which all necessary trades between places in the numbers are done before any subtractions are carried out. Some people favor this algorithm because they can concentrate on one thing at a time. See Section 11.2.2: Subtraction Algorithms.

transformation An operation on a geometric figure (the *preimage*) that produces a new figure (the *image*). The study of transformations is called transformation geometry. Transformations are often based on rules for how points compare, as in the translation shown in the next definition. Although the preimage does not actually move under a transformation, it is convenient to think and talk about transformations as moving a figure from one place to another and sometimes changing its size or shape. So *Everyday Mathematics* encourages using informal terms such as *flip, turn,* and *slide*. See *isometry transformation, reflection, rotation, translation, size change* and Section 13.7: Transformations.

translation A *transformation* in which every point in the *image* of a figure is at the same distance in the same direction from its corresponding point in the figure. Informally called a *slide*. See Section 13.7.1: Reflections, Rotations, and Translations.

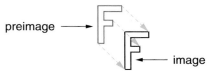

preimage image

A translation

translation tessellation A *tessellation* made of a *tile* in which one or more sides are *translation images* of the opposite side(s). Dutch artist M. C. Escher (1898–1972) created many beautiful and elaborate translation tessellations. See Section 13.10: Tessellations.

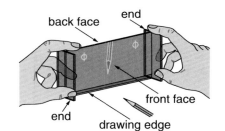

A translation tessellation

transparent mirror A piece of semitransparent plastic used to draw and study reflections. See Section 13.13.5: Transparent Mirrors.

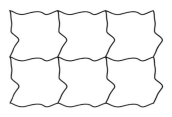

back face   end

front face

end   drawing edge

transversal A *line* that *intersects* two or more other lines. See Section 13.6.3: Relations and Orientations of Angles.

transversal

trapezoid A *quadrilateral* that has exactly one pair of *parallel* sides. In *Everyday Mathematics,* both pairs of sides cannot be parallel; that is, a parallelogram is not a trapezoid. See Section 13.4.2: Polygons (*n*-gons).

Trapezoids

tree diagram A network of points connected by *line segments* and containing no closed loops. *Factor trees* and *probability trees* are tree diagrams used, respectively, to factor numbers and to represent probability situations in which there is a series of events. The first tree diagram below shows the prime factorization of 30. The second tree diagram models flipping one coin two times to get HEADS H or TAILS T.

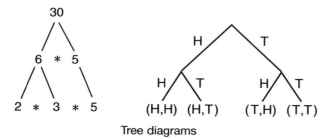

Tree diagrams

tri- A prefix meaning three, as in tricycle.

trial-and-error method A method for finding the *solution of an equation* by trying a sequence of *test numbers*. See Section 17.2.4: Solving Open Sentences.

triangle A 3-sided polygon. See *equilateral triangle, isosceles triangle, scalene triangle, acute triangle, right triangle, obtuse triangle,* and Section 13.4.2: Polygons (*n*-gons).

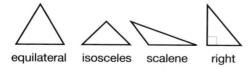

equilateral   isosceles   scalene   right

Triangles

triangular numbers *Figurate numbers* that can be shown by triangular arrangements of dots. The triangular numbers are {1, 3, 6, 10, 15, 21, 28, 36, 45, . . .}. See Section 17.1.2: Sequences.

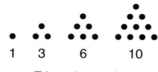

1   3   6   10

Triangular numbers

triangular prism A *prism* whose *bases* are *triangles.* See Section 13.5.2: Polyhedrons.

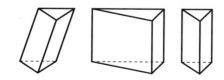

Triangular prisms

triangular pyramid A *pyramid* in which all *faces* are *triangles,* any one of which is the *base.* A regular tetrahedron has four *equilateral triangles* for faces and is one of the five *regular polyhedrons.* See Section 13.5.2: Polyhedrons.

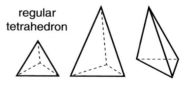

regular tetrahedron

Triangular pyramids

true number sentence A *number sentence* stating a correct fact. For example, $75 = 25 + 50$ is a true number sentence. See Section 10.2: Reading and Writing Number Sentences.

truncate (1) In a *decimal,* to cut off all *digits* after the decimal point or after a particular place to the right of the decimal point. For example, 12.345 can be truncated to 12.34, 12.3, or 12. *Integers* cannot be truncated. Same as rounding down in places to the right of the decimal point. See *round* and Section 16.2: Approximation and Rounding. (2) Informally, to cut off a part of a solid figure.

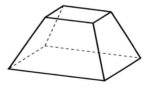

A truncated pyramid

turn An informal name for a *rotation.*

turn-around facts A pair of multiplication (or addition) facts in which the order of the factors (or addends) is reversed. For example, $3 * 9 = 27$ and $9 * 3 = 27$ are turn-around multiplication facts, and $4 + 5 = 9$ and $5 + 4 = 9$ are turn-around addition facts. There are no turn-around facts for subtraction or division. Turn-around facts are instances of the *Commutative Properties of Addition* and *Multiplication.* See Section 16.3.2: Basic Facts and Fact Power.

turn-around rule A rule for solving addition and multiplication problems based on the *Commutative Properties of Addition* and *Multiplication.* For example, if you know that $6 * 8 = 48$, then, by the turn-around rule, you also know that $8 * 6 = 48$.

twin primes Two prime numbers with a difference of 2. For example, 3 and 5 and 11 and 13 are pairs of twin primes.

2-dimensional (2-D) coordinate system A reference frame in which any point on a *2-dimensional figure* can be located with an *ordered pair* of coordinates relative to the *origin* of two intersecting perpendicular axes in space. Compare to *1-* and *3-dimensional coordinate systems*. See Section 15.3.2: 2- and 3-Dimensional Coordinate Systems.

2-dimensional (2-D) figure A figure whose points are all in one *plane* but not all on one *line*. Examples include polygons and circles, all of which have length and width but no height. See Section 13.1: Dimension.

unfair game A game in which every player does not have the same chance of winning. See Section 12.1.2: The Language of Chance.

unit A label used to put a number in context. In measuring *length,* for example, inches and centimeters are units. In a problem about 5 apples, apple is the unit. In *Everyday Mathematics,* students keep track of units in *unit boxes.* See Section 10.3.1: Addition and Subtraction Use Classes.

unit box In *Everyday Mathematics*, a box displaying the *unit* for the numbers in the problems at hand. See Section 1.3.6: Unit Boxes.

A unit box

unit fraction A *fraction* whose *numerator* is 1. For example, $\frac{1}{2}$, $\frac{1}{3}$, $\frac{1}{12}$, $\frac{1}{8}$, and $\frac{1}{20}$ are unit fractions. Unit fractions are especially useful in converting among units within measurement systems. For example, because 1 foot = 12 inches you can multiply a number of inches by $\frac{1}{12}$ to convert to feet. See Section 14.2.3: Converting between Measures.

unit interval The *interval* between 0 and 1 on a *number line.*

unit percent One *percent* (1%).

unit price The price for one item or *per* unit of measure. For example, the unit price of a 5-ounce package of onion powder selling for $2.50 is $0.50 per ounce. In recent years, grocery stores have begun posting unit prices to help consumers compare prices of different brands of a similar product or different size containers of the same product. See Section 14.2.3: Converting between Measures.

unit ratio Same as *n*-to-1 ratio.

unit whole Same as *whole* or *ONE.*

unlike denominators *Denominators* that are different, as in $\frac{1}{2}$ and $\frac{1}{3}$.

unlike fractions *Fractions* with *unlike denominators.*

upper quartile In *Everyday Mathematics,* in an ordered data set, the middle value of the *data* above the *median.* Data values at the median are not included when finding the upper quartile. Compare to *lower quartile.* See Section 12.2.3: Organizing and Displaying Data.

U.S. customary system The measuring system used most often in the United States. Units for *length* include inch, foot, yard, and mile; units for *weight* include ounce and pound; units for *volume* or *capacity* include cup, pint, quart, gallon, and cubic units; and the main unit for *temperature* change is degrees Fahrenheit. See Section 14.2.1: U.S. Customary System.

use class In *Everyday Mathematics,* a problem situation that one of the basic arithmetic operations can be used to solve. Students use *situation diagrams* to help model problems from the different use classes. See *addition/subtraction use classes, multiplication/division use classes,* and Section 10.3: Use Classes and Situation Diagrams.

value of a variable A specific number or quantity represented by a *variable.* For example, in $y = 4x + 3$, if the value of x is 7, then the value of y that makes the equation true is 31. See Section 17.2.2: Reading and Writing Open Sentences.

vanishing line A line connecting a point on a figure in a *perspective drawing* with a *vanishing point*.

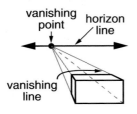

vanishing point In a *perspective drawing,* the point at which *parallel* lines that extend away from the viewer seem to meet. It is located on the *horizon* line. See *vanishing line* and Section 13.5.4: Connecting 2-D and 3-D.

variable A letter or other symbol that represents a number. A variable can represent a single number, as in $5 + n = 9$, because only $n = 4$ makes the sentence true. A variable can also stand for many different numbers, as in $x + 2 < 10$, because any number x less than 8 makes the sentence true. In *formulas* and *properties,* variables stand for all numbers. For example, $a + 3 = 3 + a$ for all numbers a. See Section 17.2.1: Uses of Variables.

variable term A *term* that contains at least one *variable.* For example, in $4b - 8 = b + 5$, $4b$ and b are variable terms. See Section 17.2.2: Reading and Writing Open Sentences.

Venn diagram A picture that uses circles or rings to show relationships between sets. In this diagram, $22 + 8 = 30$ girls are on the track team, and 8 are on both the track and the basketball teams. See Section 12.2.3: Organizing and Displaying Data.

Number of Girls on Sports Teams

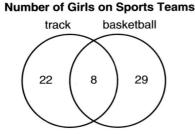

vernal equinox The first day of spring, when the sun crosses the plane of Earth's equator and day and night are about 12 hours each. "Equinox" is from the Latin *aequi-* meaning "equal" and *nox* meaning "night." Compare to *autumnal equinox.*

vertex The point at which the *rays* of an angle, the *sides* of a polygon, or the *edges* of a polyhedron meet. Plural is vertexes or vertices. In *Everyday Mathematics,* same as *corner.* See Section 13.4: Planes and Plane Figures and Section 13.5: Space and 3-D Figures.

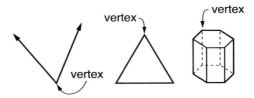

vertex point A point where the corners of *tessellation tiles* meet.

vertical Upright; perpendicular to the *horizon.* Compare to *horizontal.*

vertical angles The angles made by *intersecting* lines that do not share a common side. Same as *opposite angles.* Vertical angles have equal measures. See Section 13.6.3: Relations and Orientations of Angles.

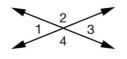

Angles 1 and 3; angles 2 and 4
are pairs of vertical angles.

volume (1) The amount of space occupied by a *3-dimensional figure.* Same as *capacity.* (2) Less formally, the amount a container can hold. Volume is often measured in cubic units, such as cm^3, cubic inches, or cubic feet. See the Tables of Formulas and Section 14.5: Volume (Capacity).

weight A measure of how heavy something is; the force of gravity on an object. An object's *mass* is constant, but it weighs less in weak gravity than in strong gravity. For example, a person who weighs 150 pounds in San Diego weighs about 23 pounds on the moon. See Section 14.6: Weight and Mass.

"What's My Rule?" problem In *Everyday Mathematics,* a problem in which two of the three parts of a *function (input, output,* and rule) are known, and the third is to be found out. See Section 17.1.3: Functions.

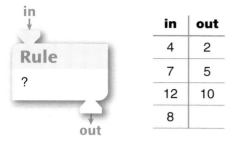

in	out
4	2
7	5
12	10
8	

A "What's My Rule?" problem

whole An entire object, collection of objects, or quantity being considered in a problem situation; 100%. Same as *ONE* and *unit whole.* See Section 9.3.2: Uses of Fractions.

whole numbers The *counting numbers* and 0. The set of whole numbers is {0, 1, 2, 3, . . .}.

width of a rectangle The *length* of one side of a *rectangle* or rectangular object, typically the shorter side.

wind-chill temperature A measure of how cold the air feels, based on a combination of wind speed and air temperature.

winter solstice The shortest day of the year, when the sun is farthest south of Earth's equator. The number of hours of daylight depends on the latitude of a location. In Colorado, the winter solstice averages a little more than 9 hours of daylight. Compare to *summer solstice.*

yard (yd) A U.S. customary unit of *length* equal to 3 feet, or 36 inches. To Henry I of England, a yard was the distance from the tip of the nose to the tip of the middle finger. In *Everyday Mathematics,* it is from the center of the chest to the tip of the middle finger. See the Tables of Measures and Section 14.1: Personal Measures.

Z

zero fact In *Everyday Mathematics:* (1) The *sum* of two 1-digit numbers when one of the *addends* is 0, as in $0 + 5 = 5$. If 0 is added to any number, there is no change in the number. Same as the additive identity. (2) The product of two 1-digit numbers when one of the factors is 0, as in $4 * 0 = 0$. The product of a number and 0 is always 0.

zero point Same as *origin.*

General Reference

Symbols

$+$	plus or positive
$-$	minus or negative
$*$, $\times$	multiplied by
$\div$, $/$	divided by
$=$	is equal to
$\neq$	is not equal to
$<$	is less than
$>$	is greater than
$\leq$	is less than or equal to
$\geq$	is greater than or equal to
$\approx$	is approximately equal to
x^n, $x\char`^n$	nth power of x
$\sqrt{x}$	square root of x
$\%$	percent
$a{:}b$, a/b, $\frac{a}{b}$	ratio of a to b or a divided by b or the fraction $\frac{a}{b}$
a [bs]	a groups, b in each group
$n/d \rightarrow a$ Rb	n divided by d is a with remainder b
{ }, ( ), [ ]	grouping symbols
∞	infinity
$n!$	n factorial
$\circ$	degree
(a,b)	ordered pair
$\overleftrightarrow{AS}$	line AS
$\overline{AS}$	line segment AS
$\overrightarrow{AS}$	ray AS
$\llcorner$	right angle
$\perp$	is perpendicular to
$\parallel$	is parallel to
$\triangle ABC$	triangle ABC
$\angle ABC$	angle ABC
$\angle B$	angle B
$\cong$	is congruent to
$\sim$	is similar to
$\equiv$	is equivalent to
$|n|$	absolute value of n

Prefixes

Prefix	Value	Prefix	Value
uni-	one	tera-	trillion (10^{12})
bi-	two	giga-	billion (10^9)
tri-	three	mega-	million (10^6)
quad-	four	kilo-	thousand (10^3)
penta-	five	hecto-	hundred (10^2)
hexa-	six	deca-	ten (10^1)
hepta-	seven	uni-	one (10^0)
octa-	eight	deci-	tenth (10^{-1})
nona-	nine	centi-	hundredth (10^{-2})
deca-	ten	milli-	thousandth (10^{-3})
dodeca-	twelve	micro-	millionth (10^{-6})
icosa-	twenty	nano-	billionth (10^{-9})

Constants

Pi (π)	3.14159 26535 89793
Golden Ratio (ϕ)	1.61803 39887 49894
Radius of Earth at equator	6,378.388 kilometers 3,963.34 miles
Circumference of Earth at equator	40,076.59 kilometers 24,902.44 miles
Velocity of sound in dry air at 0°C	331.36 m/sec 1087.1 ft/sec
Velocity of light in a vacuum	2.997925×10^{10} cm/sec

The Order of Operations

1. Do operations inside grouping symbols following Rules 2–4. Work from the innermost set of grouping symbols outward.
2. Calculate all expressions with exponents.
3. Multiply and divide in order from left to right.
4. Add and subtract in order from left to right.

Tables of Measures

Tables of Measure

Metric System

Units of Length

1 kilometer (km)	= 1,000 meters (m)
1 meter	= 10 decimeters (dm)
	= 100 centimeters (cm)
	= 1,000 millimeters (mm)
1 decimeter	= 10 centimeters
1 centimeter	= 10 millimeters

Units of Area

1 square meter (m^2)	= 100 square decimeters (dm^2)
	= 10,000 square centimeters (cm^2)
1 square decimeter	= 100 square centimeters
1 are (a)	= 100 square meters
1 hectare (ha)	= 100 ares
1 square kilometer (km^2)	= 100 hectares

Units of Volume and Capacity

1 cubic meter (m^3)	= 1,000 cubic decimeters (dm^3)
	= 1,000,000 cubic centimeters (cm^3)
1 cubic centimeter	= 1,000 cubic millimeters (mm^3)
1 kiloliter (kL)	= 1,000 liters (L)
1 liter	= 1,000 milliliters (mL)

Units of Mass and Weight

1 metric ton (t)	= 1,000 kilograms (kg)
1 kilogram	= 1,000 grams (g)
1 gram	= 1,000 milligrams (mg)

U.S. Customary System

Units of Length

1 mile (mi)	= 1,760 yards (yd)
	= 5,280 feet (ft)
1 yard	= 3 feet
	= 36 inches (in.)
1 foot	= 12 inches

Units of Area

1 square yard (yd^2)	= 9 square feet (ft^2)
	= 1,296 square inches ($in.^2$)
1 square foot	= 144 square inches
1 acre	= 43,560 square feet
1 square mile (mi^2)	= 640 acres

Units of Volume and Capacity

1 cubic yard (yd^3)	= 27 cubic feet (ft^3)
1 cubic foot	= 1,728 cubic inches ($in.^3$)
1 gallon (gal)	= 4 quarts (qt)
1 quart	= 2 pints (pt)
1 pint	= 2 cups (c)
1 cup	= 8 fluid ounces (fl oz)
1 fluid ounce	= 2 tablespoons (tbs)
1 tablespoon	= 3 teaspoons (tsp)

Units of Mass and Weight

1 ton (T)	= 2,000 pounds (lb)
1 pound	= 16 ounces (oz)

System Equivalents (Conversion Factors)

1 inch ≈ 2.5 cm (2.54)	1 liter ≈ 1.1 quarts (1.057)
1 kilometer ≈ 0.6 mile (0.621)	1 ounce ≈ 28 grams (28.350)
1 mile ≈ 1.6 kilometers (1.609)	1 kilogram ≈ 2.2 pounds (2.21)
1 meter ≈ 39 inches (39.37)	1 hectare ≈ 2.5 acres (2.47)

Body Measures

1 *digit* is about the width of a finger.

1 *hand* is about the width of the palm and thumb.

1 *span* is about the distance from the tip of the thumb to the tip of the first (index) finger of an outstretched hand.

1 *cubit* is about the length from the elbow to the tip of the extended middle finger.

1 *yard* is about the distance from the center of the chest to the tip of the extended middle finger of an outstretched arm.

1 *fathom* is about the length from fingertip to fingertip of outstretched arms. Also called an arm span.

Units of Time

1 century	= 100 years
1 decade	= 10 years
1 year (yr)	= 12 months
	= 52 weeks (plus one or two days)
	= 365 days (366 days in a leap year)
1 month (mo)	= 28, 29, 30, or 31 days
1 week (wk)	= 7 days
1 day (d)	= 24 hours
1 hour (hr)	= 60 minutes
1 minute (min)	= 60 seconds (s or sec)

Tables of Formulas

Formulas	Meaning of Variables

Rectangles
  Perimeter: $P = (2 * l) + (2 * w)$
  Area: $A = (b * h)$
	$P =$ perimeter; $l =$ length; $w =$ width
	$A =$ area; $b =$ length of base; $h =$ height

Squares
  Perimeter: $P = 4 * s$
  Area: $A = s^2$
	$P =$ perimeter; $s =$ length of side
	$A =$ area

Parallelograms Area: $A = b * h$	$A =$ area; $b =$ length of base; $h =$ height
Triangles Area: $A = \frac{1}{2} * b * h$	$A =$ area; $b =$ length of base; $h =$ height
Regular Polygons Perimeter: $P = n * s$	$P =$ perimeter; $n =$ number of sides; $s =$ length of side

Circles
  Circumference: $C = \pi * d,$ or $C = 2 * \pi * r$
  Area: $A = \pi * r^2$
	$C =$ circumference; $d =$ diameter; $r =$ radius
	$A =$ area

Pick's Formula for the Area of Polygons Area: $A = (\frac{1}{2} * P) + I - 1$	$A =$ area; $P =$ number of grid points on polygon; $I =$ number of grid points in the interior
Polyhedrons Euler's Formula: $e = (f + v) - 2$	$e =$ number of edges; $f =$ number of faces; $v =$ number of vertices

Mobiles
  Fulcrum at center: $W * D = w * d$
  Fulcrum not at center: $(W * D) + (R * L) = w * d$
	$W =$ weight of object farthest from fulcrum
	$D =$ distance of object farthest from fulcrum
	$w =$ weight of object closest to fulcrum
	$d =$ distance of object closest to fulcrum
	$R =$ weight of rod
	$L =$ distance from center to fulcrum

Tables of Formulas

Formulas (continued)	Meaning of Variables
Prisms Volume: $V = B * h$, or $V = l * w * h$ Surface area: $S = 2 * ((l * w) + (l * h) + (w * h))$	V = volume; B = area of base; l = length; w = width; h = height S = surface area (for right prisms only)
Cubes Volume: $V = e^3$ Surface area: $S = 6 * e^2$	V = volume; e = length of edge S = surface area
Cylinders Volume: $V = B * h$, or $V = \pi * r^2 * h$ Surface area: $S = (2 * \pi * r^2) + ((2 * \pi * r) * h)$	V = volume; B = area of base; h = height; r = radius of base S = surface area (for right cylinders only)
Pyramids Volume: $V = \frac{1}{3} * B * h$	V = volume; B = area of base; h = height
Cones Volume: $V = \frac{1}{3} * B * h$, or $V = \frac{1}{3} * \pi * r^2 * h$	V = volume; B = area of base; h = height; r = radius of base
Spheres Volume: $V = \frac{4}{3} * \pi * r^3$ Surface area: $S = 4 * \pi * r^2$	V = volume; r = radius S = surface area
Temperatures Fahrenheit to Celsius conversion: $C = \frac{5}{9} * (F - 32°)$ Celsius to Fahrenheit conversion: $F = (\frac{9}{5} * C) + 32°$	C = degrees Celsius; F = degrees Fahrenheit
Distance traveled (linear) $d = r * t$	d = distance traveled; r = rate of speed; t = time of travel
Pythagorean theorem $a^2 + b^2 = c^2$	a, b = lengths of legs of a right triangle; c = length of hypotenuse of a right triangle

Properties of Rational Numbers

The following properties are true for all rational numbers. The variables *a, b,* and *c* can be any rational numbers, except for zero when a variable is a divisor.

Properties

Binary Operations Property

The sum, difference, product, or quotient of any two numbers is a single number.

$a + b$, $a - b$, $a * b$, and a/b are single numbers.

Commutative Properties

The sum or product of two numbers is the same, regardless of the order of the numbers.

$$a + b = b + a$$
$$a * b = b * a$$

In *Everyday Mathematics,* these are *turn-around rules.*

Associative Properties

The sum or product of three or more numbers is the same, regardless of how the numbers are grouped.

$$a + (b + c) = (a + b) + c$$
$$a * (b * c) = (a * b) * c$$

Distributive Properties

If a number *a* is multiplied by the sum or difference of two numbers, *a* is multiplied times each of the other numbers.

$$a * (b + c) = (a * b) + (a * c)$$
$$a * (b - c) = (a * b) - (a * c)$$

In other words, *a* is "distributed" over the sum or difference.

Addition Property of Zero

The sum of a number *a* and 0 is equal to *a*.

$$a + 0 = 0 + a = a$$

Zero is the *additive identity.*

Opposites Property

The opposite of a number *a* is written $-a$ or, in *Everyday Mathematics,* OPP(a).

If *a* is positive, then $-a = $ OPP(a) is negative.

If *a* is negative, then $-a = $ OPP(a) is positive.

If $a = 0$, then $-a = $ OPP(a) $= 0$.
Zero is the only number that is its own opposite.

Opposite of Opposites Property

The opposite of the opposite of a number *a* is equal to *a*.

$$-(-a) = a$$
$$\text{OPP(OPP}(a)) = a$$

Sum of Opposites Property

The sum of a number and its opposite is 0.

$$a + (-a) = (-a) + a = 0$$

a and $-a$ are *additive inverses.*

Multiplication of Reciprocals Property

The product of a number and its reciprocal is 1.

$$a * \frac{1}{a} = \frac{1}{a} * a = 1$$

a and $\frac{1}{a}$ are *multiplicative inverses.*

Multiplication Property of 1

The product of a number *a* and 1 is equal to *a*.

$$a * 1 = 1 * a = a$$

One is the *multiplicative identity.*

Properties of Rational Numbers

The following properties are true for all rational numbers. The variables a, b, and c can be any rational numbers, except for zero when a variable is a divisor.

Properties (continued)

Addition Properties of Positive and Negative Numbers

The sum of two positive numbers is a positive number.

The sum of two negative numbers is the opposite of the sum of the "number parts" of the addends.

To find the sum of a positive number and a negative number, subtract the smaller number part from the larger number part. The sum has the sign of the addend with the larger number part.

The number parts are called *absolute values*.

Multiplication Property of Positive and Negative Numbers

The product of two positive numbers or two negative numbers is a positive number.

The product of a positive number and a negative number is a negative number.

Subtraction and Division Properties

All subtraction problems can be solved by addition, and all division problems can be solved by multiplication.

$$a - b = a + (-b)$$

$$\frac{a}{b} = a * \frac{1}{b}$$

$$a \div b = a * \frac{1}{b}$$

Addition and Subtraction of Fractions Properties

The sum or difference of fractions with *like denominators* is the sum or difference of the numerators over the denominator.

$$\frac{a}{c} + \frac{b}{c} = \frac{a+b}{c}$$

$$\frac{a}{c} - \frac{b}{c} = \frac{a-b}{c}$$

To add or subtract fractions with *unlike* denominators, rename the fractions so that they have a common denominator.

$$\frac{a}{b} + \frac{c}{d} = \frac{ad + bc}{bd}$$

$$\frac{a}{b} - \frac{c}{d} = \frac{ad - bc}{bd}$$

Equivalent Fractions Property

If the numerator and denominator of a fraction $\frac{a}{b}$ are multiplied or divided by the same number, the resulting fraction is equivalent to $\frac{a}{b}$.

$$\frac{a}{b} = \frac{a * c}{b * c} \qquad \frac{a}{b} = \frac{a \div c}{b \div c}$$

Multiplication of Fractions Property

The product of two fractions is the product of the numerators over the product of the denominators.

$$\frac{a}{b} * \frac{c}{d} = \frac{a * c}{b * d}$$

Division of Fractions Property

The quotient of two fractions is the product of the dividend and the reciprocal of the divisor.

$$\frac{a}{b} \div \frac{c}{d} = \frac{a}{b} * \frac{d}{c}$$

$$= \frac{a * d}{b * c}$$

Powers of a Number Property

For any number a and any positive whole number b, a^b is the product of b factors of a.

$$a^b = \underbrace{a * a * a * \ldots * a}_{b \text{ factors}}$$

a^0 is equal to 1.

For any number a and any positive whole number b, a^{-b} is the reciprocal of a^b.

$$a^{-b} = \frac{1}{a^b} = \frac{1}{\underbrace{a * a * a * \ldots * a}_{b \text{ factors}}}$$

Properties of Rational Numbers

4–6 Games Correlation Chart

Games	Grade 4 Lesson	Grade 5 Lesson	Grade 6 Lesson	Basic Facts	Operations	Calculator	Numeration	Geometry	Data	Algebra	Meas./Ref. Frames	Mental Math	Strategy
Addition Top-It (Extended-Facts Version)	1-2			●	●		●					●	
Addition Top-It (Decimal Version)		2-2			●		●					●	
Algebra Election		4-7	6-11		●	●			●	●	●		●
Angle Add-Up	6-6				●			●			●		
Angle Tangle	6-6	3-6	5-1		●			●			●		
Base-10 Exchange	4-2						●						
Baseball Multiplication	3-3	*		●	●							●	
Beat the Calculator	3-5	*		●	●	●						●	
Beat the Calculator (Extended-Facts Version)		1-3		●	●	●						●	
Build-It		8-1	4-2				●						●
Buzz and Bizz Buzz	3-2				●		●						
Calculator 10,000	*					●	●						
Chances Are	7-11								●				
Coin Top-It	4-3				●		●					●	
Coordinate Search		12-8									●		●
Credits/Debits Game	10-6		3-7		●							●	
Credits/Debits Game (Advanced Version)	11-6	7-8	6-3		●							●	
Divisibility Dash		4-4	2-6	●	●		●					●	●
Division Arrays	3-5			●	●							●	
Division Dash	6-3	4-2			●							●	
Division Top-It	*	4-5	2-7		●		●					●	
Doggone Decimal			2-4		●	●	●					●	●
Estimation Squeeze		5-5				●	●					●	
Exponent Ball		7-1	2-10		●	●	●					●	
Factor Bingo		1-7		●	●							●	
Factor Captor		1-4	3-2	●	●		●					●	●
Factor Top-It		*		●	●		●					●	
Finish First		6-2		●	●							●	
First to 100		4-7	8-12	●	●					●		●	
Fishing for Digits	2-4				●	●	●						●
500		7-8			●							●	
Frac-Tac-Toe		5-7	4-8		●		●					●	●
Fraction Action, Fraction Friction		8-4	4-4		●		●					●	●
Fraction Capture		6-9	4-1		●		●					●	●
Fraction Match	7-6						●					●	●
Fraction Of	7-2	5-11			●		●					●	●
Fraction/ Percent Concentration	9-3	5-8				●	●					●	
Fraction Spin		8-5			●		●						●
Fraction Top-It	7-9	5-1			●		●						
Fraction Top-It (Advanced Version)		6-8			●		●					●	

Number indicates first exposure at grade level. *Available in the Games section of the *Student Reference Book*.

4–6 Games Correlation Chart continued

Games	Grade 4 Lesson	Grade 5 Lesson	Grade 6 Lesson	Basic Facts	Operations	Calculator	Numeration	Geometry	Data	Algebra	Meas./Ref. Frames	Mental Math	Strategy
Fraction/Whole-Number Top-It		*	6-1		●		●					●	
Getting to One	7-10	*	3-10			●	●						●
Grab Bag	7-3		7-1		●				●	●		●	●
Greedy			7-7						●			●	●
Grid Search	6-8										●		●
Hidden Treasure		9-1									●		●
High-Number Toss	2-7	2-10	1-2				●						●
High-Number Toss (Decimal Version)		2-5	1-11		●		●						●
Landmark Shark			1-5						●			●	●
Mixed-Number Spin		8-3	4-7		●		●			●		●	●
Multiplication Bull's-Eye		2-7	2-5		●	●	●					●	
Multiplication Top-It	3-3	3-3	2-5	●	●		●					●	
Multiplication Top-It (Extended-Facts Version)		1-8		●	●		●					●	
Multiplication Wrestling	5-2	*	9-1		●		●			●		●	●
Name That Number	2-2	1-9	1-8		●		●				●	●	●
Number Top-It (7-Digit Numbers)	5-11	2-10	2-1				●					●	
Number Top-It (Decimals)	4-4	5-6					●					●	
Over and Up Squares	6-9		1-6								●	●	●
Percent/Sector Match-Up			1-9				●						●
Polygon Capture		3-7	5-8					●					
Polygon Pair-Up	1-6							●					
Product Pile-Up	4-3			●			●					●	●
Rugs and Fences	8-7	11-4								●	●	●	●
Scientific Notation Toss		7-3	2-9				●				●		
Seega	3-6												●
Sides and Angles: Triangles		3-6						●	●				
Solution Search			6-12		●					●			
Spoon Scramble		12-6	5-4		●		●					●	
Spreadsheet Scramble			3-7		●							●	●
Sprouts	1-2							●					●
Subtraction Target Practice	2-9	*			●	●							●
Subtraction Target Practice (Decimal Version)		2-3			●	●							●
Subtraction Top-It (Extended-Facts Version)	1-4			●	●		●					●	
Sz'kwa	1-4							●					●
3-D Shape Sort		11-2	5-10					●					
Top-It with Positive and Negative Numbers		7-11	6-4		●		●					●	
Triangle Sort		3-6						●					
Venn Diagram Challenge			7-6					●	●				●
"What's My Attribute Rule?"		3-7						●				●	
Where Do I Fit In?		3-6						●					
X and O—Tic Tac Toe			5-4								●		●

Number indicates first exposure at grade level. *Available in the Games section of the *Student Reference Book*.

Index

Index

Index

Index

Index